Neuroscience for Psychologists and Other Mental Health Professionals

Jill Littrell, PhD, LCSW, is an associate professor at Georgia State University, where she teaches psychopathology, drug and alcohol addictions, and research methods to social work students. After 8 years as a social worker, she obtained a doctorate in clinical psychology from Arizona State University. Following a U.S. Department of Veterans Affairs internship in alcohol and drug abuse, she worked as a psychologist in the Alcohol and Drug Dependency Department at Cigna. During her time at Cigna, she completed a two-volume work on alcoholism. This endeavor further acquainted her with the neuroscience literature and the proliferating research on how stress influences the immune system and mood. Having been intrigued by the connections between mind and body, she pursued a master's degree in biology (molecular genetics and biochemistry) while on faculty at Georgia State. Much of her class work and laboratory experience was focused on immunology and neuroscience. She continues to work in the immunology lab of Dr. Yuan Liu. In recent years, she has published various papers on the links among behavior, disease, and immune system function, as well as on the efficacy of antidepressants.

Neuroscience for Psychologists and Other Mental Health Professionals

Promoting Well-Being and Treating Mental Illness

Jill Littrell, PhD, LCSW

SPRINGER PUBLISHING COMPANY
NEW YORK

Springer Publishing Company, LLC
11 West 42nd Street
New York, NY 10036
www.springerpub.com

Acquisitions Editor: Stephanie Drew
Composition: Newgen KnowledgeWorks

ISBN: 978-0-8261-2278-0
e-book ISBN: 978-0-8261-2279-7

15 16 17 18 19 / 5 4 3 2 1

The author and the publisher of this Work have made every effort to use sources believed to be reliable to provide information that is accurate and compatible with the standards generally accepted at the time of publication. The author and publisher shall not be liable for any special, consequential, or exemplary damages resulting, in whole or in part, from the readers' use of, or reliance on, the information contained in this book. The publisher has no responsibility for the persistence or accuracy of URLs for external or third-party Internet websites referred to in this publication and does not guarantee that any content on such websites is, or will remain, accurate or appropriate.

Library of Congress Cataloging-in-Publication Data
Littrell, Jill, author.
  Neuroscience for psychologists and other mental health professionals : promoting well-being and treating mental illness / Jill Littrell.
     p. ; cm.
  Includes bibliographical references and index.
  ISBN 978-0-8261-2278-0 — ISBN 978-0-8261-2279-7 (e-book)
  I. Title.
  [DNLM: 1. Mental Disorders—physiopathology. 2. Mental Disorders—therapy. 3. Brain—physiopathology. 4. Brain Chemistry—immunology. 5. Mental Disorders—etiology. 6. Psychophysiology. WM 140]
  RC454.4
  616.89—dc23   2015000573

Printed in the United States of America by McNaughton & Gunn.

*This work is dedicated to my husband, Gus Levine,
who makes everything I do better.*

Contents

Preface

A wealth of information has emerged in recent decades about neurotransmitters, receptors for neurotransmitters, and the different
areas of the brain that are more or less active in synchrony with
different types of thoughts. Not only have empirical findings with
regard to traditional areas of neuroscience exploded, but a rich literature now exists on how the immune system affects the brain in ways
that result in reliable changes in mood and behavior. My goal here is
to present information about brain function and its chemical underpinnings in a way that contributes to a conceptual understanding of
distress and subjective well-being. Along with the emerging conceptual understanding of particular brain functions, our understanding
of how pharmaceuticals, foods, and lifestyle changes influence mood
and behavior has advanced. The integration of neuroscience and
immunology has identified the mechanisms through which lifestyle
changes and what we eat can obviate distress, giving us new avenues
for improving well-being.

The study of distress was initially the province of psychiatry, but
a willing partner was found when clinical psychology emerged as a
profession after World War II. Chapter 1 provides a history of thought
in psychiatry and explains how we arrived at our current system for
categorizing distress. In order to understand the physiology behind
the major categories of distress, background information on how the
brain operates is required. Chapter 2 offers information on physiology,
including brain circuits undergirding anxiety and depression, circuits
for emotional or impulse regulation, and circuits for robust motivated
behaviors. Chapter 2 also presents information on how hormones, neurotransmitters, and the immune system can influence behavior. (At the

end of Chapter 2, exercises for increasing retention of key terms used in subsequent chapters are provided.) Pharmaceuticals currently constitute a major strategy used to ameliorate distress. Chapter 3 offers information on pharmacology, including the major classes of drugs used to influence behavior. In addition, Chapter 3 covers how drugs are brought to market and the current controversies over the regulation of pharmaceuticals. Chapters 4 through 8 consider categories of distress that afflict adults, whereas Chapter 9 focuses on categories of distress in children. In the chapters considering specific disorders, the physiology pertinent to each disorder is presented. Then, the efficacy and side effects of various treatments, including pharmaceuticals, are reviewed.

Chapters 4, 6, and 10 contain some material of special note. Chapter 6, on psychosis, tells the story of the relatively new research on fast-spiking gamma-aminobutyric acid (GABA) interneurons and the role of N-methyl-d-aspartate (NMDA) receptors in psychosis. Chapter 4, on depression, includes the relatively new story of the role of inflammatory processes in mood disorders. Chapter 4 also describes the emerging story on gut microbiota's influence on inflammation. With the burgeoning awareness of the dramatic impact of systemic inflammation on mood, new avenues to prevention and treatment are gaining prominence. The role of diet and exercise in controlling inflammation has been clear for some time now. Putting all the information together offers strong support for the conclusion that diet and exercise not only have strong influence on people's general health, but in turn affect people's mental states; and this effect is not merely incidental, but occurs at a level suitable for therapeutic application. The integrated information on physiology provides the rationale for the efficacy of treatment focused on diet, exercise, and maintaining interpersonal support from others. In keeping with this new approach, the last chapter (Chapter 10) focuses on the physiology undergirding health and resilience, offering a research-based rationale for viewing the mind and body as an inseparable unit for both therapeutic and prophylactic purposes. The rich, cellular-level detail from the new empirical findings has made it possible, in this presentation, to offer the latest not just on how to ameliorate distress, but on how to enhance well-being.

A MENTAL HEALTH ROLE FOR HEALTHY LIVING

Some readers may be surprised to learn that maintaining a healthy body, particularly avoiding systemic inflammation, is sometimes the key to the amelioration of mental and emotional distress. New interventions intended to ameliorate mental distress will include practices that are familiar to those with interests in healthy living. The mechanisms through which lifestyle changes can be effective in alleviating distress are explained. Implementation of healthy lifestyle choices may require significant lifestyle modifications for some. In the chapter on addictions (Chapter 8), orientations for approaching clients about lifestyle changes are discussed in the context of three treatment models: motivational interviewing, relapse prevention, and the transtheoretical model of change. In the last chapter, ways to maintain lifestyle changes (e.g., diet, exercise) and mechanisms for bolstering adherence to plans are covered.

THIS BOOK'S TARGET AUDIENCE

Traditional training for psychologists has focused primarily on psychological theories explaining mood, attitudes, thoughts, and behaviors. However, a literature is emerging in psychology journals that has identified activities in various areas of the brain, including changes in blood flow, changes in hormone levels in the blood, and markers of inflammation in blood as critical variables in the psychobiological story. Mind–body connections are being appreciated in many areas. A number of interprofessional journals have emerged examining how psychological variables integrate with physiology, bringing together diverse areas such as immunology and neuroscience, social psychology, and affective neuroscience. This book seeks to provide students of human behavior with an understanding of this widely dispersed literature. If offers a more articulated understanding of how subjective distress occurs, pointing to a broader armamentarium for assisting clients.

Psychiatric journals are also reporting many of these findings. However, because so much of this information appears in the sea of medical specialty and biological journals, as well as psychological journals, psychiatrists will probably encounter a good deal of new, professionally pertinent information here.

The material presented in this book is also relevant to behavioral health clinicians who work in primary care settings and to those clinicians working in more traditional mental health settings. With the advent of the Patient Protection and Affordable Care Act, behavioral health clinicians are being trained to work in primary care. (More information on this topic can be found in Chapter 10, the final chapter.) Behavioral health clinicians in primary care identify those who are in distress and discuss with these clients alternatives for modifying their distress. Thus, behavioral health clinicians (in most cases trained as psychologists or social workers) have the responsibility of explaining various treatment options. This book offers them a theoretical basis for their suggestions. Exploring treatment options is part of the process of securing informed consent. In Chapter 3, the process of securing informed consent and the sometimes vexing issue of how psychologists and social workers can discuss medications without "practicing medicine without a license" are addressed.

HARNESSING INFORMATION FOR BETTER LIVING

The emerging story on the physiology underpinning happiness and distress offers a useful frame of reference. In sharing this new perspective, this book centers on two related themes: how neuroscience, along with integrated findings from immunology, has been able to explain behavioral syndromes, and the new alternatives these findings suggest for ameliorating distress and promoting well-being. This book tells that story.

1

Ways of Thinking About Behavioral Syndromes

Traditionally, mental health professions have relied on the American Psychiatric Association and its forerunners to establish the mental health agenda. The American Psychiatric Association has delineated and labeled those behaviors and syndromes that the larger society regards as mental illness. In recent times, especially with the publication of the *Diagnostic and Statistical Manual of Mental Disorders*, Fifth Edition (*DSM-5*; American Psychiatric Association [APA], 2013), the role that the American Psychiatric Association has played in setting the agenda has been challenged. This chapter looks at the evolution of psychiatry and offers an explanation of why the earlier prevailing paradigm is being challenged.

THE CURRENT PARADIGM AND HOW WE GOT THERE

American psychiatry has been primarily focused on afflictions. The *DSM* of the American Psychiatric Association, since its inception in 1952, has always been a categorical system of disorders. Although the name of the National Institute of Mental Health (NIMH) suggests a promise to focus on more than mental illness, much of the training in psychiatry assumes the medical model. The medical model, a term coined by R. D. Laing (1971) in *The Politics of the Family and Other Essays,* construes clinicians as treating disorders or diseases. The assumption is that the individual needs to be fixed. Proper diagnosis involves evaluation of the initiating complaint, a history, a physical examination, and ancillary tests. The correct diagnosis will identify the culprit responsible for the less than optimal behavior. Some strategy, usually designed to affect the biochemistry, will alter the physiology giving rise to the problem. Clinical social workers, clinical psychologists, and counseling psychologists are often involved in treatment. They are schooled in psychopathology, which focuses on identification of what is wrong and ways to (one hopes) ameliorate the distress. Thus, the current paradigm in mental health treatment is focused on correcting what is wrong rather than promoting what is right.

Jaak Panksepp (2004) divides the history of psychiatry into three 20-year intervals. The first is the Kraepelin era, which extended from 1942 to 1962. Kraepelin ran governmental psychiatric hospitals in Europe during the late 1800s. Kraepelin categorized his patients according to their symptoms. He published descriptions of the behaviors of persons in each category and documented the lifetime trajectory of persons in each category. In the years following Kraepelin, psychiatrists read Kraepelin's work. Kraepelin is credited with inspiring those who wrote the *DSM-III* (APA, 1980) in their quest for establishing reliable categories. The second period of psychiatry was dominated by the thinking of Adolph Meyer, who ran a clinic for mental patients at Johns Hopkins. Meyer believed that it was vital to understand the social and environmental stressors impinging on each patient. Panksepp (2004) suggests that Meyer's approach was the inspiration for the axes system in the *DSM-III*, which encouraged evaluation of each patient's individual functioning and environmental factors. (With the *DSM-5*, the axes were dropped.) The third (and current) phase of psychiatry was ushered in by the discovery of chlorpromazine by Jean Delay and Pierre Deniker for the treatment of psychosis. This third phase is characterized by a search for pharmacological interventions for most of life's difficulties.

HISTORY OF THE DIAGNOSTIC AND STATISTICAL MANUALS OF THE AMERICAN PSYCHIATRIC ASSOCIATION

With the census of 1840, the U.S. government began collecting statistics on the prevalence of "idiocy/insanity" in America. In 1843, the American Statistical Association reported to the U.S. House of Representatives that "the most glaring and remarkable errors are found in the statements respecting nosology, prevalence of insanity, blindness, deafness, and dumbness, among the people of this nation" (American Psychiatric Association, 2015). In fact, whole towns of African Americans were declared "insane." For the 10th census of 1880, Fredrick H. Wines was appointed to write a report on the prevalence of mental disorders in the U.S. population, entitled "Report on the Defective, Dependent, and Delinquent Classes of the Population of the United States, As Returned at the Tenth Census" (Grob, 1991).

Although the census was focused on counting the number of Americans in mental distress, several professions (law, medicine, social work, and psychiatry) were developing in the United States in the 1800s. The Association of Medical Superintendents of American Institutions for the Insane was formed in 1844. This association became the American Medico-Psychological Association in 1892, and then became the American Psychiatric Association in 1921 (Noll, 2011). Soon the newly formed professional associations addressed the task of creating categories for classifying those in their care. In 1917, the National Commission on Mental Hygiene and the American Medico-Psychological Association developed the *Statistical Manual for the Use of Institutions for the Insane,* which complemented the nomenclature developed by the New York Academy of Medicine's Standard Classified Nomenclature of Disease. During World War II, many soldiers required treatment for distress. Under the auspices of the Office of the Surgeon General, Brigadier General William C. Menninger issued a new classification system called the *Medical 203.* Menninger brought in current concepts of the day in revising the Standard Classified Nomenclature of Disease of the New Academy of Medicine. After the war, many clinical psychologists were trained in Veteran Administration hospitals, which used the *Medical 203.* When the American Psychiatric Association published its first *DSM* in 1952, it used the conceptual framework of the *Medical 203.* The *DSM* was 130 pages long and listed 106 mental disorders. The manual was divided into overarching categories of psychosis, neurosis, and character disorders (Grob, 1991; Houts, 2000).

In 1968, the *DSM-II* was published by the American Psychiatric Association. It was very similar to the *DSM-I.* It listed 182 disorders. It used the term "neurosis" and was infused with the psychoanalytic dogma of the day. Again, neurosis and psychosis were major divisions. The *DSM-II* clearly differentiated the categories associated with severe disability (psychosis) from those not associated with incapacitating disability (neurosis; Decker, 2013).

During the 1960s and 1970s, the *DSM* was being broadly criticized. Psychiatrist Thomas Szasz (1961) published *The Myth of Mental Illness,* which argued that attributing antisocial acts to uncontrollable disease processes would weaken societal sanctions against antisocial behavior.

Sociologist Erving Goffman characterized psychiatric labels as a mechanism for punishing and controlling nonconformists. In the *DSM-II*, homosexuality was categorized as a sociopathic personality disturbance. In response, Evelyn Hooker conducted a study in 1956, finding that many homosexuals were well adjusted. Gay activists staged demonstrations at the American Psychiatric Association convention in 1970. Later, members of the APA voted. Homosexuality was discarded from the manual in 1974 with the seventh printing of the *DSM-II* (Decker, 2013).

Hanna Decker (2013), who contributed a book on the history of the *DSM-III*, suggests that a crisis in the credibility of psychiatry was the impetus for the *DSM-III* (APA, 1980). There were protests from gay rights groups and dramatically argued objections from Irving Goffman and Thomas Szasz. David Rosenhan's (1973) article in *Science* told of a normal person who was admitted to a psychiatric facility with the complaint of hearing voices (part of an experiment Rosenhan was conducting). Although the patients recognized that the man was normal, none of the professionals realized this. Hospital directors challenged Rosenhan to try this again. Believing that Rosenhan was repeating his experiment, the doctors identified real patients as Rosenhan plants. (Rosenhan, in fact, had not repeated his experiment.) Rosenhan's publication was a major challenge to the psychiatric profession's claim to be able to differentiate the sane from the insane. Further questions about psychiatry followed. Studies contrasting diagnostic practices in Europe with practices in the United States indicated that the same patients would not receive the same diagnoses if evaluated by an American versus a European doctor. Spitzer and Fleiss (1974) published a paper decrying the lack of reliability for all *DSM-II* categories with the exception of alcoholism, mental deficiency, and organic brain damage. The association of psychiatry with those who performed lobotomies further damaged the reputation of the profession. If the society was to continue to rely on the psychiatrists' expert opinions, the public trust in these opinions needed to be reinstated (Decker, 2013).

In contrast to the psychoanalytic school dominating the thinking on the East and West Coasts, the empiricists were gaining ground in the middle of the country during the late 1970s. Samuel Guze, George Winokur, Eli Robins, and his sociologist wife, Lee Robins, were at Washington University in St. Louis and Nancy Andreasen was at the University of Iowa. The empiricists inspired Robert Spitzer, who was selected as the chairperson to supervise the production of the *DSM-III*. The empiricists operated in the tradition of Kraepelin, who sought descriptive criteria for assignment to categories of mental illness. Spitzer was atheoretical. Conjectures about the etiology of various behavioral syndromes were not included in the *DSM-III*. Ideas about internal conflicts, which relied on speculation and not description, were out. The emphasis was on achieving reliability. Reliance on discrete observable behaviors was the best way to achieve reliability. According to Decker (2013), Spitzer corralled the leading experts on various categories into a room. Although there was a great deal of disagreement, Spitzer took notes on whatever consensus occurred. The result was the *DSM-III*, published in 1980.

James Davies (2014), for his book *Cracked*, interviewed members of the *DSM-III* taskforce: Robert Spitzer, Donald Klein, Theodore Millon, and Renee Garfinkel. All agreed that the process of creating the *DSM-III* involved very little weighing of scientific information, because this information was lacking. According to Renee Garfinkel, the process was more like a group of friends deciding where to have lunch than a group of people making judgments about evidence. Thus, the *DSM-III* categories arose. For each diagnosis, there was a list of relevant behaviors. An individual met criteria for a disorder based on observations of some specified number of behaviors off the disorder's list. Spitzer worked with the psychometrician Jean Endicott on developing standardized diagnostic interviews for asking about the occurrence of specific behaviors. Spitzer and Janet B. Williams, his social-worker wife, held workshops all over the country.

In the *DSM-III*, clinicians were encouraged to not only provide a diagnosis but also to make assessments on various dimensions relevant to the individual's functioning. Axis I was for diagnostic categories that were the focus for treatment. Axis II was for personality characteristics and stable patterns of behavior, such as personality disorders or levels of intellectual functioning. Axis III allowed for specification of physical illnesses, such as stroke, Alzheimer's disease, diabetes, or autoimmune disorder. Axis IV allowed assessment of current stressors in the individual's life. Axis V asked for assessment of the individual's current level of functioning. As psychiatry moved toward reliance on pharmacology, few clinicians completed the axes (Probst, 2014). The developers of the *DSM-5* abandoned the axes except for the evaluation of the level of function.

Major Depression and Anxiety Used to Be Neurosis

Ghaemi (2013) characterizes the *DSM-III* as a serious revision to how neurotic depressive symptoms and psychotic depression were differentiated. In the *DSM-II* era, the concept of depression frequently included psychosis and referred to the enduring and debilitating depression associated with manic-depressive illness. In contrast to psychotic conditions, in the *DSM-II* era, neurosis covered the depressive and anxious behaviors of those who were treated by psychoanalysts. The depressive symptoms of neurotics were highly responsive to life stressors or associated with personality characteristics. Neurotic depression was seldom debilitating and never involved psychosis. In the *DSM-II*, manic depression was included in the section on psychosis.

A big change occurred with the *DSM-III*. For the first time, with the *DSM-III*, manic depression was classified as a mood disorder along with depression experienced by persons who never exhibited mania. That is, the *DSM-III* category of mood disorders merged severe depressive symptoms associated with psychosis with the less severe depressive symptoms associated with neurosis. Thus, those with severe debilitation were merged with the "worried well." Of course, being a member of the "worried well" is pretty common. In a 2007 interview with Adam Curtis for the British Broadcasting Corporation, Spitzer acknowledged that the changes in the *DSM-III* resulted in the medicalization of 20% to 30% of the population. Spitzer further noted that a manual based on behavioral description that does not include the contexts in which these behaviors occurred will sometimes construe normal reactions to a bad situation as pathology (Davies, 2014).

The *DSM-IV* Continues the Tradition of Medicalizing More of Us

The *DSM-IV* was released in 1994. Allen Frances (2013), in his book *Saving Normal*, reports that he was selected as the chair for the process of revising the *DSM-III-R* (APA, 1987) because of his involvement in the production of *DSM-III* and *DSM-III-R*. There was not much competition for the position of the chair for the *DSM-IV*. Perhaps one of the biggest changes in the *DSM-IV* was the expansion of the categories under bipolar disorders. The category of bipolar II was added in the *DSM-IV*. Henceforth, the original bipolar diagnosis would be known as bipolar I.

As will be discussed in Chapter 7, "Bipolar Disorders," since the addition of the bipolar II category, the rates of bipolar diagnoses have soared as have the rates of autism, depression, and attention deficit hyperactivity disorder (ADHD) diagnoses. In his book, *Saving Normal*, Allen Frances (2013) regrets the expanded numbers of the American population being diagnosed with depression, bipolar disorders, and ADHD, which he attributes to the looseness of the criteria in establishing membership in the categories. Possibly in anticipation of the large number of individuals who would be diagnosed, the *DSM-IV* included the criterion of causing major impairment or distress in social, occupational, or other areas of life before making any diagnosis. In fact, a very large survey conducted by Kessler, Chiu, Demler, Merikangas, and Walters (2005) found that more than 50% of the U.S. population met criteria for a *DSM* disorder at some point in their lives and a study by Moffitt et al. (2010) reported that 65% of the general population had met criteria for a *DSM-IV* disorder during their lifetime. Paul McHugh, a psychiatrist professor emeritus at Johns Hopkins, commenting on the Kessler et al. study to *The New York Times*, reflected, "the problem is that the diagnostic manual we are using in psychiatry is like a field guide and it just keeps expanding and expanding" (Carey, 2005). McHugh further quipped regarding the expanding number of *DSM* categories, "pretty soon, we'll have a syndrome for short, fat Irish guys with a Boston accent, and I'll be mentally ill" (Carey, 2005).

Controversy Over the *DSM-5*

Prior to the publication of the *DSM-5*, which was released in May 2013, there was a groundswell of negative press about American psychiatry and the *DSM* processes. Senator Charles Grassley from Iowa held hearings on the connections between luminaries in psychiatry and the pharmaceutical houses. Ghostwriting, wherein drug company employees write articles and academic psychiatrists attach their names, was found to be common (Lacasse & Leo, 2010). As a result of congressional hearings, several luminaries, Harvard's Joseph Biederman and Emory's Charles Nemeroff, were prohibited from submitting grants to federal funding agencies for a period of time (Harris & Carey, 2008). Charles Nemeroff lost his departmental chair position at Emory because of the controversy.

Allen Frances began a campaign to stop the addition of diagnoses in the *DSM-5* that would further increase the number of Americans being classified as mentally ill. He explained his activism to Gary Greenberg (2010) in an online interview, referencing the newly instituted practice of diagnosing children with pediatric bipolar disorders and treating them with antipsychotic drugs, "kids getting unneeded antipsychotics that would make them gain 12 pounds in 12 weeks hit me in the gut. It was uniquely my job and my duty to protect them. If not me to correct it, who? I was stuck without an excuse to convince myself."

Allen Frances's (2009, 2010, 2011a, 2011b, 2011c, 2011d) specific objections to the *DSM-5* included the possible inclusion of the category of pre-psychosis; adding the category of disruptive mood dysregulation disorder in the children's section, which Frances characterized as "medicalizing" temper tantrums; the inclusion of minor forgetting in the elderly as indicative of disease; the merging of drug abuse and drug dependence categories; allowing everyday worries to meet criteria for anxiety disorders; labeling the bereaved as suffering from major depression; and the expansion of the categories for eating disorders. The Humanistic Psychology Division of the American Psychological Association (2011) launched a petition addressed to the American Psychiatric Association requesting that the American Psychiatric Association abandon the category of pre-psychosis, which would encourage treatment with antipsychotics. The petition referenced the recent finding by Ho, Andeasen, Ziebell, Pierson, and Magnotta (2011) that antipsychotic drugs result in shrinkage of the cortex. Allen Frances urged people to sign the petition, which was eventually signed by 14,000 people and endorsed by 50 mental health organizations (Deacon, 2013). The American Psychiatric Association did abandon the inclusion of pre-psychosis in the *DSM-5*. When the APA published the *DSM-5* in 2013, which allowed for the medicalization of temper tantrums and bereavement, Allen Frances urged the boycott of the *DSM-5*. According to Frances and Jones (2014), commenting on the process of the development of the *DSM-5*, "[e]verything has been done in a disorganized way: constant missing deadlines, inconsistent methods for conducting literature reviews, poor research design for the field trials, and finally the cancellation of the crucial quality control step because time was running out" (p. 11).

Beyond specific objections to the *DSM-5*, Frances and Jones (2014) questioned why the American Psychiatric Association is the final authority on defining mental illness. Psychiatrists have had the leadership role in defining mental illness for years and many psychiatrists are devoted to their patients. However, the revelations about the influence of the pharmaceutical industry on American psychiatry raise legitimate concerns. Many committee members developing criteria for schizophrenia, major depression, and bipolar disorders have documented ties to the pharmaceutical industry (Cosgrove & Krimsky, 2012).

THE LIMITATIONS OF CURRENT DIAGNOSTIC CATEGORIES

Diagnostic categories are useful to the extent that they are reliable, allow for better understanding of the etiology of the category, and guide clinical practice. Critics have examined how well these criteria have been met by the various versions of the *DSM*. After the publication of the *DSM-III*, Kirk and Kutchins (1992) published their book on the lack of reliability on the *DSM-III* categories as evaluated during the field studies. Estimates of the percentage of time that clinicians disagree on a diagnosis are between 33% and 46% of the time (Aboraya, Rankin, France, El-Missiry, & John, 2006). Since the *DSM-III*, findings regarding category reliabilities have deteriorated further. In *Saving Normal*, Allen Frances (2013) discusses the rushed field studies of the categories in the *DSM-5*. He suggests that the reliability of categories in the *DSM-5* is considerably weaker than that of categories in the *DSM-IV*. Thus, in terms of criteria for having a useful system of categories, the *DSM-5* fails the reliability test.

The lack of validity of the *DSM-5* categories has also been acknowledged by prominent individuals. Thomas Insel (2013), psychiatrist and director of the NIMH, in his blog characterized the *DSM-5* as "lacking validity" and "at best a dictionary." S. Nassir Ghaemi (2013), an expert in bipolar disorders, also voiced his skepticism regarding the categories in the *DSM*: "The leaders of those *DSMs* don't believe there are scientific truths in psychiatric diagnoses—only mutually agreed upon falsehood. They call it reliability" (p. 16). Ghaemi (2013) reflected on the days before the pathologizing of depression, which used to be referred to as neurosis or community depression. He finds little evidence of improvement with the advent of convincing individuals with ordinary forms of distress that they are suffering from a major illness requiring attention and treatment. Indeed, a survey by the WHO (WHO World Mental Health Survey

Consortium, 2004) found that the prevalence and severity of diagnosed mental disorders were higher in the United States, home of the *DSM*, than in any other country in the world.

With regard to the categories informing etiology, it is widely acknowledged that the *DSM* diagnoses refer to symptoms. In physical medicine, the same symptoms can be caused by many underlying causes. For example, a runny nose may reflect allergies, viral or bacterial infection, or irritation. Everyone acknowledges that basing category membership on symptoms lumps together apples and oranges. Indeed, Spitzer and First (2005) reflected, "little progress has been made toward understanding the pathophysiological processes and etiology of mental disorders. If anything, the research has shown the situation is even more complex than initially imagined, and we believe not enough is known to structure the classification of psychiatric disorders according to etiology" (p. 1898). Thus, Insel is probably correct in characterizing the *DSM-5* as a dictionary.

Another reasonable criterion for a system of diagnostic categories is that the categories should guide treatment, as commonly occurs in most of modern medicine. However, it is becoming apparent that diagnoses do not guide treatment in clinical practice in mental health. For those who subscribe to a neurotransmitter deficiency as the "root" of the diagnostic problem, drugs used to treat the disorder should all drive the culprit neurotransmitter in the same direction. However, in current practice, drugs that increase a particular neurotransmitter and drugs that decrease the same neurotransmitter are recommended for the same condition. The selective serotonin reuptake inhibitors, such as Prozac, are antidepressants and are believed to increase serotonin levels. Now, antipsychotic drugs (e.g., Abilify), which decrease dopamine signaling and block particular serotonin receptors (Stahl, 2013), have been approved by the Food and Drug Administration (FDA) for treatment of refractory depression. Children with ADHD may be treated with stimulant atomoxetine (Strattera), which is a norepinephrine-signaling enhancer. However, clonidine, a blood pressure medication that decreases norepinephrine-signaling, is also used to treat ADHD (Adler & Chua, 2002). Antidepressants, which increase norepinephrine, are sometimes prescribed for those with obsessive-compulsive disorders (OCDs). However, beta-blockers, which decrease norepinephrine function, are also used (Taylor, McKay, & Abramowitz, 2010). More children are being treated today with antipsychotic medications than ever. However, a study by Dosreis et al. (2011)

found that children for whom antipsychotics were prescribed carried all kinds of diagnoses (see Chapter 9, Foster Care section).

In summary, the criteria for a good system of categories include reliability, association with etiology, and ability to guide treatment. The current nomenclature fails on all criteria.

Abandonment of the *DSM-5*

The Patient Protection and Affordable Care Act (2010) will not be using the *DSM-5*. Under the Patient Protection and Affordable Care Act, the *International Classification of Diseases-9* (*ICD-9*) and the to-be-published *ICD-10*, when it is released, will be used for billing (Frances & Jones, 2014). As the insurance industry will be using the *ICD-10* categories for billing purposes, there is no compelling reason to read or purchase the *DSM-5*. (The *DSM-5* will cost $200; the *ICD* can be downloaded for free.) Insel (2013) announced that the NIMH would no longer be using *DSM* categories but rather would be focused on brain circuits underpinning particular behavioral syndromes, called research domain criteria. Many sectors of current society, the NIMH, and the insurance industry are planning on just ignoring the *DSM-5*.

EXTENSIVE NATURE OF THE MIND–BODY CONNECTION

I began my career in mental health working as a ward aide in a state mental hospital in order to finance my undergraduate education in 1967. The *DSM-II* (APA, 1968) had not yet been released. Although *psychosis* and *neurosis* were common terms, *functional* and *organic* were also commonly made distinctions. Organic behavioral symptoms were thought to be based on physiology. Persons who had suffered strokes were considered "organic." There were people who suffered from syphilis of the central nervous system or who had been infected with syphilis during gestation. They were also "organic." However, at that time, the bulk of the patients with psychotic diagnoses were considered "functional." According to the extant dogma in the 1960s, physiological explanations could not explain their behavior, at least not in a causative sense.

Modern research has discredited the idea that the mind and body are separate. Humans do vary in their behaviors. Some of this variation is attributable to genetic differences. Scientists can identify which variations in the gene recipe for making a protein (called an allele) are associated with particular behavioral manifestations. There are many examples of particular allelic variations of a gene predisposing to behavioral syndromes. Men with two copies of a particular genetic version of the receptor for vasopressin (a particular hormone) are less satisfied with their marriages and more likely to have considered divorce. Their wives were also less happy (Walum et al., 2008). Researchers in the field of behavioral genetics have established that religiosity (Kandler & Riemann, 2013), conscientiousness, enjoyment of exercise, and procrastination (Gustavson, Miyake, Hewitt, & Friedman, 2014; Huppertz et al., 2014; Matteson, McGue, & Iacono, 2013) all have genetic roots. Being a "night" or "morning" person is also genetically influenced by the version (allele) of the period gene that one carries. In flies (*Drosophila*), variation of this "period" gene is related to the amount of sunlight the ancestors of the fly were exposed to. Thus, timing of the sleep cycle is also inherited (Flint, Greenspan, & Kendler, 2010).

Just as the body can affect behavior, subjective states, and even attitudes, the reverse is also true. The field of psychoneuroimmunology has established that mood and stress can definitely influence physiology and disease processes (Littrell, 2008a, 2008b). Sheldon Cohen, whose research involves bringing people into the hospital and then spraying flu virus into their noses, established that stressors and level of social support influence whether a person will exhibit symptoms of a cold (Cohen, Doyle, Skoner, Rabin, & Gwaltney, 1997; Cohen et al., 1998). Persons who were raised by parents who owned their homes are less susceptible to disease as adults (Cohen, Doyle, Turner, Alper, & Skoner, 2004). Persons undergoing a great deal of stress, such as caregivers of those with Alzheimer's disease, produce lower levels of antibodies after vaccination (Glaser et al., 1992). Psychological stress retards wound healing (Kiecolt-Glaser, Marucha, Malarkey, Mercado, & Glaser, 1995), and social support improves the immune function of elderly persons (Kiecolt-Glaser et al., 1985). The studies of Whitehall employees, the British Civil Service agency at which everyone had health insurance, found that employees of lower grade status exhibited higher inflammatory markers in blood and thus were predisposed to cardiovascular diseases (Marmot, 2004; Steptoe & Marmot, 2002). These are examples of psychological events influencing negative health outcomes. Examples of psychological events improving brain function are also available. Siegle, Ghinassi, and Thase (2007) enumerate the large list of studies demonstrating that successful talk therapy does alter brain function as verified on imaging studies. Panksepp (2004) cites changes in brain following cognitive behavioral therapy for depression and OCD. Moreover, placebos can produce measurable changes in the brain (Panksepp, 2004). Thus, psychological interventions can definitely alter physiology. Once again, the mind and the body are a two-way street.

Throughout this book, we will identify physiological factors associated with the presentation of behavioral syndromes. Some allelic variations of genes have been substantiated as factors that increase the risk of development of particular behavioral syndromes. In terms of what people believe, the belief that a condition has a physiological basis often implies the need for a pharmacological intervention. For example, there is a correlation between the belief that depression has a physical basis and support for a drug as a treatment for depression (Deacon & Baird, 2009; Reavley & Jorm, 2012). However, the mind influences the body and the body influences the mind. Identifying physiology as a causal factor in producing a behavioral syndrome need not imply that pharmacology is the only way or a desirable way to alter a behavioral syndrome.

Throughout this book, the ways in which diet, social support, meditation, yoga, and exercise can alter physiology will be reviewed. If one accepts that anxiety, major depression, and psychosis have physiological underpinnings, pharmacological treatments need not be implied. Other interventions can work as well. In deciding which interventions are best, the criteria should be efficacy and fewer side effects. In each chapter of this book, various ways of intervening to ameliorate distress will be considered.

ARE DIAGNOSES NEEDED?

The January 2014 issue of *Research in Social Work Practice* was devoted to discussion of the *DSM-5*. Elaine Gambrill (2014), a social work educator noted for her publications on critical thinking, considered the function of diagnoses. She proffered the idea that diagnoses do offer an illusion of control as explanation for the continued prominence of diagnoses. In fact, there might be something to be said for an illusory sense of control. A number of studies have found that even when people work at rigged games with random outcomes, people infer that they have control (Baumeister, 2008; Langer, 1975). There is a large literature attesting to a sense of control attenuating levels of distress when people operate in a stressful environment (Bandura, 2001). Having a label for explaining distress usually implies that the cause is known and thus, a solution is available. Although such is not the case for mental disorders, the diagnosis may, nonetheless, provide a sense of comfort. Apparently, labels are comforting for clinicians as well. The Divisions of Counseling Psychology and Humanistic Psychology have established a forum on diagnoses (dxsummit.org). According to Jonathan Raskin (2013), chairperson for this endeavor, counseling psychologists do want a system of diagnoses. Moreover, insurance companies like diagnoses because diagnoses limit insurance company expenditures to those cases with legitimate need. So, apparently, there is a case to be made for some system of diagnoses.

Ironically, although having a diagnosis may confer an illusory sense of control over the future, most mental health diagnoses also carry the implication that the behavior associated with the disorder reflects the physiology to which one is fated (an absence of control). The late Thomas Szasz (Aftab, 2014) is famous for his view that mental illness is a myth. Szasz did not dispute that some people hear voices or that some people commit suicide. What he did dispute was that physiology could determine an individual's behavior and that people can be condemned by their genes to engage in particular ways. Szasz believed that people should be held accountable for their acts. Is there evidence that people can be condemned by their genes to act in particular ways? Contrary to Szasz's argument that the mentally ill are not fated by their genes, it might be argued that no one, including those considered normal, has free will. As previously stated, men with particular alleles for the receptor for vasopressin will be less satisfied with their marriages and more likely to engage in extramarital affairs (Walum et al., 2008). Adoption studies on children suggest that even when raised in a privileged environment, people rarely achieve beyond the economic-status level of their biological parents (Clarke, 2014). Biology probably does constrain the choices and outcomes of everyone. However, from the societal point of view, there is something to be gained when people think they have free will. Persons who are informed that obesity is a disease are less likely to stay on a diet (Hoyt, Burnette, & Auster-Gussman, 2014). In the laboratory, people have been shown to cheat more when they believe that they do not have free will (Vohs & Schooler, 2008). The academic achievement gap between Asian children and U.S. children has been explained by the fact that Asians tend to believe that achievement is a function of effort, whereas Americans tend to believe that achievement is a function of innate ability (Hsin & Xie, 2014). Hence, believing that one has control and free will really does influence behavior. As a society, it pays to maintain the belief that people have free will. Because diagnoses are associated with presumably ineluctable behavior patterns, diagnoses limit the subjective sense of free will.

There is another consideration against the utility of diagnoses. Most people in mental health settings seek treatment for marital problems, conflicts at work, being undecided about what to do in a marriage, and feeling overwhelmed with their children. Clients rarely come into treatment seeking a diagnosis. The strongest predictor of outcome in psychotherapy is the therapeutic alliance, which means that the therapist and the client agree on the nature of the problem and the strategy for achieving a change (DiClemente, 2007; Martin, Garske, & Davis, 2000). Thus, to decide how to proceed, good therapists conceptualize strategies, which are guided by the frames of reference of their clients. Then, in order to get paid, the clinician struggles to find some category in the *DSM* that might capture the client's distress. Some people do seek treatment for moods (e.g., anxiety or depression) or discomfort in social situations, which are more directly related to diagnostic categories. However, with mood disorders, the treatment requires attending to the content of each situation. Thus, what the client says about his or her sadness or the content of the particular worry directs the treatment to a greater extent than the label. Again, the diagnosis is not very helpful.

Khoury, Langer, and Pagnini (2014) alert us to the impact of diagnosis on the clinician. For the clinician, a diagnosis encourages the fundamental attribution error committed by observers. According to the attribution error, actors explain their own behaviors in terms of environmental pressures, whereas observers attribute others' behaviors to enduring traits. A diagnosis assigns the cause of distress to the individual rather than to situational factors, encouraging a mindless analysis lacking in nuance by the clinician. According to Khoury et al., after making diagnoses, clinicians "are less prone to seek novel information toward their patients' environment. Such mindless orientation toward the past may lead to misdiagnosis, mistreatment, and seriously compromise the therapeutic alliance between the professional and the individual seeking help" (Khoury et al., 2014, p. 5). Thus, again diagnosis can have negative unintended consequences.

There are additional downsides of diagnoses, particularly diagnoses associated with a biological origin. For every *DSM* diagnosis, publications in the psychiatric literature on the dismal long-term outcomes abound. Efforts to destigmatize may decrease blame. However, even though more people believe that conditions such as depression and alcohol dependence are biologically based, stigma has not been reduced. In fact, holding a biological view is correlated with belief that depressed people are dangerous and a desire for social distance from them (Mehta & Farina, 1997; Pescosolido et al., 2010; Schomerus et al., 2012). Those viewing mental illness as biologically based even want social distance from the relatives of those with a biologically based disorder (Phelan, 2005). Those holding the view that panic disorder has a biological basis exhibit more pessimism regarding recovery from it and are more likely to believe that persons with panic disorder are likely to commit suicide and harm others (Lam & Salkovskis, 2007). Similar findings are obtained when depression is construed as having a biological origin (Deacon & Baird, 2009). Paula Caplan (1995) argues against psychiatric diagnoses because these diagnoses are used in making legal decisions, such as awarding child custody. In some states, those who have been committed to state hospitals lose voting privileges, driving privileges, and are excluded from serving on juries. Although having a diagnosis may decrease blame, it does not reduce stigma and exclusion from the larger society.

Aside from the stigma imposed by others, diagnoses, particularly when they have a physiological basis, can become self-fulfilling prophecies for the persons receiving them. In a sample of depressed persons, those holding the biochemical or genetic view of depression expected depression to endure for a longer period of time (Lebowitz, Ahn, & Nolen-Hoeksema, 2013). In a review of the literature on how belief in biological explanations impacts self-concept, Lebowitz (2014) found that holding the biological view was associated with increased pessimism.

In summary, there are many disadvantages to diagnoses, particularly when they imply less personal control. However, diagnoses of disorders perhaps serve the reasonable function of getting some people off the hook of accountability. (A manic individual who has cleaned out his bank account needs a label as an excuse as much for himself as for his family.) Even those of us who believe that the truly disabled should receive disability insurance and perhaps be treated in a hospital rather than in a prison recognize that the present system of categories labels too many of us.

What Should Be the Criteria for Disorder?

Science cannot answer the question of which behavioral syndromes should be regarded as disorders. Science can inform whether a behavioral pattern is genetic or influenced by physiology. Science can inform regarding the prevalence of a behavioral pattern. Science can inform whether a physiologically based behavioral pattern results in desired outcomes for the individual and the society as a whole. Sometimes, the rationale for viewing a behavioral pattern as a disorder is that it is physiologically based and results in bad outcomes. (The rationale that the disorder is unusual has clearly been abandoned in America; apparently, "normal" no longer means "normative.") However, where to draw the line requires a value judgment. Perhaps, the current lines are in the wrong place. Many would probably object to 50% of us who meet criteria for a *DSM* label (Kessler et al., 2005, study estimate) being granted rights under the Americans with Disabilities Act or receiving Social Security disability benefits because of our impairment.

Has Labeling Ordinary Behavior as Mental Illness Resulted in Better Outcomes?

The practice of labeling and then treating common behavioral syndromes should result in better outcomes. Thomas Insel questions whether current practices of diagnoses and treatments have produced less suffering for humanity. Insel (2009) has acknowledged, "The unfortunate reality is that current medications help too few people to get better and very few people to get well" (p. 704). Indeed, the WHO (2011) reports that mental illness is among the leading causes of disability. Robert Whitaker's (2010) *Anatomy of an Epidemic* examines the swelling rates of disability rolls attributable to psychiatric conditions in the United States. More of us are considered mentally ill now than in the past.

Ghaemi (2008) reflects on the dominant philosophy in current medical practice, which regards disease entities as requiring a frontal attack through some external means. Ghaemi regards current practices as failing to appreciate how any dysfunction is deeply entwined in the intrinsic functions of the body. Ghaemi recognizes that modern medicine is far from the practice of medicine as envisioned by Hippocrates. Hippocrates is famous for such admonitions as "first, do not harm" and "It's more important to know what sort of person has a disease than to know what sort of disease a person has." Hippocrates believed that the healer should harness the body's natural mechanisms for correcting itself, rather than imposing foreign processes. According to Ghaemi (2008), modern medicine fails to recognize possible strengths in the patient that can be harnessed in the service of limiting distress. Indeed, the *DSM-5* abandonment of the axes system is further evidence of failure to acknowledge the impact of the environment in exacerbating distress or the possibility that the environment might offer resources for ameliorating distress.

THE APPROACH IN THIS BOOK

Tom Insel is probably correct in his assessment that the *DSM* is a dictionary. Most of the categories in the *DSM* have become part of daily terminology for everyone. We are stuck with the categories we have been given, so we continue to use them. In this book, the physiology and environmental stressors giving rise to particular behavioral syndromes in the *DSM* are reviewed. The efficacy and side effects of pharmacological interventions are discussed. Additionally, the outcome studies of more naturalistic interventions (diet, exercise, meditation, and social support) and ways to harness the individual's capacity for health are considered. The pathways through which various interventions influence biology are explained.

This book is designed to assist clinicians in articulating the physiology undergirding specific distress and assisting clients in selecting a strategy for ameliorating their distress. In the last chapter of this book, rather than focusing on distress, the focus switches to ways to promote well-being. As discussed in the last chapter, the Patient Protection and Affordable Care Act does allow for prevention. Perhaps the future will allow us to provide desired support to all people with a minimum of labeling.

REFERENCES

Aboraya, A., Rankin, E., France, C., El-Missiry, A., & John, C. (2006). The reliability of psychiatric diagnosis revisited. *Psychiatry, 3*(1), 41–50.

Adler, L. A., & Chua, H. C. (2002). Management of ADHD in adults. *Journal of Clinical Psychiatry, 63* (Suppl. 12), 29–35.

Aftab, A. (2014). Mental illness vs. brain disorders: From Szasz to *DSM-5*. *Psychiatric Times, 31*(2), 20G–20H.

American Psychiatric Association. (1952). *Diagnostic and statistical manual of mental disorders*. Washington, DC: Author.

American Psychiatric Association. (1968). *Diagnostic and statistical manual of mental disorders* (2nd ed.). Washington, DC: Author.

American Psychiatric Association. (1980). *Diagnostic and statistical manual of mental disorders* (3rd ed.). Washington, DC: Author.

American Psychiatric Association. (1987). *Diagnostic and statistical manual of mental disorders* (3rd ed., rev.). Washington, DC: Author.

American Psychiatric Association. (1994). *Diagnostic and statistical manual of mental disorders* (4th ed.). Washington, DC: Author.

American Psychiatric Association. (2013). *Diagnostic and statistical manual of mental disorders* (5th ed.). Washington, DC: Author.

American Psychiatric Association. (2015). *DSM: History of the manual.* Retrieved from http://www.psychiatry.org/practice/dsm/dsm-history-of-the-manual

Bandura, A. (2001). Social cognitive theory: An agentic perspective. *Annual Review of Psychology, 52*, 1–26.

Baumeister, R. F. (2008). Free will in scientific psychology. *Perspectives on Psychological Science, 3*(1), 14–17.

Caplan, P. (1995). *They say you're crazy: How the world's most powerful psychiatrists decide who's normal.* Cambridge, MA: De Capo Press.

Carey, B. (2005, June 7). Most will be mentally ill at some point, study says. *The New York Times.* Retrieved from http://www.nytimes.com/2005/06/07/health/07mental.html?_r=0

Clarke, G. (2014, February 23). Your ancestors, your fate. *The New York Times: Sunday Review*, pp. 1, 6, 7.

Cohen, S., Doyle, W. J., Skoner, D. P., Rabin, B. S., & Gwaltney, J. M. (1997). Social ties and susceptibility to the common cold. *Journal of the American Medical Association, 277*(24), 1940–1944.

Cohen, S., Doyle, W. J., Turner, R. B., Alper, C. M., & Skoner, D. P. (2004). Childhood socioeconomic status and host resistance to infectious illness in adulthood. *Psychosomatic Medicine, 66*(4), 553–558.

Cohen, S., Frank, E., Doyle, W. J., Skoner, D. P., Rabin, B. S., & Gwaltney, J. M. (1998). Types of stressors that increase susceptibility to the common cold in healthy adults. *Health Psychology, 17*(3), 214–223.

Cosgrove, L., & Krimsky, S. (2012). A comparison of *DSM-IV* and *DSM-5* panel members' financial associations with industry: A pernicious problem persists. *PLoS Medicine, 9*(3), e1001190.

Davies, J. (2014). *Cracked: The unhappy truth about psychiatry.* London: Pegasus Books.

Deacon, B. J. (2013). The biomedical model of mental disorder: A critical analysis of its validity, utility, and effects on psychotherapy research. *Clinical Psychology Review, 33*(7), 846–861.

Deacon, B. J., & Baird, G. (2009). The chemical imbalance explanation of depression: Reducing blame at what cost? *Journal of Clinical and Social Psychology, 28,* 415–435.

Decker, H. (2013). *The making of the DSM-III: A diagnostic manual's conquest of American psychiatry.* New York, NY: Oxford University Press.

DiClemente, C. C. (2007). Mechanisms, determinants and processes of change in the modification of drinking behavior. *Alcoholism, Clinical and Experimental Research, 31* (10, Suppl.), 13s–20s.

Dosreis, S., Yoon, Y., Rubin, D. M., Riddle, M. A., Noll, E., & Rothbard, A. (2011). Antipsychotic treatment among youth in foster care. *Pediatrics, 128*(6), e1459–e1466.

Flint, J., Greenspan, R. J., & Kendler, K. S. (2010). *How genes influence behavior.* New York, NY: Oxford University Press.

Frances, A. (2009, June 26). A warning sign on the road to the *DSM-V*: Beware of its unintended consequences. *Psychiatric Times, 26*(8). Retrieved from http://psychiatrictimes.com/display/article/10168/1425378

Frances, A. (2010, March 1). It's not too late to save "normal." *Los Angeles Times.* Retrieved January 1, 2012, from http://articles.latimes.com/2010/mar/01/opinion/la-oe-frances1–201mar01

Frances, A. (2011a, October). Debate: Does early intervention help or hinder mental health outcomes? *Psychiatric Times, 28*(10), 9–12.

Frances, A. (2011b, November 11). *DSM-5*: Living document or dead on arrival? *Psychiatric Times.* Retrieved from http://www.psychiatrictimes.com/blog/dsm-5/content/article/10168/1989691

Frances, A. (2011c, November 10). The user's revolt against DSM-5: Will it work? *Psychiatric Times.* Retrieved from http://www.psychiatrictimes.com/blog/dsm-5/content/article/10168/1988483

Frances, A. (2011d, November 4). Why psychiatrists should sign the petition to reform *DSM-5. Psychiatric Times.* Retrieved from http://www.psychiatrictimes.com/dsm-5-0/why-psychiatrists-should-sign-The-Petition-To-Reform-DSM-5

Frances, A. (2013). *Saving normal: An insider's revolt against out-of-control psychiatric diagnosis, DSM-5, big pharma, and the medicalization of ordinary life.* New York, NY: HarperCollins.

Frances, A., & Jones, K. D. (2014). Should social workers use *Diagnostic and Statistical Manual of Mental Disorders-5? Research on Social Work Practice, 24,* 11–12.

Gambrill, E. (2014). The *Diagnostic and Statistical Manual of Mental Disorders* as a major form of dehumanization in the modern world. *Research on Social Work Practice, 24,* 13–36.

Ghaemi, S. N. (2008). *Mood disorders, 2nd edition.* New York, NY: Lippincott Williams & Wilkins.

Ghaemi, S. N. (2013, July 17). Requiem for *DSM. Psychiatric Times.* Retrieved from www.pychiatrictimes.com/dsm-5–0/requiem-dsm

Glaser, R., Kiecolt-Glaser, J. K., Bonneau, R. H., Malarkey, W., Kennedy, S., & Hughes, J. (1992). Stress-induced modulation of the immune response to recombinant hepatitis B vaccine. *Psychosomatic Medicine, 54*(1), 22–29.

Greenberg, G. (2010, December 10). *Inside the battle to define mental illness* [Web log post]. Retrieved January 1, 2012, from www.wired.com/magazine/2010/12/ff_dsmv/all/1

Grob, G. N. (1991). Origins of *DSM-I:* A study in appearance and reality. *American Journal of Psychiatry, 148*(4), 421–431.

Gustavson, D. E., Miyake, A., Hewitt, J. K., & Friedman, N. P. (2014). Genetic relations among procrastination, impulsivity, and goal-management ability: Implications for the evolutionary origin of procrastination. *Psychological Science, 25*(6), 1178–1188.

Harris, G., & Carey, B. (2008, July 12). Psychiatric Association faces Senate scrutiny over drug industry ties. *The New York Times,* A13.

Ho, B. C., Andeasen, N. C., Ziebell, S., Pierson, R., & Magnotta, V. (2011). Long-term antipsychotic treatment and brain volume, *Archives of General Psychiatry, 68*(2), 126–137.

Houts, A. C. (2000). Fifty years of psychiatric nomenclature: Reflections on the 1943 War Department Technical Bulletin, Medical 203. *Journal of Clinical Psychology, 56*(7), 935–967.

Hoyt, C. L., Burnette, J. L., & Auster-Gussman, L. (2014). "Obesity is a disease": Examining the self-regulatory impact of this public-health message. *Psychological Science, 25*(4), 997–1002.

Hsin, A., & Xie, Y. (2014). Explaining Asian Americans' academic advantage over whites. *Proceedings of the National Academy of Sciences of the United States of America, 111*(23), 8416–8421.

Humanistic Psychology Division of the American Psychological Association. (2011). *Open letter to the DSM-5.* Retrieved from http://www.petitions.com/petition/dsm5/

Huppertz, C., Bartels, M., Jansen, I. E., Boomsma, D. I., Willemsen, G., de Moor, M. H., & de Geus, E. J. (2014). A twin-sibling study on the relationship between exercise attitudes and exercise behavior. *Behavior Genetics, 44*(1), 45–55.

Insel, T. R. (2009). Disruptive insights in psychiatry: Transforming a clinical discipline. *Journal of Clinical Investigation, 119*(4), 700–705.

Insel, T. R. (2013, April 13). *Director's blog: Transforming diagnosis.* Retrieved from www.nimh.nih.gov/about/director/2013/transforming-diagnosis.shtml

Kandler, C., & Riemann, R. (2013). Genetic and environmental sources of individual religiousness: The roles of individual personality traits and perceived environmental religiousness. *Behavior Genetics, 43*(4), 297–313.

Kessler, R. C., Chiu, W. T., Demler, O., Merikangas, K. R., & Walters, E. E. (2005). Prevalence, severity, and comorbidity of 12-month *DSM-IV* disorders in the National Comorbidity Survey Replication. *Archives of General Psychiatry, 62*(6), 617–627.

Khoury, B., Langer, E. J., & Pagnini, F. (2014). The DSM: Mindful science or mindless power? A critical review. *Frontiers in Psychology, 5*, 602.

Kiecolt-Glaser, J. K., Glaser, R., Williger, D., Stout, J., Messick, G., Sheppard, S.,...Bonnell, G. (1985). Psychosocial enhancement of immunocompetence in a geriatric population. *Health Psychology, 4*(1), 25–41.

Kiecolt-Glaser, J. K., Marucha, P. T., Malarkey, W. B., Mercado, A. M., & Glaser, R. (1995). Slowing of wound healing by psychological stress. *Lancet, 346*(8984), 1194–1196.

Kirk, S. A., & Kutchins, H. (1992). *The selling of the DSM: The rhetoric of science in psychiatry.* Hawthorne, NY: Aldine de Gruyter.

Lacasse, J. R., & Leo, J. (2010). Ghostwriting at elite academic medical centers in the United States. *PLoS Medicine, 7*(2), e1000230.

Laing, R. D. (1971). *The politics of the family and other essays.* New York, NY: Routledge.

Lam, D. C., & Salkovskis, P. M. (2007). An experimental investigation of the impact of biological and psychological causal explanations on anxious and depressed patients' perception of a person with panic disorder. *Behaviour Research and Therapy, 45*(2), 405–411.

Langer, E. J. (1975). The illusion of control. *Journal of Personality and Social Psychology, 32*(2), 311–328.

Lebowitz, M. S. (2014). Biological conceptualizations of mental disorders among affected individuals: A review of correlates and consequences. *Clinical Psychology: Science and Practice, 21*, 67–83.

Lebowitz, M. S., Ahn, W. K., & Nolen-Hoeksema, S. (2013). Fixable or fate? Perceptions of the biology of depression. *Journal of Consulting and Clinical Psychology, 81*(3), 518–527.

Littrell, J. (2008a). The mind–body connection: Not just a theory anymore. *Social Work in Health Care, 46*(4), 17–37.

Littrell, J. (2008b). New developments in understanding cardiovascular disease and the implications for social work. *Social Work in Health Care, 46*(2), 35–49.

Marmot, M. (2004). *The status syndrome: How social standing affects our health and longevity.* New York, NY: Times Books.

Martin, D. J., Garske, J. P., & Davis, M. K. (2000). Relation of the therapeutic alliance with outcome and other variables: A meta-analytic review. *Journal of Consulting and Clinical Psychology, 68*(3), 438–450.

Matteson, L. K., McGue, M., & Iacono, W. (2013). Is dispositional happiness contagious? The impact of the well-being of family members on individual well-being. *Journal of Individual Differences, 34*(2), 90–96.

Mehta, S., & Farina, A. (1997). Is being "sick" really better? Effect of the disease view of mental disorder on stigma. *Journal of Social and Clinical Psychology, 16*(4), 405–419.

Moffitt, T. E., Caspi, A., Taylor, A., Kokaua, J., Milne, B. J., Polanczyk, G., & Poulton, R. (2010). How common are common mental disorders? Evidence that lifetime prevalence rates are doubled by prospective versus retrospective ascertainment. *Psychological Medicine, 40*(6), 899–909.

Noll, R. (2011). *American madness: The rise and fall of dementia praecox.* Boston, MA: Harvard University Press.

Panksepp, J. (2004). Biological psychiatry sketched—Past, present, and future. In J. Panksepp (Eds.), *Biological psychiatry* (pp. 3–32). Hoboken, NJ: Wiley-Liss.

Patient Protection and Affordable Care Act of 2010, Pub. L. No. 111–148, 124, Stat. 119 (2010).

Pescosolido, B. A., Martin, J. K., Long, J. S., Medina, T. R., Phelan, J. C., & Link, B. G. (2010). "A disease like any other"? A decade of change in public reactions to schizophrenia, depression, and alcohol dependence. *American Journal of Psychiatry, 167*(11), 1321–1330.

Phelan, J. C. (2005). Geneticization of deviant behavior and consequences for stigma: The case of mental illness. *Journal of Health and Social Behavior, 46*(4), 307–322.

Probst, B. (2014). The life and death of Axis IV: Caught in the quest for a theory of mental disorder. *Research on Social Work Practice, 24*(1), 123–131.

Raskin, J. (2013, November 3). *Panel on DSM-5.* Annual Conference of the International Society for Ethical Psychology and Psychiatry, Greensboro, NC.

Reavley, N. J., & Jorm, A. F. (2012). Belief in the harmfulness of antidepressants: Associated factors and change over 16 years. *Journal of Affective Disorders, 138*(3), 375–386.

Rosenhan, D. L. (1973). On being sane in insane places. *Science, 179,* 250–258.

Schomerus, G., Schwahn, C., Holzinger, A., Corrigan, P. W., Grabe, H. J., Carta, M. G., & Angermeyer, M. C. (2012). Evolution of public attitudes about mental illness: A systematic review and meta-analysis. *Acta Psychiatrica Scandinavica, 125*(6), 440–452.

Siegle, G. J., Ghinassi, F., & Thase, M. E. (2007). Neurobehavioral therapies in the 21st century: Summary of an emerging field and an extended example of cognitive control training for depression. *Cognitive Therapy and Research, 31,* 235–262.

Spitzer, R. L., & First, M. R. (2005). Classification of psychiatric disorders. *Journal of the American Medical Association, 294*(15), 1898–1899.

Spitzer, R. L., & Fleiss, J. L. (1974). A re-analysis of the reliability of psychiatric diagnosis. *British Journal of Psychiatry, 125*(0), 341–347.

Stahl, S. M. (2013). *Stahl's essential psychopharmacology: Neuroscientific basic and practical applications, 4th edition.* New York, NY: Cambridge University Press.

Steptoe, A., & Marmot, M. (2002). The role of psychobiological pathways in socio-economic inequalities in cardiovascular disease risk. *European Heart Journal, 23*(1), 13–25.

Szasz, T. S. (1961). *The myth of mental illness: Foundations of a theory of personal conduct.* New York: Harper Perennial.

Taylor, S., McKay, D., & Abramowitz, J. S. (2010). More on the brain disease model of mental disorders. *Behavior Therapist, 33,* 16–17.

Vohs, K. D., & Schooler, J. W. (2008). The value of believing in free will: Encouraging a belief in determinism increases cheating. *Psychological Science, 19*(1), 49–54.

Walum, H., Westberg, L., Henningsson, S., Neiderhiser, J. M., Reiss, D., Igl, W.,... Lichtenstein, P. (2008). Genetic variation in the vasopressin receptor 1a gene (AVPR1A) associates with pair-bonding behavior in humans. *Proceedings of the National Academy of Sciences of the United States of America, 105*(37), 14153–14156.

Whitaker, R. (2010). *Anatomy of an epidemic: Magic bullets, psychiatric drugs, and the astonishing risk of mental illness in America.* New York, NY: Broadway Books.

WHO World Mental Health Survey Consortium. (2004). Prevalence, severity, and unmet need for treatment of mental disorders in the World Health Organization World Mental Health Surveys. *Journal of the American Medical Association, 291,* 2581–2590.

World Health Organization. (2011). *Global status report on non-communicable diseases 2010.* Geneva, Switzerland: Author.

2

Physiology

This chapter is a primer on physiology, which will offer a foundation for the material covered in the rest of the text. The technical terms are introduced in six different sections.

Section 1 of this chapter focuses on genes and epigenetics. Section 2, which discusses some of the major neurotransmitters, explains how neurons function and how they communicate with each other through neurotransmitters. Section 3 offers information about the immune system, which interacts with the nervous system to influence mood and behavior. Section 4 focuses on three circuits that are relevant to styles of behavior: the appetitive or approach system, the regulatory control system, and the learned helplessness system. At the end of Section 4, two additional circuits are explained, the behavioral activation system (BAS) and the behavioral inhibition system (BIS). The discussion of the BAS and BIS utilizes findings involving the other circuits. Section 5 focuses on emotion, using the material in the prior sections to explain various emotions. Section 5 also covers the physiological systems supporting emotional behavior: the autonomic nervous system and hormones. Section 6 considers how social connections influence the brain and its physiology.

There is a great deal of information in this chapter, perhaps too much to be appreciated in one sitting for those who are not yet familiar with the material. It is not necessary to have command of all the material in this chapter before moving on. Some of the material in this chapter will be referenced again in later chapters. The reader might wish to refer to relevant sections in this chapter when reading subsequent chapters. Exercises are included at the end of this chapter (following the chapter's References section), which will aid in the retention of the terms that are used again in subsequent chapters.

SECTION 1: GENES AND EPIGENETICS

Inheritance refers to the process of passing along the instructions for building the machinery of the body from parents to offspring. Genes are the physical mechanism used for the process of inheritance. A gene is a recipe for making a protein. Depending on the recipe you get from your parents, you will make a particular version of the protein. Proteins can be enzymes, and enzymes are the workhorses for making all of the other molecules in the body as well as the workhorses for acting on the molecules that you consume in your diet. Proteins can also be structural components of your body, such as the collagen in your nose or the keratin in your hair. Effectively, the versions of the proteins that you inherit play a big role in determining the characteristics that differentiate you from other people who have had similar experiences and live in similar environments.

Genes are made up of a string of nucleotides. Many genes are strung together to comprise a longer string of nucleotides called a chromosome. In fact, for storing the DNA, two strings of nucleotides bond horizontally with each other, forming a ladder-like structure. The ladder is twisted into the familiar double helix (Figure 2.1). The two strings are easily pulled apart because the connecting bonds between the sides of the rungs of the ladder are of a fragile nature. The gene recipe is present only on one of the strings.

Every cell in the body (with the exception of red blood cells) contains chromosomes in the nucleus of the cell. (The nucleus of the cell is enclosed in a membrane and is found in the larger area of the cell, called the cytoplasm of the cell.) In the nucleus there are 23 pairs of chromosomes, one from the mother and the other from the father. The actual chromosome string can be very long, albeit very narrow. In order to fit into the tiny nucleus inside the cell, the string has to be compressed. The chromosome is comprised of a DNA string that is wound around other proteins so that it gets compressed into a tiny space.

The Two-Step Process of Making a Protein

A nucleotide has a base linked to sugar and phosphate groups. The identity of the nucleotide is determined by its base. There are only four DNA bases: adenine, cytosine, thymine, and guanine. The familiar letters A,

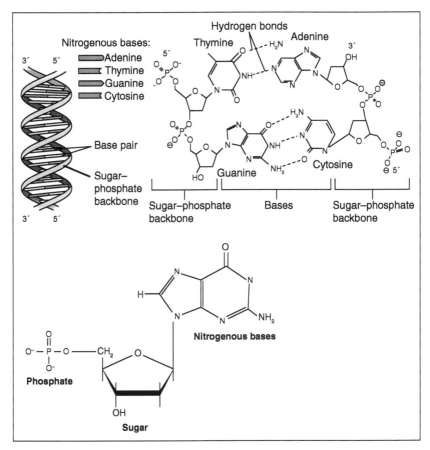

FIGURE 2.1 Image of DNA.

Source: Wikicommons.

C, T, and G seen in the popular press refer to the bases. (The reader may wish to look at the image of DNA, Figure 2.1.)

In order to use the recipe in the gene to make a protein, several steps need to occur. First, an enzyme complex (machinery that knows how to build another nucleotide string) sits on top of the beginning of the gene at the start of the string. The machinery uses the DNA template to make a string of ribonucleic acid (RNA) nucleotides. (RNA nucleotides are very similar to DNA nucleotides except that the sugar in an RNA nucleotide differs slightly from the sugar in a DNA nucleotide.) The resulting RNA nucleotide string copy of the DNA gene string is called messenger RNA (mRNA). The mRNA can leave the nucleus and move into the cytoplasm of the cell. This is the first step in the protein-making process. The second step occurs when the mRNA encounters another complex of machinery in the cell cytoplasm. In the second step, machinery uses the mRNA nucleotides as instructions for stringing together individual amino acids (there are 20 amino acid possibilities) into a string of amino acids called a peptide or protein. In fact, different sequences of three nucleotides in the mRNA string, called a codon, specify which amino acid should be added to the emerging chain. The machinery just slides along the mRNA string, recognizing the appearance of a start codon, and sequentially adds on amino acids according to the instructions from the mRNA.

How the Cell Decides Whether to Make a Protein

Whether a gene will be used to make mRNA is a highly controlled decision. Often, transcription of the DNA into mRNA is controlled by other proteins called transcription factors. Transcription factors help to assemble the machinery that will make an mRNA string using the DNA string as the recipe. Many transcription factors, usually proteins, only operate when particular molecules, for example, hormones like glucocorticoids, are bound to these proteins. The docking of all the machinery for transcribing a DNA nucleotide sequence into mRNA also depends on the DNA sequence in the promoter region (the place close to where the copying machinery, including enzymes and transcription factors, assembles).

Some genes, that is, the nucleotide strings that are recipes for making proteins, are polymorphic in a given population. *Polymorphic* means that there are multiple versions of the recipe or nucleotide string in a given group of people. Sometimes the difference in the nucleotide string is in a single nucleotide in the region, which is used to determine the sequence of amino acids in the protein. Even a single change in a base can create an enormous functional difference in the protein. (The gene that codes for the version of the hemoglobin protein that a person carries requires only one base change to yield a propensity to sickle cell anemia.) Sometimes the difference is seen in the promoter region of the gene. A change in a nucleotide or nucleotides in the promoter region of the gene will not alter the version of the protein that gets produced. However, variation across people in a gene's promoter region can determine how frequently the protein gets made (expressed) (Alberts et al., 2008; Schaaf, Zschocke, & Potocki, 2012).

The U.S. government does provide a wonderful resource. If one goes to the government PubMed website (National Center for Biotechnology Information) and hits online Mendelian inheritance in man (OMIM), typing in any disease will bring up the various allelic variations that have been associated with the disease. Clicking on the number of the allele provides a synopsis of current research reports. In later chapters on disorders, we will be considering allele variants associated with various disorders. A synopsis of genetic information relevant to any disorder can be found through OMIM.

Epigenetics

Epigenetics is a newly developing field. It has long been recognized that cells of different tissues look very different. How can this be, if all cells contain the same DNA? It turns out that as cells differentiate to become a particular type of cell belonging to a particular organ, particular genes in the chromosome get "packed away" so that the gene becomes inaccessible for making mRNA. The packing up, unpacking, and opening of the DNA so that it can be copied into mRNA constitutes the new field of epigenetics (Carey, 2012).

Epigenetics has resurrected the Lamarckian notion that the environment can change the genome (Szyf, 2014). Environmental factors do not often change the sequence of a DNA string (unless in the case of strong chemicals or exposure to strong sunlight). However, environmental influence, such as starvation or types of food in the diet, can determine whether a gene gets packed away or unpacked. The packing process usually involves adding a methyl group (methylation) in the promoter region of the gene. The methylation makes it hard to open the DNA string to get at the DNA recipe for copying. It turns out that the care and feeding of a youngster or exposure to particular aversive events have an influence on epigenetic modifications that determine which proteins get made.

Epigenetic modifications do influence behavioral outcomes. The rat pups of low-licking mothers are more anxious. (Licking rat pups is a form of nurturing by the mother.) Michael Meaney and colleagues (Weaver et al., 2007) showed that given more licking by the mother, the gene for the cortisol receptor (in the hippocampus of the rat pup, explained later) gets unpacked so that it is readily available for making the cortisol receptor protein. (The receptor offers a mechanism for discerning when there is enough cortisol in the body.) Thus, the nurtured rat pup has a mechanism for turning off the system so that there is a break on the production of cortisol, a stress hormone. In contrast to the frequently licked pup, in the low-licked pup, the DNA sequence (gene) for the cortisol receptor is packed away. The animal lacks a feedback mechanism for decreasing the cortisol-producing system. When Meaney and colleagues (McGowan, Meaney, & Szyf, 2008) introduced a chemical that increases openness of the DNA into the hippocampus to reopen the cortisol receptor gene in the nervous rats, the epigenetic modifications in the rat were reversed. The rats were no longer anxious. To prove that the anxiety of the rat pup depended on the expression of the cortisol receptor, Meaney et al. also infused an amino acid (methionine) into the brain of the high-licked rat, which led to packing away (methylation) of the cortisol receptor gene. Adding the amino acid resulted in anxiety in the rat pups of even the high-licking mother. This work is relevant to humans. The same cortisol receptor gene is packed away (methylated) in those who have committed suicide and who have been abused or neglected as children (Suderman et al., 2012).

A study done by Roth, Lubin, Funk, and Sweatt (2009) found that the gene for brain-derived neurotropic factor (BDNF), a factor required for brain health, was packed away (methylated) in rat pups of low-licking mothers. Additionally, Champagne (2008) found epigenetic modifications of the oxytocin receptor gene in the low-licked pups. (Oxytocin is a hormone that induces caring for young in mothers; the oxytocin receptor is the protein that receives the message delivered by the hormone.) In the rat pups that were not licked, the receptor for the oxytocin was packed away so that the pups could not receive the instruction to care for their young, which was carried by the oxytocin hormone. This epigenetic modification in a low-licked female rat resulted in transmission of the failure to nurture young to the female offspring. The Champagne finding showed that neglect of offspring in rats can be transferred across generations through epigenetic changes.

Not only can a tendency toward general "nervousness" be transmitted through epigenetic means, but specific fears can be transmitted as well. Dias and Ressler (2014) showed that if a rat is shocked in the presence of say an orange scent (actually they used acetophenone), then an epigenetic modification of the receptor for the scent occurs. (There is less methylation or packing away of the gene, so more of the receptor is made.) This epigenetic modification is transmitted to the gamete (the sperm or egg) such that the pups of the parents who were shocked were fearful of oranges. In fact, in the Dias and Ressler study, the epigenetic modification was transmitted to many generations.

The Dias and Ressler experiment has profound implications. The experiment showed that the environmental challenges faced by the parents can shape the genome of the offspring. From a survival-of-the-species perspective, epigenetic changes are a much more targeted mechanism for adapting to the environment than evolution. For example, an animal might get sick from eating food with a particular characteristic (a particular odor), and that experience could be transmitted to progeny, through a quick change in methylation. In contrast, evolutionary changes rely on a random mutation (change of a sequence of nucleotides) in a DNA sequence during copying of the gene for the formation of eggs or sperm. Those mutations that make the animal more fit for survival and reproduction persist in later progeny. Evolutionary changes normally take a long time and rely on a chance alteration in the genome for which the environment selects. In contrast, epigenetic changes, when they occur, are targeted and fast.

Telomeres

Telomeres are a specific sequence of nucleotides at the end of a chromosome. They are produced by a specific enzyme (telomerase). Because of the way that DNA is copied in preparation for cell division, with each copying event the length of the telomere will be a little shorter, unless the cell has activated telomerase. Researchers have realized that the length of the telomere serves as a marker for stress (Epel et al., 2004). Those individuals who have spent more of their life span in a state of depression have, as a group, shorter telomeres in their white blood cells (Wolkowitz et al., 2011).

Some of the interventions that will be discussed in subsequent chapters have been found to influence telomere length. Those whose diets are higher in omega-3s (fish oil) have longer telomeres in their white blood cells (Kiecolt-Glaser et al., 2013). Meditation is associated with higher telomerase activity. The higher telomerase activity induced by meditation was statistically mediated by (associated with) an increased sense of purpose in life and greater sense of perceived control (Jacobs et al., 2011).

SECTION 2: NEURONS AND NEUROTRANSMITTERS

Neurons are the major cells of the brain and the peripheral nervous system. One neuron fires and then transmits a message to an adjacent neuron. However, the neurons do not touch each other. They communicate with each other through a chemical called a neurotransmitter, which is released into a space between the two neurons called the synaptic cleft (Figure 2.2).

Like other cells, neurons have a nucleus where the chromosomes are located. Like other cells, the "skin" of the neuron is called a cell membrane. Unlike other cells, the neuron's morphology (shape) has been adapted so that neurons can communicate with other neurons. (The reader might want to look at Figure 2.2 at this point and notice that the central neuron is receiving input from "upstream neurons" and is sending information out to "downstream" neurons. To simplify the explanation we will discuss a three-neuron chain of communication.) Coming off the central neuron's cell body are many branches called dendrites. The dendrites receive a message from an adjacent neuron, which is "upsteam" in the communicating chain of neurons. Another bigger projection, the central neuron's axon, is the structure used by the central neuron to send a message to a receiving neuron. In order to communicate with a receiving "downstream" neuron, a packet or vesicle containing a neurotransmitter is propelled down the central neuron's axon. At the end of the axon, when the central neuron "fires," the vesicles containing neurotransmitter fuse with the membrane of the central neuron. The contents of the vesicles are then "dumped" into a space called the synaptic cleft. At the other side of the synaptic cleft is the dendrite of a receiving downstream neuron (the neuron at the end of the three-neuron chain). On the dendrites of the receiving, downstream neuron are receptors for particular neurotransmitters.

The receptors for neurotransmitters are generally classified as ionotropic, metabotropic, or as an autoreceptor. Ionotropic receptors open channels in the membrane of a neuron and allow ions (charged particles) to move into the cell. This process can quickly result in the firing of the receiving neuron. Metabotropic receptors change the internal environment of the neuron, which will have an effect on the neuron's firing at a later time. The ionotropic and metatropic receptors are usually on dendrites receiving the signal from another neuron. In contrast to ionotropic and metabotropic receptors, which receive messages from other

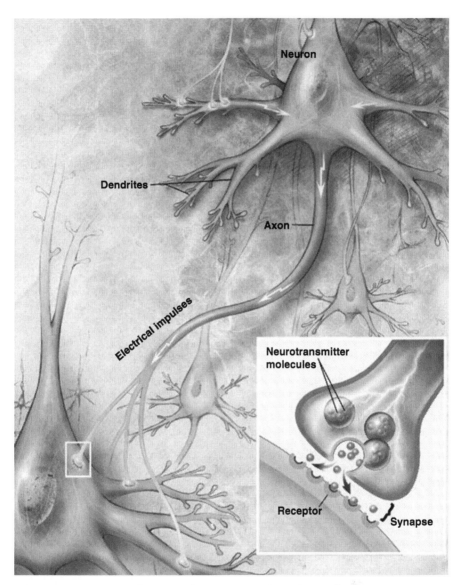

FIGURE 2.2   Image of a central neuron receiving input from an upstream neuron and communicating with a downstream neuron through a synapse.

Source: U.S. National Institutes of Health, National Institute on Aging.

neurons, are autoreceptors. Autoreceptors are found on the cell body of the very neuron that released the neurotransmitter. Autoreceptors monitor the behavior of the neuron's own activity. Autoreceptors constitute a negative feedback system, which decreases the probability that the neuron will release a great deal of neurotransmitters within a short period of time.

The Life Cycle of a Neurotransmitter

Generally, neurons use only one neurotransmitter to communicate. The neuron must produce (synthesize) its neurotransmitter. Once produced, the neurotransmitter must be packaged into vesicles, ready for delivery down the axon and release into the synaptic cleft. How is the neurotransmitter removed from the synaptic cleft? Sometimes it is broken down by an enzyme in the synaptic cleft. Some neurotransmitters (serotonin, dopamine, and norepinephrine) are transported back into the presynaptic neuron by a protein, called a transporter. The neurotransmitter is then ready to be repackaged into a vesicle and reused. Sometimes, not all of the neurotransmitter inside the cell gets repackaged. Some of the neurotransmitter can get degraded inside the cell by another enzyme.

How Are the Functions of Neurotransmitters Investigated?

The neurons that utilize serotonin, norepinephrine, acetylcholine, and dopamine are located in clusters. Neuroscientists can destroy (ablate) the entire cluster. After this specific destruction, researchers investigate how the animal's behavior has changed.

As mentioned, neurons utilizing the neurotransmitters serotonin, norepinephrine, and dopamine (the monoamines) are found in clusters. Neurons making other types of neurotransmitters are located much more diffusely throughout the brain. For example, neurons utilizing gamma-aminobutyric acid (GABA), the brain's major inhibitory neurotransmitter, and glutamate, the brain's major excitatory neurotransmitter, are found throughout the brain.

Presently, for just about every known receptor type, chemicals that will activate the receptor (agonist) or deactivate the receptor (antagonists) are available. Neuroscientists, because they can bore into a live animal's brain, can provide targeted delivery of an agonist or antagonist and then examine how behavior is affected.

Scientists have procedures for finding the location of neurons with receptors for particular neurotransmitters. They can find out which neurotransmitter any neuron is waiting for. Antibodies are molecules that bind to specific molecules, in our case, a receptor for a particular neurotransmitter. Biologists know how to make antibodies to receptors for a particular neurotransmitter. They can tag the antibody with a molecule that shines when given a light source. Slices of the brain can be prepared. The antibody sticks to the receptor. It is then possible to look at where the antibody sticks in the brain to identify which neurotransmitter the neurons in various locations are waiting for.

For each neurotransmitter, there are multiple subtypes of receptors (each produced from a different gene) waiting for that neurotransmitter. Receptor subtypes vary in their sensitivity to the neurotransmitter, that is, their affinity for the neurotransmitter. Some receptor types need a great amount of neurotransmitter to respond to the message. Others, with high affinity, respond to low amounts of the neurotransmitter. Particular subtypes of receptor can also vary in terms of the impact they will have on the receiving neuron. For the most part, this book will not detail receptor subtypes. However, if there is a number next to the receptor (e.g., dopamine receptor type 2), this just provides information on the particular receptor subtype.

Because much of the discussion that follows refers to particular substructures in the brain. Table 2.1 lists the basic function of most of the structures mentioned in this chapter and elsewhere in the text. Figure 2.3 provides a map of particular nuclei found in the brain stem. Figure 2.4 offers a side or lateral view of outer brain structures. Figure 2.5 is a view of brain structures from the front facing the brain, called a coronal view. Figure 2.6 gives a lateral view of deeper brain structures. Figure 2.7 offers a view of what are referred to as limbic structures, which will be further explained later in the text. These images can be consulted to determine the location of particular structures in the brain.

Specific Neurotransmitters

In Chapter 3, we will cover psychotropic drugs. Psychotropic drugs are drugs that alter mood or behavior. Psychotropic drugs are generally referred to as agonists or antagonists for a particular neurotransmitter system. As previously pointed out, an agonist increases the function of

TABLE 2.1
Brief Explanation of Some Major Brain Structures

Structure	General Function
Amygdala	Evaluates the emotional significance of stimuli; best known for its role in signaling fear
Basal ganglia: caudate, putamen, globus pallidus, subthalamic nucleus	Involved in fine-tuning movement; involved in habits
Bed nucleus of the stria terminalis (BNST)	Output structure of the amygdala; whereas the amygdala is needed for fear, the BNST is needed for anxiety (distinction is explained in the section Creating Anxiety/Fear in this chapter)
Brain stem: medulla, pons, midbrain	Area of the brain containing nuclei of the autonomic nervous system; nuclei producing the catecholamines and the raphe producing serotonin
Cerebellum	Coordinates fine movements providing feedback on motor plans generated elsewhere in the brain; plays role in allocating attention
Corpus callosum	Fiber tracks connecting the right and left hemispheres of the cortex
Dorsal anterior cingulate	Registers pain from psychological and physical sources; sometimes referred to as an error detector or a conflict monitor
Fornix	Output structure extending from the hippocampus to the hypothalamus
Habenula	Area in the brain that receives information from the retina to set up wake–sleep cycles; plays a major role in learned helplessness
Hippocampus	Creates and retrieves memories about what happened where (episodic memories); restrains the HPA
Hypothalamus	Regulates appetite and thirst, controls pituitary gland function, controls the autonomic response to complex stimuli; some areas involved in sexual behavior, caretaking of young, and rage
Insula	Area that receives information from internal organs; needed to experience disgust

(continued)

TABLE 2.1 (*continued*)

Medial forebrain bundle	Axons from ventral tegmental area, raphe, and locus coeruleus and other brain stem nuclei projecting broadly and with output to the lateral hypothalamus; axons carry information between areas
Nucleus accumbens	Area that receives input from the ventral tegmental area
Periaqueductal gray	Area around the aqueduct (hollow space filled with cerebrospinal fluid in midbrain); plays a role in sexual function, caring for young, and freezing behavior (ventral area) or fighting/fleeing (dorsal area)
Pineal gland	Responds to information about daylight; releases melatonin to increase the propensity toward sleep
Pituitary gland	Master gland in the body; releases hormones that influence output of other glands in the body. ACTH, a hormone that controls cortisol release, is discussed in this chapter
Striatum	Region of the mid brain; the dorsal striatum contains the basal ganglia; the ventral striatum contains the nucleus accumbens
Substantia nigra	Area of dopaminergic neurons in the midbrain that project to the basal ganglia in the dorsal striatum
Thalamus	The "Delta hub" of the brain; the area into which sensory information is fed before it is sent to areas of the cortex, which will interpret the information
Ventral tegmental area	Area in the midbrain containing dopaminergic neurons that project to the nucleus accumbens and broadly to the cortex
Ventricles	Hollow spaces in brain filled with cerebrospinal fluid

ACTH, adrenocorticotropic hormone; HPA, hypothalamic–pituitary–adrenal axis.

the neurotransmitter; an antagonist decreases the function. In this chapter, we will cover some of the major neurotransmitters in the brain that inform where the neurons that synthesize or make the neurotransmitters are found and what the function of the neurotransmitter might be. This information is presented so that when, for example, you are told that a

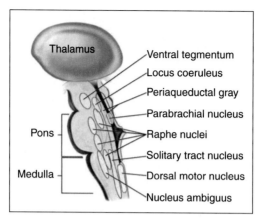

FIGURE 2.3 Brain stem.

Source: Wolters Kluwer: Lippincott Williams & Wilkins; published in Lane et al. (2009b).

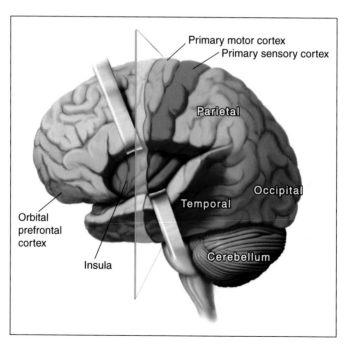

FIGURE 2.4 Lateral view of outer brain structures.

Source: Wolters Kluwer: Lippincott Williams & Wilkins; published in Lane et al. (2009b).

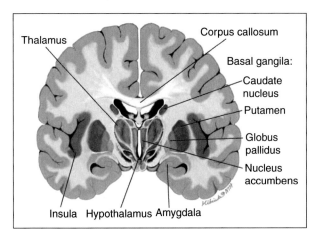

FIGURE 2.5   Coronal view of the brain.

Source: Wolters Kluwer: Lippincott Williams & Wilkins; published in Lane et al. (2009b).

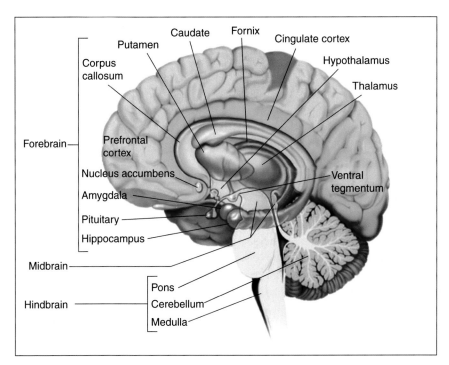

FIGURE 2.6   Midsagittal view of the brain.

Source: Wolters Kluwer: Lippincott Williams & Wilkins; published in Lane et al. (2009b).

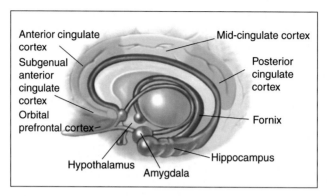

FIGURE 2.7 Limbic structures of the brain.

Source: Wolters Kluwer: Lippincott Williams & Wilkins; published in Lane et al. (2009b).

drug is a dopamine agonist in Chapter 3, you can predict how the drug will affect mood and behavior and you can predict which brain structures might be impacted by the drug.

Dopamine

There are four major circuits for dopamine in the brain (Figure 2.8). One pathway (the tuberoinfundibular pathway) controls the release of hormones from a gland located inside the brain (the pituitary). (The pathway is at the base of the hypothalamus, just above the pituitary.) In this pathway, dopamine inhibits the release of prolactin, a hormone that controls milk production in the breast (Dunlop & Nemeroff, 2007). With dopamine depletion, as occurs in heavy cocaine abusers or with blockade of dopamine receptors by antipsychotic drugs, breast development in men may occur.

A second dopamine pathway (the nigrostriatal pathway) is important for controlling movement and habit learning. Neurons in the midbrain (substantia nigra pars compacta) project to the striatum, an area controlling movement. In Parkinson's patients, the midbrain substantia nigra neurons die. The result is an extreme movement disorder. The muscles are flexed, but are unable to move. Resting tremor and pill-rolling movements in the fingers are observed. The facial muscles are motionless and eye blink is gone. Disruption of this pathway also impairs habit learning and the learning of stimulus response associations (Dunlop & Nemeroff,

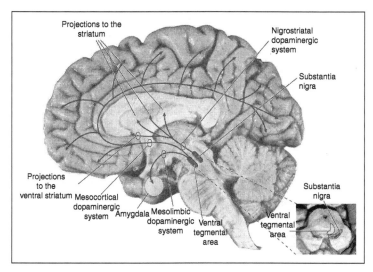

FIGURE 2.8   The dopaminergic systems. Midline sagittal section demonstrating the projections. *Inset*: Axial section of the midbrain demonstrating the location of the dopaminergic neurons.

Source: Nadeau et al. (2004).

2007; O'Doherty et al., 2004; Treadway & Zald, 2011). Antipsychotic drugs, which are dopamine antagonists, also cause Parkinson's disease symptoms.

A third pathway (the mesolimbic pathway) has been intensely studied because all drugs of abuse (alcohol, nicotine, cocaine, amphetamine, and opioids) increase activity in this pathway. Here, dopamine neurons from the ventral tegmental area (VTA; in the midbrain) project to the nucleus accumbens. Dopamine is released into the nucleus accumbens with ingestion of drugs of abuse, the opportunity for food, opportunities for copulation, and the occurrence of unexpected rewards (see Chapter 8, "Addictions").

Consideration of the context in which dopamine release occurs led to some hypothesizing about the significance of dopamine. The first hypothesis was that dopamine release was associated with pleasure. This hypothesis was discarded because of the work of Kent Berridge. First, Berridge and others observed that when an animal is about to be shocked, dopamine is also released into the nucleus accumbens (Faure, Reynolds, Richard, & Berridge, 2008; Pruessner, Champagne, Meaney, & Dagher, 2004; Salamone, Correa, Farrar, & Mingote, 2007). Second, dopamine release occurs as the animal works to find food or sex, not while the animal is consuming food or copulating (Baldo & Kelley, 2007; Berridge & Robinson, 1998). Finally, when Berridge and colleagues wiped out the dopamine neurons in the VTA, the animal clearly displayed signs of enjoyment if force fed; however, the animal would no longer work for the food (Berridge & Robinson, 1998; Robinson & Berridge, 2008). Salamone, Correa, Farrar, and Mingote (2007) showed that when dopamine input into the nucleus accumbens is inhibited, animals become lazy and lethargic. The current view is that dopamine is the neurotransmitter of motivation. It is the neurotransmitter of "wanting" rather than the neurotransmitter for "liking" (Berridge, 2009b).

The fourth pathway (the mesocortical pathway) refers to neurons from the VTA that project broadly throughout the cortex, including to the hippocampus (where memories are formed) and the prefrontal cortex (PFC) (where executive function occurs; Treadway & Zald, 2011). In the hippocampus, dopamine plays a major role in changing synapses in the hippocampus to create memories. When these dopaminergic VTA neurons are active, the animal is more alert and maintains vigilance. The animal is ready to learn about the environment, particularly about how stimuli are related to consequences (O'Doherty et al., 2004). As stated by Der-Avakian and Markou (2012, p. 5), "one role of dopamine is to transfer positive incentive value from the reward to the cue that predicts reward." Another way of characterizing the VTA projections to the prefrontal cortex is that dopamine is involved in appreciating the emotional significance of stimuli (Dunlop & Nemeroff, 2007; Rilling, Sanfey, Aronson, Nystrom, & Cohen, 2004). The VTA dopaminergic neurons (in addition to the "wanting neurons") are sometimes referred to as the "incentive salience system." The projections from the VTA to the cortex are about learning what is important, that is, assigning significance to the stimuli that surround us (Robinson & Berridge, 2008).

A second function of dopamine in the mesocortical pathway may be to focus attention and maintain information in working memory (short-term memory is required to hold ideas in awareness sufficiently long to figure things out). In the cortex, receptors are primarily of the D1 type. They are found on GABA neurons as well. They probably function to help a person ignore irrelevant stimuli (Ledoux, 2014).

Panksepp, Wright, Döbrössy, Schlaepfer, and Coenen (2014) summarize the dopamine tracks emerging from the VTA (called the medial forebrain bundle) as "a general-purpose neuronal system that coaxes animals and humans to move energetically (enthusiastically) from where they are to the places where they can find and consume resources needed for survival. It permits learning by readily assimilating predictive reward in the world" (Panksepp et al., 2014).

Serotonin

Serotonin-producing neurons are located at the midline of the brain stem in an area called the raphe (Figure 2.3). Research investigation of the serotonin system has yielded puzzling, contradictory results. For example, particular antidepressant drugs increase levels of serotonin. Presumably, antidepressants decrease distress, but in the short term these drugs can increase anxiety and precipitate suicidal ideation. The research of Chris Lowry and colleagues (Hale & Lowry, 2011; Hale, Shekhar, & Lowry, 2012) has cleared up some of the mystery. Lowry identified multiple serotonergic circuits for the neurons in the raphe. One of these circuits creates anxiety, whereas other circuits enhance regulation of emotion and decrease anxiety. Each circuit operates independently of other circuits. The function of serotonin is therefore difficult to characterize, because it plays different roles depending on the circuit.

In the section on brain circuits in this chapter (Section 4: Circuits: Creating Learned Helplessness), the learned helplessness circuit will be described. When subjected to uncontrollable shock, animals exhibit anxiety and depression. Serotonin is vital for the creation of learned helplessness. If serotonergic neurons in a particular section of the raphe (the caudal part of the dorsal raphe) are destroyed, the animal will not display learned helplessness behaviors of anxiety and "giving-up" (Hale, Raison, & Lowry, 2013; Maier & Watkins, 2005).

Another set of serotonergic neurons in the raphe (interfascicular part of the dorsal raphe nucleus and neurons near the ventrolateral periaqueductal gray [PAG]) are the antipanic neurons (Hale & Lowry, 2011; Hale et al., 2012; Hanusch et al., 2013; Paul, Johnson, Shekhar, & Lowry, 2014). They project to the prefrontal cortex and to the dorsal PAG. A reliable way to induce panic in most animals is to infuse the animal with lactic acid. Those animals that fail to panic exhibit stronger activity of the serotonin antipanic neurons (Hale et al., 2012, 2013). The antipanic serotonergic neurons respond to an anti-inflammatory white blood cell hormone (interleukin 10, discussed later) and to warm and cold temperatures. This may explain why sitting in warm sunlight reduces anxiety.

The brain contains many hollow spaces (called ventricles) that are filled with cerebrospinal fluid (CSF). Yet another set of serotonergic neurons control cilia (hair-like projections) on the cells lining the ventricles. Here serotonin increases the movement of the cilia so that CSF is moved through the system at a faster rate, allowing for pathogens or toxic chemicals associated with stress to be quickly removed from the brain. Finally, another group of serotonergic neurons controls sleep stages (Hale & Lowry, 2011).

In the literature, many studies have involved the assessment of serotonin metabolites in the CSF. A consistent finding is that those with low levels of serotonin metabolites in their CSF are more impulsive and aggressive (Korte, Koolhaas, Wingfield, & McEwen, 2005). Those who have been violent or who have committed suicide in a violent manner also are distinguished by low levels of serotonin metabolites in their CSF (Davidson, Putnam, & Larson, 2000). Unfortunately, measuring serotonin metabolites in the CSF does not inform about which circuit the metabolite came from. However, the findings suggest that some circuits that use serotonin may perform an inhibitory function on negative mood or impulses.

Norepinephrine/Noradrenaline

The locus coeruleus is a group of neurons in the brain stem that is the major producer of norepinephrine in the brain (Figure 2.3). Neurons in the locus coeruleus fire more rapidly during high arousal states as contrasted with low arousal states (Brennan & Arnsten, 2010). During normal levels of arousal, neurons in the prefrontal cortex are activated by norepinephrine through a specific type of norepinephrine receptor. These normal levels of arousal improve memory (Brennan & Arnsten, 2010). Under stress, neurons in the locus coeruleus increase the tonic firing rate to even higher levels. Under stress, norepinephrine activates another set of norepinephrine receptors in the prefrontal cortex and impairs memory (Brennan & Arnsten, 2010). Thus, norepinephrine can have opposing effects on the PFC depending on the rate of release and the subtype class of norepinephrine receptor that receives the message. At midlevels of arousal, memory improves. At very high levels, memory deteriorates (Brennan & Arnsten, 2010).

Norepinephrine is also the signal to the astrocytes (a type of supporting cell) to release fuel (which can be converted to sugar) for working neurons. Dysfunction of the release of fuel by the supporting cells has been implicated in attention deficit hyperactivity disorder (ADHD; Killeen, Russell, & Sergeant, 2013). Norepinephrine also tones down inflammation in the brain by influencing microglia, a type of white blood cell that is resident in the brain (Kalinin et al., 2012). It is known that norepinephrine neurons are destroyed early on in Alzheimer's disease, allowing for more inflammation in the brain. Inflammation, which entails activated white blood cells spewing out damaging molecules, is a big factor in Alzheimer's disease (Levey, 2014).

Acetylcholine

Acetylcholine is released in the brain, where it plays a role in memory. Acetylcholine is also used by neurons outside the brain. Acetylcholine is the neurotransmitter involved in the division of the peripheral nervous system that controls internal organs (the involuntary, autonomic nervous system). In the voluntary peripheral nervous system, acetylcholine is the neurotransmitter that commands striated muscle tissue so that one can move around (Nolte, 2009).

As mentioned previously, all drugs leading to compulsive use result in the release of dopamine into the nucleus accumbens (see Chapter 8, "Addictions"). Nicotine, for example, is a drug that operates on acetylcholine receptors (the nicotinic subtype). In the brain, nicotinic acetylcholine receptors ($\alpha 4\beta 2$ receptors) are present on dopaminergic neurons and control the release of dopamine into the nucleus accumbens (Lüscher, 2013; Purves et al., 2012). Thus, acetylcholine plays a role in appetitive structures, largely dopaminergic structures, described later.

Glutamate

Glutamate is the brain's major excitatory neurotransmitter. Although glutamate uses both metabotropic and ionotropic receptors, the ionotropic receptors are relevant for the excitatory function. α-amino-3-hydroxy-5-methyl-4-isoxazolepropionic acid receptor (AMPA) and N-methyl-d-aspartate (NMDA) receptors are two types of receptors for glutamate that open an ion channel. Interestingly, the ionotropic receptors, AMPA and NMDA receptors, work together. NMDA receptors are called silent receptors unless they are near an AMPA receptor. When glutamate binds to an AMPA receptor and sufficient ions move through the AMPA channel, then a magnesium atom blocking the NMDA receptor-associated channel is displaced out of the ion channel. When glutamate next binds to the NMDA receptor, calcium enters the cell making it very likely to fire. After this, the AMPA receptor moves nearer to the NMDA receptor, strengthening the sensitivity of the neuron to glutamate. The synchrony between the NMDA and AMPA receptors makes their conjoint activity "coincidence detectors." AMPA and NMDA receptors are critical players in the formation of long-term potentiation, meaning the way in which the brain encodes new memories (Purves et al., 2012). The NMDA receptor also needs glycine to bind on part of the receptor to respond to glutamate.

Glutamate is key to formation of new memories and learning. Because most of us want to improve our ability to learn, neuroscientists have focused on understanding glutamate. Neuroscientist Joe Tsien and colleagues created a mouse called the "Doogie Howser mouse" (in reference to the 1980 television program about a boy genius) by mutating the receptor for glutamate (Tang et al., 1999). The mutant mouse then performed much better on thinking tasks. Tsien speculated about why nature had not just created all mice as super-smart. The trade-off is that too much signaling through a glutamate receptor provokes a seizure. There is a critical threshold between brilliance and death from a seizure. Much current investigational work on performance-enhancing drugs involves glutamate receptors; it is a risky business.

After release of glutamate into the synaptic cleft, glial cells (support cells) pick up the excess glutamate (Nolte, 2009, p. 193). Astrocytes, a type of support cell, which are near the blood vessels in the brain, can thus detect where in the brain activity is occurring and shift blood supply to brain areas where more activity is occurring (Nolte, 2009, p. 135).

Gamma-Aminobutyric Acid

GABA is the brain's major inhibitory neurotransmitter. GABA neurons are dispersed throughout the brain. When GABA binds to its receptor, a channel for chloride opens. With more chloride inside the neuron, the neuron is less likely to fire. Although GABA generally inhibits neurons, sometimes GABA's function is to ensure that only a strong signal from inputting neurons activates receiving neurons (Saar, Reuveni, & Barkai, 2012).

Cannabinoids

The brain has ligands (binding partners) that will bind at cannabinoid receptors (marijuana receptors). The molecules produced by the brain that bind at receptors for marijuana are called endocannabinoids, "endo" referring to *internal* or *within*. Unlike many other neurotransmitters, which are modifications of amino acids (building blocks for proteins), endocannabinoids are altered polyunsaturated fatty acid chains. They are released after cleavage from the neuron's cell membrane. Endocannabinoids are not packaged into a vesicle. Cannabinoid receptors, which are metabotropic, are found in many areas of the brain. In addition to neurons, receptors are also found on support cells in the brain (astrocytes, microglia, and oligodendrocytes; Marco et al., 2011).

Cannabinoids play major roles in decreasing anxiety. They are essential for being able to extinguish fear memories. They potentiate GABA inhibition in the amygdala, a structure involved in anxiety (Figure 2.7 of the limbic system showing structures involved in emotional activity.) They decrease the stress hormone (cortisol). They also operate in the hypothalamus, a structure involved in the control of food intake (think, the munchies). Particular enzymes (hydrolases) degrade the endocannabinoids (Marco et al., 2011).

Opioids

Opioid receptors were so named because opium binds to these receptors. Opiate derivatives (morphine, heroin, and codeine) also bind to these receptors. There are natural opiates in the brain: endorphins, enkephalins, and dynorphins. There are three types of opioid receptors: mu receptors for the natural endorphin's binding partners, delta receptors for the natural enkephalin's binding partners, and kappa receptors for the natural dynorphin's binding partner.

Opioid receptors are found in many places, including the spinal cord, where they decrease pain transmission. The dorsal anterior cingulate cortex (dACC), an alarm center in the brain, is full of opioid receptors where opioids function to decrease alarm and physical pain. In fact, persons carrying a particular allele for the mu-opioid receptor experience both more physical and emotional pain. They exhibit stronger activation of the dACC in response to social rejection (Way, Taylor, & Eisenberger, 2009).

Opioid receptors are found on the GABA interneurons in the caudal dorsal raphe, the serotonergic structure involved in producing anxiety and defeat after exposure to uncontrollable shock (called learned helplessness). Opioids increase the release of GABA into the serotonin-releasing neurons, whose cell bodies are found in the caudal dorsal raphe. The serotonergic neurons in the caudal dorsal raphe are inhibited by opioids. The anxious behavior following inescapable shock is reduced (Maier & Watkins, 2005).

In the VTA, opioid receptors are found on the GABA neurons. GABA neurons in the VTA synapse onto dopaminergic neurons. GABA inhibits dopamine release from dopaminergic neurons, which release into the nucleus accumbens. The opioids decrease the release of GABA from the GABAnergic neurons. When GABA release is inhibited, the inhibition of dopamine release is gone. Effectively, opiates are a break on a break. Thus, when opiates hit their receptors in VTA, more dopamine is released from VTA neurons into the nucleus accumbens. The effect increases locomotion and movement (Lüscher, 2013).

As will be discussed in the section on pleasure (see Section 5: Emotions: Specific Emotions; Pleasure), opioids play a role in mediating the sensual pleasure produced by activity in another area of the brain (the ventral pallidum and parabrachial area; Berridge, 2009a, 2009b; Berridge & Kringelbach, 2008; Trezza, Baarendse, & Vanderschuren, 2010).

Dynorphin, a naturally occurring opiate, is also produced in the nucleus accumbens. Dynorphin counters the effects of endorphins and enkephalins. Dynorphins decrease dopamine release and generally increase discomfort (Bruijnzeel, 2009).

SECTION 3: THE IMMUNE SYSTEM

The immune system refers to the body's system for responding to pathogens and eliminating cancer cells. As we will see in later chapters, recent research has illuminated the impact of the immune system on mood and behavior. It is now appreciated that inflammation plays a role in psychosis. Moreover, inflammation is relevant for both depressed and anxious behavior. Targeting the immune system can alter mood, behavior, and propensity for auditory hallucinations. Thus, today's neuroscientists must also be students of the immune system. A brief overview of the major players in the immune system is provided here.

White blood cells (leukocytes) are the major players of the immune system. The word *inflammation* has been used previously without much explanation. Inflammation occurs when white blood cells are geared up for a fight, usually against a pathogen. With inflammation, the local blood vessels dilate and the skin turns red and may look swollen. This vasculature dilation occurs to get the white blood cells to the battle field fast. Some of the activated white blood cells may release destructive molecules that modify molecules (oxidizing) of either the pathogen or components of one's own body. These destructive molecules can kill pathogens, but unrestrained release of damaging molecules is very harmful to the individual. The immune system is capable of making various types of responses tailored to combat particular types of threats. In the text that follows, we will look at the divisions of the immune system.

Two Major Divisions: Innate and Adaptive Immunity

The Innate System

Two principal leukocytes of the innate system are macrophages and neutrophils. These cells respond to foreign-looking substances found in the body. Receptors for foreign-appearing molecules are found on the surface or inside the leukocytes. These receptors are not very specific; the receptors can respond to more than one particular molecule. In responding to a peculiar-looking molecule, the response of the innate system is fast. Usually, a fever is involved. Activated macrophages and neutrophils release hormones called cytokines. Some of the cytokines (hormones from white blood cells or infected cells) include interleukin (IL)-1beta, IL-6, and tumor necrosis factor–alpha. These cytokines cause the cells lining the blood vessels to express surface molecules (intercellular adhesion molecules) that allow the white blood cells to move more quickly to the invader. IL-6 stimulates the liver to release proteins, such as C-reactive protein (CRP), which facilitate the attack on the invader (Murphy, 2012). Macrophages and neutrophils, both of which can engulf pathogens, are the white blood cells that are the first responders that rush to the site of inflammation. The macrophages and neutrophils release very destructive molecules once they get to the site of inflammation. Unfortunately, because cells of the innate immune system are not terribly specific, inflammation can be costly for the host.

The innate immune system plays a role in many chronic diseases (chronic obstructive pulmonary disease, arthritis, cardiovascular disease, and cancer). For example, neutrophils, first responders to a site of infection, can release toxic chemicals (superoxide and nitric oxide) that can damage tissue. The superoxide can alter (oxidize) fats in the bloodstream. In a blood vessel, the oxidized fat particle can look like a foreign invader to a macrophage. The macrophage goes after the altered fat particle, sticks to the wall of the blood vessel, and results in cardiovascular disease (plaque on the vasculature wall). Additionally, cancer also appears to be advanced by an activated innate immune system (Caielli, Banchereau, & Pascual, 2012; Mantovani, 2010; Slavich & Irwin, 2014). The supporting evidence for the conclusion that inflammation is also a major culprit in depression, anxiety, and psychosis appears in the sections of the text focused on these topics.

It is good to remember that if you cut your finger, the fast-responding macrophages and neutrophils are your first line of defense; sometimes inflammation is a very good thing. However, control of inflammation is vital (Murphy, 2012).

The Adaptive Immune System

The other major division for the immune system is adaptive immunity. The adaptive responders (T cells and B cells) are highly specific. T-cell and B-cell receptors respond to only one very specific protein; a change in even one amino acid in the protein chain can disrupt recognition by the receptor. After an initial encounter with a pathogen, the T and B cells require about 5 days to proliferate and mount a response. The B cells make antibodies that bind to foreign particles, so the foreign particle gets attacked by other cells. Antibodies can also prevent the foreign pathogen or particle from infecting other host cells. The job of T cells is multifaceted. Some T cells give permission to the B cells to make antibodies; other T cells attack tumor cells or cells infected with a virus.

Vaccination is a strategy for harnessing the adaptive immune system. Following an initial encounter with a foreign protein in the vaccine, the T and B cells activate and divide. Some T and B cells become memory cells. Memory cells are capable of mounting a very fast response when the same pathogen is seen on a second occasion. Although in some ways cells of the innate system (mainly macrophages and another type of cell, the dendritic cell) are involved in initiating a response from T and B cells, inflammation can be negatively correlated with the function of the adaptive system (Fleshner, Nguyen, Cotter, Watkins, & Maier, 1998; Murphy, 2012; Slavich & Irwin, 2014).

Psychoneuroimmunology is a field that investigates how emotions impact the immune system. The field was officially initiated when Robert Ader found that the immune system can be classically conditioned. Ader paired an immune system–dampening drug with needle injection. After the conditioning, Ader showed that eventually the needle alone was sufficient to suppress immune system activity in patients with autoimmune disease. Ader's work was highly relevant for persons with inflammatory conditions such as lupus (Ader & Cohen, 2001).

Since Ader's time, studies have shown that people in distress have more activation of the immune system in terms of inflammation (as summarized in Littrell, 2008b, 2012), but less of an ability to mount an adaptive immune response (as reviewed in Littrell, 2008a). Stressed individuals may also have a depressed capacity for producing antiviral cytokines (O'Connor, Schultze-Florey, Irwin, Arevalo, & Cole, 2014). As discussed in Chapter 1, people who are stressed fail to respond to vaccinations. Thus, distressed individuals are more susceptible to innate immune system activation diseases (e.g., cardiovascular disease), and are also more susceptible to diseases associated with failure to activate the adaptive system (e.g., cancer, viral infections of cells).

Chapter 4, on depression, provides details relevant to distressed individuals exhibiting activation of their innate immune systems. Inflammation is also discussed in the chapter on psychosis (Chapter 6).

The Glial Cells

Most of the cells in the brain are glial cells or support cells. (*Glial* derives from the Greek word for glue.) There are three types of glial cells: microglia, astrocytes, and oligodendrocytes. All perform vital functions. (The glial cells are discussed in this section on the immune system, because some of their functions are relevant to the immune system.) Microglia are the brain's resident macrophages. Macrophages are a type of white blood cell that can phagocytize (eat) debris. The microglia play a vital role in cleaning up old synapses and remodeling the brain. They also play a big role in brain inflammation, which may be a problem in those with depression. When the microglia are not activated to fight infection, they play a role in maintaining brain health (Kettenmann, Kirchhoff, & Verkhratsky, 2013; Littrell, 2012; Parkhurst et al., 2013).

Astrocytes are the second type of glial cell in the brain. They have receptors for glutamate (the major excitatory neurotransmitter). By detecting glutamate release, they can release factors that will impact blood vessels, resulting in a shift of blood flow to more active brain areas (Nolte, 2009). They also play a role in storing glucose and getting this fuel (in the form of lactic acid) to very active neurons. One particular theory regarding the cause of ADHD holds that the astrocytes are sluggish in their performance of this function (Killeen et al., 2013).

Oligodendrocytes are support cells that wrap around the axons of neurons and allow for faster movement of neurotransmitter packets down an axon. In multiple sclerosis, for example, oligodendrocytes are destroyed (Nolte, 2009).

SECTION 4: CIRCUITS

Appetitive Signaling

In the 1950s, Milner and Olds implanted electrodes into particular areas of the brain and allowed animals to stimulate these areas by pressing a lever. They noticed that animals would repeatedly press levers that stimulated particular areas of the brain. The areas of the brain that yielded vigorous self-stimulation involved dopamine tracks emerging from the VTA (Koob, 2013).

Much has been learned about the dopaminergic neurons projecting from the VTA to the nucleus accumbens. Motivation for many types of reinforcers (sex, food, and drugs of abuse) converge in the nucleus accumbens. In fact, in monogamous animals, there are receptors for oxytocin (a hormone released on orgasm) in this area, which may explain the mechanism for mate bonding (Young & Alexander, 2014). As stated in Section 2, this system is about motivation (wanting but not necessarily liking), about paying attention to the environment, and learning the connections between stimuli and consequences (the incentive salience system). The system strongly activates behavior as well. It is known that when this system is activated, the animal will be more lively. Locomotion and exploration are increased (Hyman, Malenka, & Nestler, 2006; Nestler & Carlezon, 2006).

In addition to activating to opportunities for sex and food, reward areas in people (the ventral striatum area in which the nucleus accumbens is located) are also activated by social cues. Research participants who read statements of love and appreciation from their friends and relatives showed activation in the reward areas. Being treated fairly and seeing others treated fairly activates this area. Additionally, these structures activate when someone else who has been treated unfairly now gets rewarded (Lieberman, 2013).

As discussed in Section 2, the appetitive signaling pathway is not always about enjoyable activities. When an animal engages in vigorous activity in response to negative aversive stimuli or positive stimuli, the nucleus accumbens is activated. The basal amygdala (area of the brain that registers fear) projects to the nucleus accumbens. When an animal runs away from an aversive stimulus, the nucleus accumbens is activated (Hartley & Phelps, 2010), although not when an aversive stimuli does not require action (as when viewing unpleasant imagery; Lang & Bradley, 2010). The nucleus accumbens can be activated when working for food as well as when the animal works to avoid shock (Lang & Bradley, 2010). In fact, various areas in the nucleus accumbens are active when responding to aversive cues, whereas other areas of the brain respond to approach stimuli (Berridge & Kringelbach, 2013). Observations of bereaved individuals longing for deceased spouses have also noted activation of the nucleus accumbens (O'Connor et al., 2008).

Turning Off Activity in the Nucleus Accumbens

The lateral habenula plays a strong role in inhibiting the neurons in the VTA that project to the nucleus accumbens (Hikosaka, 2010; Hong, Jhou, Smith, Saleem, & Hikosaka, 2011; Lammel et al., 2012). The lateral habenula is active given the absence of an expected reward and when the animal is subjected to uncontrollable shock (Hikosaka, 2011; Stamatakis et al., 2013; Figure 2.9).

As will be discussed in the text on learned helplessness that follows, uncontrollable shock initiates activity in the lateral habenula, which activates anxiety structures and suppresses the VTA.

Creating Learned Helplessness

In the 1970s, Steven Maier, Marty Seligman, and Bruce Overmier developed a paradigm called learned helplessness. Learned helplessness has been characterized as a laboratory model for depression and/ or anxiety. The paradigm entails subjecting an animal to uncontrollable shock delivery. The animals in the control condition experience the same level of shock intensity for the same duration, but unlike the animal that has learned helplessness, the animals in the control group can turn off the shock.

Both escapable and inescapable shocks induce some of the same components of anxiety. Both increase stress hormone release (the release of cortisol), reduce activity, reduce exploration in an open field, and reduce sucrose preference (Christianson et al., 2008; Maier & Watkins, 2010). However, inescapable shock induces additional components of anxiety. Animals that have been subjected to uncontrollable shock exhibit a reduction in food and water intake, a reduction in social interaction, a reduction in swimming when placed in water, a reduction in aggression and social dominance, and exaggerated fear. When learned-helpless animals are moved to another environment where they can turn off shock, they fail to exert control. They have effectively learned helplessness. They have given up (Maier & Watkins, 2005, 2010).

Neural Circuitry

The neural circuitry involved in learned-helpless behavior has been articulated. However, in keeping with the wide variety of behaviors that are associated with learned helplessness, the neural circuitry has several branches. The habenula begins the response to inescapable shock. The habenula projects to two regions: the VTA and the caudal part of the

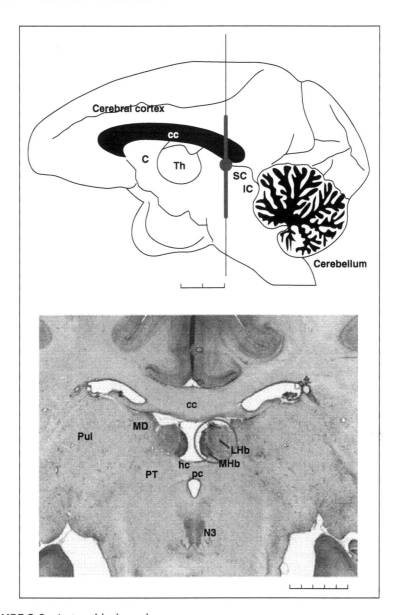

FIGURE 2.9   Lateral habenula.

The solid circle in the top image is the lateral habenula. C, caudate; CC, corpus callosum; Hc, habenular commissure; IC, inferior colliculus; LHb, lateral habenula; MD, mediodorsal nucleus of the thalamus; MHb, medial habenula; N3, oculomotor nucleus; PC, posterior commissure; PT, pretectum; Pul, pulvinar; SC, superior colliculus; Th, thalamus.

Source: Hikosaka (2007; modified 2011).

dorsal raphe nucleus. The caudal part of the dorsal raphe nucleus (which contains serotonergic neurons) projects to two regions: the amygdala and the striatum (Forgeard et al., 2011; Hale et al., 2012; Strong et al., 2011). We will look at each branch in turn.

The Habenula to the Caudal Dorsal Raphe

The habenula sends projections to the caudal part of the dorsal raphe nucleus in the brain stem, activating this structure (Amat et al., 2001). The causal dorsal raphe nucleus, with its serotonergic neurons, is critical to the learned-helpless response. If the caudal dorsal raphe structure is lesioned, then learned helplessness cannot be induced (Maier & Watkins, 2005, 2010).

Creating Anxiety/Fear

The caudal part of the dorsal raphe projects to the basolateral amygdala. The basolateral amygdala projects to other areas of the amygdala, which eventually activate other brain areas (such as the hypothalamus and PAG), resulting in the physiology of anxiety and freezing behavior (Christianson et al., 2010; Maier & Watkins, 2010; Strong et al., 2011). A critical output area of the amygdala is through the bed nucleus of the stria terminalis (BNST). Lesions of the BNST preclude failure to escape after exposure to inescapable shock, whereas lesions of other parts of the amygdala do not (Forgeard et al., 2011; Hammack, Richey, Watkins, & Maier, 2004; Maier & Watkins, 2010).

The BNST is again discussed in the chapter on anxiety (Chapter 5). Although the amygdala is about fear, the BNST is about anxiety, or being ready to be fearful (see Chapter 5, "Anxiety"). A learned-helpless animal is anxious and will exhibit enhanced fear to the next fear stimulus presentation (Maier & Watkins, 2005, 2010).

Motor Behavior Changes

The caudal part of the dorsal raphe nucleus also projects to the dorsal striatum (which influences motor behavior). The caudal dorsal raphe nucleus projection to the dorsal striatum projection establishes the escape deficits and may play a role in facilitating freezing behavior (Strong et al., 2011).

The lateral habenula is an initiating structure in producing the syndrome of learned helplessness. In addition to projecting to the caudal part of the dorsal raphe nucleus, the lateral habenula also projects to the VTA, inhibiting activity in the VTA. The result is that activity is further decreased. These connections probably are responsible for the anhedonia (lack of motivation and lack of response to reward) observed in learned-helpless animals (B. Li et al., 2011; Y. Li et al., 2013).

Creating a Resilient Animal

There are several ways to create resilient animals. In resilient animals, exposure to uncontrollable shock fails to induce anxiety symptoms and "giving up." Both exercise and exposure to controllable stress will create resilience. The mechanisms for creating resilience are known but each differs in terms of how it works.

Researchers have known that animals that have prior experience with controllable shock are less susceptible to becoming learned helpless when later exposed to uncontrollable shock. Researchers have examined which brain structures are recruited during the exposure to controllable stressors. During exposure to controllable shock, the ventromedial PFC sends projections to excite the GABA interneurons in the caudal dorsal raphe nucleus. (Recall that GABA inhibits the neurons onto which they synapse.) The GABA interneurons inhibit the firing of serotonergic neurons during the initial exposure to controllable shock (Maier & Watkins, 2010). For those animals that have an initial encounter with controllable shock, the ventromedial PFC is again recruited when, subsequently, the previously controllable shock becomes uncontrollable. (See Figures 2.5 and 2.7 for various areas in the PFC.) The ventromedial PFC will effectively tame the learned helplessness structures (the caudal dorsal raphe nucleus) when the animal is later exposed to uncontrollable shock. The experimenters did do a little bit more experimenting to prove their point. If the ventromedial PFC neurons are prevented from firing in the resilient animals, then the resilient animals are no longer immune to the effects of uncontrollable shock. Knocking out the ventromedial PFC neurons will wipe out resilience. Without the ventromedial neurons, learned helplessness in response to uncontrollable shock occurs even in those animals with prior experience with controllable shock (Maier & Watkins, 2010).

The ventromedial PFC is a pretty important area for restraining distress. As we will see in the chapter on anxiety (Chapter 5), the ventromedial PFC is also important for inhibiting the amygdala (area of the brain activated by fright) when learned fears are extinguished. Learned resilience has many ramifications. The resilience evoked by exposure to controllable shock is a generalized resilience. Those exposed to escapable shock also are less impaired when subsequently exposed to social defeat. Although resilient animals respond normally to an unconditioned fear stimulus (such as the scent of a cat), they less readily develop a conditioned fear response. Moreover, in resilient animals, previously learned conditioned fears decline to a greater extent during extinction training (Maier & Watkins, 2010).

Second Way to Create Resilience

There is another strategy for creating resilience. If animals are given access to the running wheel before exposure to uncontrollable shock, they are far less likely to become learned helpless. Greenwood et al. (2011, 2012) have identified the mechanism through which exercise creates resilient mice. As stated previously, the caudal dorsal raphe nucleus is a key structure in the circuit resulting in learned helplessness. The serotonin from the caudal part of the dorsal raphe nucleus synapses onto receptors in the amygdala and the dorsal striatum. Exercise will decrease the presence of serotonin receptors in both of these structures. Thus, when the serotonin is released, there are fewer receptors available to receive the message. Helplessness in response to inescapable shock is less likely to occur. Just as in the animals, exercise is known to decrease both anxiety and depression in humans (Herring, O'Connor, & Dishman, 2010; Saeed, Antonacci, & Bloch, 2010; Strohle, 2009).

Regulation of Impulses, Motor Activity, and Emotions

The PFC is often referred to as the area of executive control. In the previous section on resilience, we encountered the ventromedial PFC, which directly inhibits the serotonergic neurons in the caudal part of the dorsal raphe to block learned helplessness. In the chapter on anxiety (Chapter 5), we will again talk about the ventromedial PFC because it plays a vital role in unlearning learned fears by directly inhibiting the amygdala. Here, we will be looking at a few more additional regions in the PFC that may be involved in other types of restraint: the dorsolateral and the ventrolateral PFC.

Some caveats need to be stated. The PFC is more developed in humans than in other animals. Much of the work on the ventromedial PFC was done on animals, where connections between neurons can be traced. In contrast to animal work, exploration of emotional and behavioral regulation in people is done with imaging. In order to ask about which brain areas influence each other, researchers must rely on imaging of the brain as a research participant does something. Researchers investigate which areas of the brain are active or inactive at the same time. If one area is active while another area is inactive, an inference regarding one area's inhibiting another might be drawn. Human research can also use a technique called "diffusion tensor imaging" to trace the degrees of axonal connectivity between areas. Unfortunately, inferences from imaging work can fail to inform more precisely how one region might influence another. There could be a direct connection; alternatively, one region could influence another through a third connection. Neuroscientist Elizabeth Phelps (2006) works with animals and people. Phelps cautions that the ventrolateral PFC, which plays an active role in recasting emotionally evocative stimuli, does not have a direct connection in animals with the amygdala (a region involved in fear and anxiety). In people, the ventrolateral PFC may influence the amygdala through the ventromedial PFC.

Inhibiting responses across a wide variety of domains involve some of the same brain structures: a specific area in the ventrolateral PFC (the inferior frontal gyrus pars opercula, which is also referred to as Area 44), the ventromedial PFC (Aron, Robbins, & Poldrack, 2004; Jovanovic & Norrholm, 2011; Ochsner, Silvers, & Buhle, 2012), and the dorsolateral PFC (Sokol-Hessner, Camerer, & Phelps, 2013; Urry et al., 2006).

The ventrolateral PFC (more specifically, the inferior frontal gyrus) is activated when drug addicts inhibit cravings, when anyone represses the performance of a previously learned motor response, when repressing strongly associated cognitions (e.g., the moon is associated with night, and the sun with day), and when suppressing emotional reactions to grotesque photos (Tabibnai et al., 2011). Based on human-imaging work, the ventrolateral PFC (again, more specifically the inferior frontal gyrus) inhibits regions involved in motor output (the subthalamic nucleus that controls basal ganglia output), that is, when a person wants to restrain a response (Aron et al., 2004). Some imaging studies also suggest that during the process of a delay-of-gratification task, the ventromedial PFC is again involved in inhibiting activity in the nucleus accumbens (Diekhof &

Gruber, 2010; Diekhof et al., 2011). A recent study found that when the dorsolateral PFC is inhibited with electrical stimulation, people consume more junk food and perform more poorly on a task requiring inhibition of an impulsive first response (Lowe, Hale, & Staines, 2014).

The role of the lateral PFC in inhibiting first responses (prepotent responses) on tasks has been demonstrated in a variety of ways. Goel and Dolan (2003) gave people valid syllogisms, which, however, started with false premises. People were asked whether the inference from the false premise was true. The question was whether the deduction followed from the syllogism, not whether the deduction (conclusion) was false. Thus, people had to inhibit saying "false" to an obviously wrong conclusion because it was a logical deduction from the premise. This is hard to do; one has to suppress the first, more spontaneous response. On those trials in which individuals were able to exert the cognitive control, more activity in the right lateral PFC was noted. Elsewhere, it has been demonstrated that when transcranial magnetic stimulation is used to scramble the ventrolateral PFC, then people commit more errors (Verbruggen, Aron, Stevens, & Chambers, 2010).

The PFC is also involved in controlling negative emotions. For suppressing anxiety, the ventrolateral, dorsolateral, and the ventromedial PFC may all be involved. In studies in which research participants were asked to reappraise or think about a distressing image in a less provocative way, increased activity in the ventrolateral PFC is found (Ochsner, Bunge, Gross, & Gabrieli, 2002; Wagner, Davidson, Hughes, Lindquist, & Ochsner, 2008). In a particular study examining responses as people thought about distressing images in less provocative ways, there was decreased activity in the amygdala that was inversely correlated with activity in the PFC (Eippert et al., 2007). In another study, people were distracted from their reactions to distressing images by having to make non–emotion-related judgments. In the distracting task, a decrease in amygdala activity was associated with an increase in ventral PFC activity (Hariri, Mattay, Tessitore, Fera, & Weinberger, 2003). Other studies find that the dorsolateral PFC and the ventromedial PFC are activated when altering amygdala activation to negative images or to contemplating the possibility of loss (Sokol-Hessner et al., 2012; Urry et al., 2006).

In addition to the amygdala being activated in response to distressing stimuli, the dACC becomes active in response to both physical pain and the social pain associated with rejection. The PFC is involved in regulation of the dACC as well as other anxiety structures. When people are exposed to social rejection or experience physical pain, strong activation in the ventrolateral PFC is correlated with less activation of the dACC, suggesting that the ventrolateral PFC can suppress the dACC in response to physical pain or social rejection (Lieberman, 2013; Lieberman & Eisenberg, 2009). In addition to activation in the brain's distress areas, stress hormones spike when people are disturbed. When people are subjected to looking at emotional photographs, more activity in the ventromedial PFC is correlated with less stress hormone release (Shin & Liberzon, 2010). Across studies then, the dorsolateral, ventrolateral, and the ventromedial PFC play roles in suppressing distress areas of the brain (Hartley & Phelps, 2010).

In the 1970s, Walter Mischel carried out the now famous marshmallow study with 4-year-olds at Stanford University (Mischel, Ebbesen, & Raskoff-Zeiss, 1972). These 4-year-olds were given a choice of ringing a bell and receiving one marshmallow now or waiting for the experimenter to return and receiving two marshmallows. Basically, the marshmallow experiment was a test of delay of gratification. Later follow-up on the children who had delayed gratification found that they were distinguished by higher Scholastic Aptitude Test scores and grade point averages (Eigste et al., 2006). When imaged as adults in the scanner, they exhibited more activity in the right ventrolateral PFC than others (Casey et al., 2011). Thus, delay of gratification depends on structures in the PFC.

Additional findings also suggest that regulatory control capacity extends to multiple domains. Those who score high on measures of persistence show greater activity in the ventromedial PFC and regard more images as pleasant than other people viewing the same images (Gusnard et al., 2003). In a short-term study, researchers found that intentionally inhibiting a motor response enhanced capacity for dampening amygdala activity while watching an emotional face (Berkman, Burklund, & Lieberman, 2009).

The research reviewed in this section suggests that the PFC is involved in regulating behaviors and emotions across a variety of domains, including downregulating intense negative emotions, delaying gratification, inhibiting motor impulses, and inhibiting thoughts. Self-regulation will be relevant for recovery from substance abuse as well as regulating negative emotions (namely, anxiety and sadness). Self-regulation is not a static, immutable trait. Roy Baumeister has suggested that areas of the brain involved in regulation of emotions and impulses function like a muscle (discussed more in Chapter 8). The strength of these areas can be enhanced by practice over time. For example, in an experimental study, attending to one's posture increased ability to resist temptation. Using the nondominant hand in daily routines increased the ability to maintain smoking abstention (Heatherton & Wagner, 2011). In addition to increasing regulatory control through practice, it may be possible to increase regulatory control by increasing heart rate variability (HRV). This pathway will be discussed in a later section on the autonomic nervous system (Section 5).

Putting It All Together: BAS and BIS

Psychologists have developed the concepts of the behavioral activation system (BAS) and behavioral inhibition system (BIS). The terms were originated by Jeffrey Grey in the 1970s, who examined fear responding in animals. These terms were adopted by Richie Davidson in the late 1980s; he postulated that the right PFC cortex activity was more heavily connected with the BIS, whereas activity on the left PFC cortex activity reflected activity in the BAS. In fact, in imaging studies, the right PFC (the medial region of the right oribitofrontal cortex [OFC]) is responsive to punishment, whereas the left PFC (medial region of the OFC) is more active during reward (Davidson, Pizzagalli, Nitschke, & Putnam, 2002).

Across studies, operationalization of the BAS and the BIS is done in multiple ways. Davidson measured EEG activity differentials between the right and left sides of the head. (EEG is a crude measure of electrical activity in the cortex.) In 1994, Carver and White published paper-and-pencil scales designed to assess the BAS and BIS. These paper-and-pencil measures did correlate as expected with measures of the differential left versus right electrical activity measured by EEG (Amodio, Master, Yee, & Taylor, 2008).

Research categorizing individuals as high on the BIS has found that the measures do relate to behavior in the predicted manner. Early on, Davidson measured electrical activity in the two hemispheres of the brain. Davidson found that an infant's greater right side electrical activity during stranger approach was correlated with more crying, with greater stress hormone (cortisol) output, and predicted subsequent shyness at toddler age (Buss et al., 2003; Davidson & Fox, 1989). This work was consistent with previous findings in primates on how hemispheric activity related to behavior (Buss et al., 2003). Subsequent research used the paper-and-pencil measure to identify those with strong BIS. When shown images of angry people, those with high BIS scores showed greater activation of the distress area (dorsal anterior cingulate) than others (Beaver, Lawrence, Passamonti, & Calder, 2008).

Research examining how operationalization of measures of the BAS relates to personality traits has been consistent with the predictions of Davidson: Those who score high on the BAS system are less fearful and more active. People who score high on measures of BAS are much less likely to be intimidated and more likely to be activated in response to aggression. When shown anger images, those with high score on the BAS show activation in the amygdala, but less activation in an area of the brain associated with distress (dorsal anterior cingulate; Beaver et al., 2008).

Preliminary evidence does link high BAS levels with greater dopamine function in the nucleus accumbens under conditions of opportunity for reward. There is also suggestion that high BAS scorers have less dopamine function in the PFC, an area that might dampen the nucleus accumbens (Wacker, Mueller, Pizzagalli, Hennnig, & Stemmier, 2013).

Activity in the left PFC can also be used as a measure of a momentary state. Greater activity in the left PFC is associated with more activity in the nucleus accumbens, the appetitive structure (Davidson & Irwin, 1999; Sutton, Larson, Holden, Perlman, & Davidson, 1997). (Recall that the activity in the nucleus accumbens is about making an active response.) On being provoked, left-brain activity increases in those who are in a position to retaliate relative to those who cannot take action (Harmon-Jones, Lueck, Fearn, & Harmon-Jones, 2006).

Emotional Inhibition/Regulation in High BAS Scorers

It should be noted that the term *inhibition* is used in two different ways in the literature. Inhibition can refer to inhibiting active behavior as seen in shy people. Inhibition can refer to regulating emotional behavior, including fear responses. Those with strong BAS are less behaviorally inhibited as the term is used to describe shy or fear-subdued individuals; however, they are better at regulating (inhibiting) distress.

A number of observations suggest that those with strong BAS are better at emotional regulation. Those who display greater left-brain activity (those who are high on the BAS) deny any negative affect (Tomarken &

Davidson, 1994). They demonstrate decreased attention to and memory for negative stimuli (Tomarken & Keener, 1998). They exhibit less startle to a loud noise after being told to suppress their feelings to previously viewed distressing pictures (Davidson, 1998; Davidson et al., 2000). Those with high BAS scores are higher on measures of emotional control (increased HRV discussed in the section on the parasympathetic nervous system; see Section 5) and higher in the ability to inhibit motoric behavior on a stop-signal task (Sütterlin, Anderson, & Vögele, 2011).

Another researcher, George Bonanno, has been examining those with strong BAS, although he did not set out to do so. Bonanno has spent much of his career examining how people respond to bereavement. Bonanno has identified people who deny distress at the time of bereavement but who show strong activation in terms of their heart rates and sweaty palms. He labels these individuals as repressors. Other researchers have found that those who deny any negative affect are higher on left PFC activity (Tomarken & Davidson, 1994), suggesting that Bonanno's subjects have a strong BAS. Bonanno's findings attest to the benefits of having a strong BAS. Those who are repressors at the time of bereavement not only report less distress at the time of the loss of a loved one, but they also show better future recovery (Coifman, Bonanno, Ray, & Gross, 2007).

The meaning of the BAS concept is explored more thoroughly in the chapter on bipolar disorders (Chapter 7).

SECTION 5: EMOTIONS

The discussion thus far has been dealing with action tendencies, a component of emotional behavior. There is a literature examining particular emotions (sadness, disgust, anxiety, pleasure, anger) and their function. This section provides an overview of that literature.

Emotions in General

Emotion is a term used in common parlance. In fact, *emotion* refers to multiple facets of behavior. Overt action is often a component of an emotional response. The autonomic nervous system prepares the body for an overt response (Lang & Bradley, 2010). Overt action is supported by changes in heart rate and blood flow (controlled by the autonomic nervous system) and output from various glands. People are also generally aware of the experience of emotional changes and can report on their feelings. Thus, emotions involve three channels: overt behavior, subjective experience measured by self-report, and involuntary nervous system responding.

The question of how people become aware of their feelings so that they can self-report was an area of controversy between William James and Walter Cannon and Philip Bard, who proposed the Cannon–Bard theory. James believed that people decided what they felt by observing their physical response. The Cannon–Bard theory held that internal events constituted the basis for self-report (Friedman, 2010). Both theories have been supported to some extent. Support for William James's position is found in the experiments in which research participants have their facial expressions manipulated by the experimenter and are then asked to report on their feelings. Congruent facial positions can enhance subjective feeling, whereas being forced to maintain a neutral expression can dampen self-report of feeling (Duclos et al., 1989). Thus, when people describe their subjective experience, although some of their self-reports will be based on what is happening in their brains without interaction with other structures, feedback from their overt behavior may also contribute to their self-assessment.

Much of the research in neuroscience has concentrated on those brain structures associated with changes in emotional behavior. In assigning emotional significance to an environmental stimulus, the amygdala is involved. Although the circuitry in the amygdala is best articulated for fearful responding to conditioned and unconditioned stimuli, the amygdala is also involved in responding to positive stimuli (Berridge & Kringelbach, 2013; Lane et al., 2009b). The amygdala receives input from the thalamus (a structure in the middle of the brain that receives incoming information from all sensory modalities). The amygdala sends output to the hypothalamus. The hypothalamus controls the autonomic nervous system (which controls internal organs of the body) and the master gland of the body (the pituitary gland). Thus, output from the amygdala controls the autonomic nervous system and affects many of the body's major glands (Lane et al., 2009b).

Animal work suggests that emotions can be evoked by stimuli without cognitive processing of the meaning of the stimuli. For example, rats become frightened at the smell of a cat (LeDoux, 2012). Imaging work with humans confirms that subliminal presentation of a fearful face can induce activity in the amygdala. In fact, people who are blind because of damage to the occipital lobe only (which processes visual information) can still respond to fearful images. This is called blindsightedness and relies on the connection of the retina to areas in the midbrain (Liddell et al., 2005). Fear can be evoked without any cognitive processing of the stimulus. Persons with blindsightedness can have physical responses to scary faces or an object being moved (they will reach for it in the new place), although they cannot tell you why they are acting the way they do. Thus, people can exhibit an emotional response or a response to new information without any cognitive processing about what they are responding to.

Although gruesome pictures and angry faces can induce a fast visceral response without much cognitive processing, complex situations may require cognitive processing before fear is evoked. For example, realizing that your employer is laying people off requires rather sophisticated cognitive processing to induce fear in you. In regard to the complex situations, the thinking of Richard Lazarus is probably more relevant. The late Richard Lazarus, a major figure in the area of stress research, argued that situations or stimuli require appraisals regarding the dangerousness of the situation as well as appraisals of one's resources for coping with the situation before emotion would be evoked (Schooler & Mauss, 2010). The literature on emotional regulation shows that when situations are interpreted in non–emotion-provoking ways, activity in the amygdala subsides (see discussion in Phelps, 2006).

Later in this section, we consider particular types of emotions. Before considering specific emotions, we discuss the physiological mechanisms supporting emotional responding. We begin with the autonomic nervous system and then review hormonal mechanisms.

Autonomic Nervous System

Neurons in the hypothalamus as well as in the brain stem control the autonomic nervous system (Figure 2.10). The autonomic nervous system can be divided into two divisions: the sympathetic nervous system (SNS) and the parasympathetic nervous system (PNS). Both systems send projections to internal organs. Neither system is under voluntary control. Anatomically, the neurons belonging to each system are easy to distinguish. The neurons belonging to the PNS emerge at the top and bottom

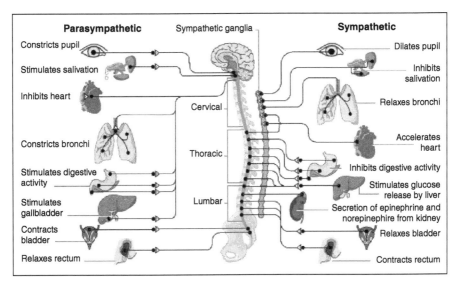

FIGURE 2.10   The autonomic nervous system.

Source: iStockphoto Support.

sections of the spinal cord. The neurons of the PNS act independently of each other. Thus, one can digest popcorn in a movie theater (PNS function onset) while one's pupils widen (offset of PNS). The neurons of SNS project from the middle sections of the cord and at their first synapse they send projections to each other (sympathetic chain ganglia) so that they all tend to act simultaneously.

There are just two synapses from neurons in the spinal cord to the target organ in both the PNS and the SNS. In the literature, the terms *preganglionic neuron* and *postganglionic neuron* are used to describe this. The term *preganglionic* refers to the first neuron in the autonomic nervous system whose cell body is in the spinal cord, which synapses onto the neuron in the ganglion (a collection of neuronal bodies). The *postganglionic neuron* is the second neuron, the neuron whose cell body is in the ganglion whose axon makes contact with the target organ.

Sympathetic Nervous System

Activation of the SNS occurs in preparation for fight or flight. The first neurotransmitter released in this response is acetylcholine and the second is norepinephrine. With activation of the SNS, pupils dilate, the heart rate accelerates, the vasculature constricts, and the pumping force of the heart is increased. Respiration is accelerated. The center of the adrenal gland (called the medulla of the adrenal gland), which secretes adrenaline (also called epinephrine), is actually formed by a postganglionic neuron of the SNS. For the most part, adrenaline/epinephrine acts with cortisol (a stress hormone) to get fat cells to release stored fuel and to get the liver to release glucose. (You need all the fuel you can get to run from the bear.)

To control the SNS, output is controlled at multiple levels. Areas in the brain stem monitor blood loss and other bodily states. Thus, the system will respond without any complex thinking. For an emotional response to complex events, areas in the hypothalamus and the amygdala are more relevant to controlling the SNS (Critchley et al., 2003).

Parasympathetic Nervous System

Both the first and second neurotransmitters of the PNS are acetylcholine. Activation of the PNS is sometimes mistakenly construed as opposing the SNS. In fact, the PNS and SNS are separate systems that often affect organs in opposite ways but occasionally act together. However, the PNS generally predominates during periods of relaxation, when the body turns to digesting food. Again, there is control on multiple levels. The hypothalamus and areas in the brain stem control the PNS.

Polyvagal Theory

Cranial nerve X is the vagus nerve. The vagus nerve belongs to the PNS. The vagus nerve projects to most major organs. Porges (2011), who developed polyvagal theory, recognized that in mammals there is more than one nucleus in the brain controlling the vagus nerve of the PNS. The phylogenetically more ancient division of the vagus nerve slows down the heart rate and controls the bradycardia of attention (slowing heart rate in order to orient to a novel stimulus). The older vagus is unmyelinated, that is, the axonal fibers lack the covering of fat cells that enable faster transmission. The more recently evolved division of the vagus nerve terminates at separate areas of the brain stem (primarily at the nucleus ambiguus and, to a lesser extent, to the nucleus of the solitary tract). The newer division of the vagus has myelinated fibers that allow fast transmission.

The myelinated vagus controls some movements of the tongue and face. The newer division of the vagus plays a role in regulating blood delivery to coordinate with breathing. HRV is a measure of the degree to which blood delivery and breathing are coordinated. Higher HRV is desirable. It is sometimes referred to as vagal tone (Appelhans & Luecken, 2006; Lane et al., 2009a).

As stated earlier, the amygdala does play a role in evaluating the emotional significance of various stimuli. The central amygdala projects directly to brain stem areas controlling HRV (nucleus ambiguus of the brain stem; Porges, 2011). An area of the PFC involved in regulating fear (medial PFC) is also involved in sustaining more HRV (Thayer & Lane, 2009).

HRV (vagal tone) has been the focus of much research. Sometimes it is examined as a momentary state measure. Changes in HRV over time are assessed in terms of how they correlate with particular behaviors. Average HRV over time is also studied as a personality trait. Both as a state and trait measure, HRV is correlated with the ability to maintain attention during strong emotions, with capacity for social function, and control over systemic inflammation. (Vagal control over inflammation will be covered in Chapter 4, on major depression.)

Self-Regulation

Stephen Porges has studied children who do and do not score highly on measures of HRV. Those children with higher vagal tone are much better at delaying gratification (Beauchaine, 2001). Children with higher social competence, who can assist other children in distress, exhibit higher HRV (Appelhans & Luecken, 2006; Eisenberg & Eggum, 2009; Fabes, Eisenberg, & Eisenbud, 1993). Moreover, those with higher HRV are able to focus attention away from threatening information (Thayer, Saus-Rose, & Johnsen, 2009) and exhibit lesser increases in the stress hormone (cortisol; Thayer & Lane, 2009). With regard to working memory, those with better working memory are higher on HRV (Lane et al., 2009). They are able to suppress prepotent (habitual) motor responses and to maintain focused attention under threat (Thayer & Lane, 2009). In contrast to those with high HRV, those who are low on HRV are more likely to display submissive behavior in response to intimidation (Sgoifo et al., 2003).

HRV also relates to momentary emotional control. When asked to reappraise or suppress reaction in response to emotional material, people increase their HRV (Butler, Wilhelm, & Gross, 2006; Critchley et al., 2003). Greater HRV is correlated with less activity in the dorsal anterior cingulate, an alarm center (Critchley et al., 2003).

Preparing for a Burst of Energy

When a person prepares for exertion, there are two ways to increase the heart rate. (During emergencies, the heart rate increases to get more fuel to the muscles.) The PNS's vagus nerve, which slows down the heart rate, can decrease its influence on heart rate. Alternatively, the SNS can release norepinephrine into the heart, which increases heart rate and strength of contraction. Increasing SNS activity is a slower process than regulation through PNS offset (Appelhans & Luecken, 2006). When the heart rate is increased through SNS onset, the vasculature will also narrow. (Recall, all SNS neurons are linked and act as a unit.) Some of the SNS neurons synapse onto the vasculature and narrow blood vessels. The heart is pumping against the pressure of constricted vessels. This will cause a much greater activation of the blood pressure and is much more taxing for the body. The research of Blascovich and Mendes (2000) finds that those individuals who construe a test as a challenge tend to display less peripheral resistance. Those who construe a test as a threat tend to display more peripheral resistance.

Cooperative Social Communication

HRV is increased in both mothers and offspring when mothers tend to their offspring. HRV is also a correlate of positive facial expressions and vocalizations. (Recall that the myelinated vagus and other PNS nerves control some of the neurons of the vocal cords, facial muscles, and the middle ear to tune for receiving human vocal communication [Porges, 2011]). The myelinated vagus, the newer division of the vagus, serves to decrease the release of stress hormones (Porges, 2011).

Hormonal Activity

A hormone is a substance secreted into the bloodstream, usually by a gland, which influences targets that are far away. There are many hormones in the body that regulate behavior. Indeed, more hormones involved in weight and appetite control seem to be discovered every year. This section considers cortisol because it is released in response to stress. Additionally, oxytocin is considered because it can affect mood and behavior associated with mood disorders.

Cortisol

Cortisol is considered a stress hormone; however, it is good to remember that it is a glucocorticoid, a name that implies that cortisol will alter the availability of blood glucose. All kinds of stress, including running or starvation, elevate cortisol in the body. The effects of cortisol are far-reaching. Cortisol can enter cells. It binds to receptors in the cytoplasm of a cell. Along with its receptor, it then goes to the cell's nucleus to increase expression of various proteins and decrease expression of others. Cortisol controls the expression of many proteins.

One of cortisol's jobs is to prepare the body for fight or flight. In response to cortisol, fatty acids get released from fat cells so that fuel is available for working muscles. Many immune system functions get suppressed. (This is why topical cortisol gets applied to inflamed areas.) Long-term cortisol secretion can erode the body, decrease bone strength, change the location of fat stores throughout the body, and decrease fat pads under the skin so skin tears more readily. Sustained levels of elevated cortisol are also believed to shrink the hippocampus (area for memory retrieval and memory formation; Chetty et al., 2014; McEwen & Milner, 2007).

Cortisol also affects psychological function. In the central amygdala, cortisol increases the production of another stress-enhancing neurotransmitter (corticotropin-releasing factor [CRF]; Davis, Walker, Miles, & Grillon, 2010; Shin & Liberzon, 2010). Cortisol also sensitizes the receptors for norepinephrine and epinephrine (adrenaline), which are distributed throughout the vascular system in the body. Persons who have lost the capacity to produce cortisol (called Addison's disease) because they cannot respond to norepinephrine sometimes do not have the stamina to climb a flight of stairs.

The control on cortisol secretion, as with most major hormones, is through the hypothalamus. The amygdala sends projections to the hypothalamus (Lane et al., 2009b; Purves et al., 2012) as does the dACC (the alarm center; Eisenberger, Taylor, Gable, Hilmert, & Lieberman, 2007). It is a two-step process to get from the hypothalamus to the release of cortisol. A part of the hypothalamus (the paraventricular nucleus) releases another hormone (CRF) to the master gland (the pituitary) of the brain. In response to the release of the hypothalamus chemical (CRF), the master gland releases another hormone (adrenocorticotropic hormone [ACTH]) into the bloodstream. The master gland hormone (ACTH) acts on the adrenal glands (which sit on top of your kidneys) to release cortisol.

There is a short-term break in this pathway (often called the hypothalamic–pituitary–adrenal axis or HPA). The ventromedial PFC, the structure involved in toning down anxiety in response to a dopamine signal, can limit the extent of the cortisol stress response (Sullivan & Dufresne, 2006).

For long-term control, the body does have a "turnoff" mechanism for stopping cortisol release. There are receptors for cortisol in the hippocampus (a brain area associated with the formation of memories about what happened where). Given excessive levels of cortisol in the blood, the hippocampus turns off the area in the hypothalamus which releases CRF. The rest of the cascade is then turned off. In very stressed out persons, who are elevated on inflammatory markers, the cytokines (white blood cell hormones) induce a loss of sensitivity in the cortisol receptor to the cortisol (Pace & Miller, 2009). In those cases, the turnoff mechanism does not work properly.

The dexamethasone suppression test is a crude measure of depression. Synthetic cortisol is administered and a blood test is taken to determine whether cortisol levels are suppressed. Persons with depression are more likely to fail this test. Their receptors for cortisol in the hippocampus just do not respond. They do not decrease their secretion of cortisol in response to the synthetic cortisol. The dexamethasone suppression test is not very specific for depression. People with systemic inflammation (alcoholism, autoimmune disease, infection) may also be "dexamethasone nonsuppressors" (Pace & Miller, 2009).

Chronic distress can induce a second aberration of the HPA system as well. The loss of a variable pattern of release during the day (called a circadian pattern) is also a sign of stress. In those who are very stressed, cortisol is released at a constant level throughout the day, rather than being highest in the morning and declining during the day (O'Connor, Wellisch, Stanton, Olmstead, & Irwin, 2012).

Oxytocin

The hormone oxytocin is a peptide chain of nine amino acids. Oxytocin is produced by cells in the nucleus of the hypothalamus. (The cells of the paraventricular area releasing oxytocin are distinct from those releasing CRF). Oxytocin does get released during childbirth and it is important for inducing contractions in the vagina and then for milk release. Stimulation of the vagina during sexual activity releases oxytocin. The perception of being trusted by others also releases oxytocin (Porges, 2007; Young & Alexander, 2014; Zak, Kurzban, & Matzner, 2004).

Young and Alexander (2014) characterize oxytocin as the hormone or neurotransmitter of social connection. In experiments in which animals have oxytocin directly injected into their brains, they are better at forming memories of members of their species. People who have their oxytocin levels increased are better able to discriminate facial expressions in photos. They are more willing to trust a stranger with their money (Young & Alexander, 2014).

Oxytocin has been evaluated in terms of its effect on social behavior. For couples discussing contentious subjects, oxytocin nasal spray increases prosocial behavior, such as touching, mutual expressions, and eye gazing. On the dark side, oxytocin also tends to increase in-group preference while enhancing out-group discriminatory behavior. Women do differ from each other in their receptors for responding to oxytocin. Those women with more responsive receptors are more satisfied with their interpersonal relationships and are more adept in terms of interpersonal relationship skills (Carter, Grippo, Pournajafi-Nazarloo, Ruscio, & Porges, 2008; De Dreu, 2012; Kemp et al., 2012; Young & Alexander, 2014). Women who have been abused as children, on average, have lower levels of oxytocin (Heim et al., 2009).

Oxytocin is generally an anxiety reducer. If oxytocin is administered, it attenuates anxiety levels and increases HRV. Oxytocin downregulates cortisol. People given a nasal spray containing oxytocin (which gets into the brain) are especially responsive to happy faces and less responsive to frowning faces, as evidenced by activation of the amygdala (Young & Alexander, 2014). Those with higher levels of oxytocin heal wounds faster (Gouin et al., 2010). In a laboratory test of oxytocin on pain perception, an intranasal spray of oxytocin decreased pain intensity as well as decreased the pain-induced increase in heart rate (Rash & Campbell, 2014).

Specific Emotions

We now consider information regarding those areas of the brain that are active during various emotional experiences. In reviewing this material, it is clear that both basic sensory experiences and complex thought processes often activate the same brain structure during a particular emotional experience. Emotional pain and psychological pain register in the same brain regions, as does the experience of a disgusting taste or a disgusting thought. It is also the case that our language uses the same word (emotional label) to describe experiences that may utilize different brain circuitry. As we will see, this is probably the case with pleasure and with rage.

Distress/Anxiety

The amygdala is a key structure involved in responding to both innate fears and learned fears. The BNST is involved in maintaining a strong propensity to respond to fearful situations. Parts of the amygdala are also involved in fear conditioning. The specifics are examined in more detail in Chapter 5, the chapter on anxiety.

Higher order brain structures also participate in the subjective experience of distress. The dorsal anterior cingulate is involved in registering pain, whether emotional or physical pain, and potentiating anxiety. (A high density of opioid receptors is found in this brain area.) The dorsal anterior cingulate activates in response to social exclusion, and when an individual perceives himself or herself to be stressed (Eisenberger et al., 2007; Lieberman, 2013). The dorsal anterior cingulate is active in processing physical pain, the pain of a broken heart (Eisenberger, 2012), and the pain of envy (Takahashi et al., 2009). When rat pups are separated from their mothers, distress signals register in the dACC. The dACC is also active during the experience of frustration. Based on brain imaging with humans, the dorsal anterior cingulate has been characterized as involved in error detection, conflict monitoring, and processing emotion (Lieberman, 2013; Paus, 2001). This region receives input from the amygdala, from the locus coeruleus (releasing norepinephrine) and the VTA, and has reciprocal connections with the PFC (Paus, 2001).

In terms of the neurotransmitter involved in distress, agonists at acetylcholine receptors in the brain stem (periaqueductal gray or PAG) are associated with distress calls (Kroes, Burgdorf, Otto, Panksepp, & Moskal, 2007). The PAG, in the midbrain, is an output structure for the amygdala. The regions in the dorsal area of the PAG induce fight or flight. The regions in the ventral area of the PAG induce freezing. However, parts of the PAG also are involved in sexual response, maternal behavior, and analgesia (Farook et al., 2004; Panksepp et al., 2014).

Disgust

The insula plays a role in responding to mixed emotions involving disgust and anxiety (Figures 2.4 and 2.5). The insula receives information about the state of the body and the skin (Craig, 2002). This area of the brain is activated by disgust induced by unpalatable tastes but also in response to psychologically disgusting imagery (Calder et al., 2007; Wicker et al., 2003).

Some distressing situations involve both the activation of the dACC and the anterior insula. Both the dACC and the anterior insula are active when processing emotionally distressing and disgusting images, when responding to aversive tastes, when processing the distressing aspects of pain, and when thinking about sad events (Lieberman, 2013; Shin & Liberzon, 2010). In addition to the anterior insula and the dACC, the basal ganglia are also activated during disgust or recognition of disgust in others. Similar responses are evoked, given disgusting images or smells, but also morally disgusting ideas as well (Chapman & Anderson, 2013; Paulmann, Pell, & Kotz, 2009).

Pleasure

Kent Berridge, who began his research asking questions about what causes organisms to develop compulsive use of drugs, spent a great deal of time investigating whether dopamine is the neurotransmitter of pleasure. (As discussed earlier in this chapter, dopamine is now viewed as the neurotransmitter of motivation.) In the process of disentangling motivation from pleasure, Berridge did learn a great deal about which areas of brain are active in response to pleasure. According to Kent Berridge, pleasure-producing nuclei are found in the ventral pallidum, part of the nucleus accumbens, and the parabrachial nucleus, which is found in the midbrain.

The neurotransmitters in these nuclei are cannabinoids, GABA, and opioids (Berridge, Robinson, & Aldridge, 2009; Kringelbach & Berridge, 2012). Although dopamine is involved in signaling to these nuclei, it is not the neurotransmitter used in creating the subjective experience of pleasure. The subjective sense of pleasure also registers in the OFC (Der-Avakian & Markou, 2012). Kringelbach (2010) and Kringelbach and Berridge (2009) suggest that the degree of activation in the OFC may differentiate whether the subjective experience is positive or negative.

Of course, pleasure is a complicated emotion, if it can be called an emotion. Kringelbach (2010) views pleasure as the result of a process of valuation, that is, the result of reaching a conclusion. Anticipating reward can be distinguished from appreciating a reward (Der-Avakian & Markou, 2012). Moreover, pleasure comes in many flavors: relaxed satisfaction, excitement, pleasure from eating, and pleasure from sex. Pleasure can also derive from personal achievement or from connection to others. Each of these experiences is likely to involve its own circuitry. Parsing positive affective experiences encompasses a range of qualitative experiences. For those pleasurable states that are associated with excitement (e.g., hearing beautiful music), activity is frequently registered in the OFC and the ventral striatum, including the nucleus accumbens (Kringelbach, 2010). The pleasure of seeing one's enemies suffer registers in the nucleus accumbens (Takahashi et al., 2009). For rough-and-tumble play in animals, the medial PFC and the parietal cortex play a prominent role (Burgdorf, Kroes, Beinfeld, Panksepp, & Moskal, 2010; Burgdorf, Panksepp, & Moshal, 2011) as do endocannabinoids in the amygdala and nucleus accumbens (Trezza et al., 2012). In fact, Porges (2011) argues that the evolutionarily newer divisions of the vagus nerve (part of the PNS), when active, are correlated with subjective comfort, possibly a component of some forms of pleasure.

Rage/Anger

Rage/anger is another emotion that probably comes in many flavors and is evoked by several different circuitry systems. For example, sham rage (when an animal aggressively bares its teeth) can be evoked by stimulating various regions of the hypothalamus or the septal area. Anger can be provoked by activating the circuitry associated with protecting the young and staking out mating opportunities (Young & Alexander, 2014). Carver and Harmon-Jones (2009) suggest that some types of anger are associated with activation of the BAS, involving dopamine. For predatory aggression aimed at acquisition, activation of appetitive, dopaminergic structures may be involved. Making people angry is also associated with activity of the BAS (Harmon-Jones & Sigelman, 2001). However, predatory aggression may not be the same as aggression involved in defending territory or defensive aggression associated with fear.

SECTION 6: THE HUMAN BRAIN IS SOCIAL

Much of the information on various circuits underpinning anxiety and learned helplessness comes from work on rodents and sometimes primates, such as monkeys. Fear circuitry evolved very long ago in older species. The human brain emerged later in the evolutionary timetable. What is clear about the human brain is that much of its function is devoted to social processes. In fact, when humans are imaged in the scanner without a task to perform, the default system comes online. According to Lieberman (2013), the default system is activated when people process information about social interactions. This is where most people's thoughts will go spontaneously, when they are not engaging in another type of problem-solving task.

Giacomo Rizzolatti and colleagues (Rizzolatti, Fogassi, & Gallese, 2001) discovered that both primates and human beings possess mirror neurons. These mirror neurons are dispersed widely throughout the cortex and cerebellum (Decety & Meyer, 2008; Gallese & Goldman, 1998). These neurons are activated both when an individual performs a particular action and when an individual watches another person performing some action. The neurons enable the capacity for imitation through which language and culture are conveyed.

A series of clever experiments have yielded the conclusion that the mirror neurons respond to similar intentions to produce an end state, not just motoric behaviors. This led to the theorizing that mirror neurons allow humans to develop theories of the mind, that is, to observe another person and speculate on his or her motives and intentions. Experiments conducted by Matt Lieberman (see discussion in Lieberman, 2013) confirmed that the motor neurons probably allow observers to intuit the intended effect of another person's action (e.g., watching a person sipping through a straw or gulping a drink may activate the same mirror neurons). However, determining the reason why another person wants to achieve an intended effect (he is hungry vs. he needs to take his medicine) activates additional areas of the brain required for complex thinking (Lieberman, 2013).

Another capacity that we share with primates is empathy. In fact, identifying emotion in others is facilitated when we adapt facial expressions that are congruent with the expressions of the persons we are observing. Those who have been injected with Botox (a treatment for wrinkles that paralyzes facial muscles) have difficulty identifying emotions in others (Lieberman, 2013). When viewing another in pain, areas of our brain associated with our own physical pain are activated (Lieberman, 2013). Feeling another's pain is not sufficient to activate helping. Prosocial behavior requires more than empathy. In order to help another, it is necessary to distinguish one's self from the other person. (The right temporoparietal junction is active when we distinguish ourselves from others [Decety & Meyers, 2008].) Additionally, the areas for inhibiting the amygdala, the ventrolateral PFC, come online in those who can help. Children with higher HRV, an indicator of emotional regulation, are more likely to assist another child in distress (Eisenberg & Eggum, 2009). When we are overwhelmed by fear, we can not do much to assist others (Decety & Lamm, 2006).

Neuroscience and work with primates have also revealed the extent to which our phylogenetic order is concerned with fairness. In fact, Franz DeWalls (2014) has demonstrated that monkeys are very aware of fairness. When one monkey is given a lesser reward than another monkey for the same amount of work, the unfairly compensated monkey becomes agitated and throws the food back at the experimenter. In work with people in the scanner, an unfairly compensated individual exhibits activity in the dACC and the anterior insula. Not only do people respond to unfairness toward themselves, they also respond to unfairness to others. While in the scanner, distress areas in the anterior cingulate cortex are activated when a person views another person being unjustly compensated. When an unfairly treated individual is finally seen to be compensated, the reward circuitry in the viewer is activated (Civai, Crescentini, Rustichini, & Rumiati, 2012; Lieberman, 2013; Tricomi, Rangel, Camerer, & O'Doerty, 2010). A sense of justice is hardwired in most primates.

Because the survivability of all humans is dependent on the group, we are set up to conform. In addressing the issue of why so many ordinary Germans conformed to Adolph Hitler's madness, Solomon Asch developed a paradigm to investigate whether individuals would make an obviously wrong judgment when the majority of others made this wrong judgment. The "Asch paradigm" asks research participants to indicate whether two lines are of equal length, when it is obvious that they are not of equal length. When others in the group say that the lines are equal, then 41% of people will also say that they are equal. Berns et al. (2005) investigated this conformity phenomenon using brain imaging. The Berns et al. results suggest that parts of the brain involved in perception are activated when people rendered the wrong answer in the Asch paradigm. Thus, what people believe they see may in fact be altered by the opinions of others. People appear to rely heavily on social proof. What the Berns et al. investigation also revealed was the cost associated with nonconformity. Those who went against the group judgment exhibited more activation in their amygdalae.

In the chapters to follow, the primacy of our interdependence with others will be explored as a vehicle for achieving better physical and mental health. The case will be advanced that human interactions can change physiology. Each chapter considers mechanisms for harnessing our capacity for utilizing mutual support.

REFERENCES

Ader, R., & Cohen, N. (2001). Conditioning and immunity. In R. Ader, D. Felten, & N. Cohen (Eds.), *Psychoneuroimmunology: Vol 1* (3rd ed., pp. 3–34). San Diego, CA: Academic Press.

Alberts, B., Johnson, A., Lewis, J., Raff, M., Roberts, K., & Walter, P. (2008). *Molecular biology of the cell* (5th ed.). New York, NY: Garland Science.

Amat, J., Sparks, P. D., Matus-Amat, P., Griggs, J., Watkins, L. R., & Maier, S. F. (2001). The role of the habenular complex in the elevation of dorsal raphe nucleus serotonin and the changes in the behavioral responses produced by uncontrollable stress. *Brain Research, 917*(1), 118–126.

Amodio, D. M., Master, S. L., Yee, C. M., & Taylor, S. E. (2008). Neurocognitive components of the behavioral inhibition and activation systems: Implications for theories of self-regulation. *Psychophysiology, 45*(1), 11–19.

Appelhans, B. M., & Luecken, L. J. (2006). Heart rate variability as an index of regulated emotional responding. *Review of General Psychology, 10*(3), 229–240.

Aron, A. R., Robbins, T. W., & Poldrack, R. A. (2004). Inhibition and the right inferior frontal cortex. *Trends in Cognitive Science, 8*(4), 170–177.

Baldo, B. A., & Kelley, A. E. (2007). Discrete neurochemical coding of distinguishable motivational processes: Insights from nucleus accumbens control of feeding. *Psychopharmacology, 191*(3), 439–459.

Beauchaine, T. P. (2001). Vagal tone, development, and Gray's motivational theory: Toward an integrated model of autonomic nervous system functioning in psychopathology. *Development and Psychopathology, 13*(2), 183–214.

Beaver, J. D., Lawrence, A. D., Passamonti, L., & Calder, A. J. (2008). Appetitive motivation predicts the neural response to facial signals of aggression. *Journal of Neuroscience, 28*(11), 2719–2725.

Berkman, E. T., Burklund, L., & Lieberman, M. D. (2009). Inhibitory spillover: Intentional motor inhibition produces incidental limbic inhibition via right inferior frontal cortex. *NeuroImage, 47*(2), 705–712.

Berns, G. S., Chappelow, J., Zink, C. F., Pagnoni, G., Martin-Skurski, M. E., & Richards, J. (2005). Neurobiological correlates of social conformity and independence during mental rotation. *Biological Psychiatry, 58*(3), 245–253.

Berridge, K. C. (2009a). "Liking" and "wanting" food rewards: Brain substrates and roles in eating disorders. *Physiology & Behavior, 97*(5), 537–550.

Berridge, K. C. (2009b). Wanting and liking: Observations from the Neuroscience and Psychology Laboratory. *Inquiry, 52*(4), 378.

Berridge, K. C., & Kringelbach, M. L. (2008). Affective neuroscience of pleasure: Reward in humans and animals. *Psychopharmacology, 199*(3), 457–480.

Berridge, K. C., & Kringelbach, M. L. (2013). Neuroscience of affect: Brain mechanisms of pleasure and displeasure. *Current Opinion in Neurobiology, 23*, 294–303.

Berridge, K. C., & Robinson, T. E. (1998). What is the role of dopamine in reward: Hedonic impact, reward learning, or incentive salience? [Review]. *Brain Research. Brain Research Reviews, 28*(3), 309–369.

Berridge, K. C., Robinson, T. E., & Aldridge, J. W. (2009). Dissecting components of reward: "liking," "wanting," and learning. *Current Opinion in Pharmacology, 9*(1), 65–73.

Blascovich, J., & Mendes, W. B. (2000). Challenge and threat appraisals: The role of affective cues. *Feeling and Thinking: The Role of Affect in Social Cognition*, 59–82.

Brennan, A. R., & Arnsten, A. F. T. (2010). Neuronal mechanisms underlying attention deficit hyperactivity disorder. *Annals of the New York Academy of Sciences, 1129*, 236–245.

Bruijnzeel, A. W. (2009). Kappa-opioid receptor signaling and brain reward function. *Brain Research Reviews, 62*(1), 127–146.

Burgdorf, J., Kroes, R. A., Beinfeld, M. C., Panksepp, J., & Moskal, J. R. (2010). Uncovering the molecular basis of positive affect using rough-and-tumble play in rats: A role for insulin-like-growth factor 1. *Neuroscience, 168*, 769–777.

Burgdorf, J., Panksepp, J., & Moskal, J. R. (2011). Frequency-modulated 50kHz ultrasonic vocalizations a tool for uncovering the molecular substrates of positive affect. *Neuroscience and Biobehavioral Reviews, 35*(9), 1831–1836.

Buss, K. A., Schumacher, J. R., Dolski, I., Kalin, N. H., Goldsmith, H. H., & Davidson, R. J. (2003). Right frontal brain activity, cortisol, and withdrawal behavior in 6-month-old infants. *Behavioral Neuroscience, 117*(1), 11–20.

Butler, E. A., Wilhelm, F. H., & Gross, J. J. (2006). Respiratory sinus arrhythmia, emotion, and emotion regulation during social interaction. *Psychophysiology, 43*(6), 612–622.

Caielli, S., Banchereau, J., & Pascual, V. (2012). Neutrophils come of age in chronic inflammation. *Current Opinion in Immunology, 24*(6), 671–677.

Calder, A. J., Beaver, J. D., Davis, M. H., van Ditzhuijzen, J., Keane, J., & Lawrence, A. D. (2007). Disgust sensitivity predicts the insula and pallidal response to pictures of disgusting foods. *European Journal of Neuroscience, 25*(11), 3422–3428.

Carey, N. (2012). *The epigenetics revolution.* New York, NY: Columbia University Press.

Carter, C. S., Grippo, A. J., Pournajafi-Nazarloo, H., Ruscio, M. G., & Porges, S. W. (2008). Oxytocin, vasopressin and sociality. *Progress in Brain Research, 170,* 331–336.

Carver, C. S., & Harmon-Jones, E. (2009). Anger is an approach-related affect: Evidence and implications. *Psychological Bulletin, 135*(2), 183–204.

Carver, C. S., & White, T. L. (1994). Behavioral inhibition, behavioral activation, and affective responses to impending reward and punishment: The BIS/BAS scales. *Journal of Personality and Social Pscyhology, 67,* 319–333.

Casey, B. J., Somerville, L. H., Gotlib, I. H., Ayduk, O., Franklin, N. T., Askren, M. K.,…Shoda, Y. (2011). Behavioral and neural correlates of delay of gratification 40 years later. *Proceedings of the National Academy of Sciences of the United States of America, 108*(36), 14998–15003.

Champagne, F. A. (2008). Epigenetic mechanisms and the transgenerational effects of maternal care. *Frontiers in Neuroendocrinology, 29*(3), 386–397.

Chapman, H. A., & Anderson, A. K. (2013). Things rank and gross in nature: A review and synthesis of moral disgust. *Psychological Bulletin, 139*(2), 300–327.

Chetty, S., Friedman, A. R., Taravosh-Lahn, K., Kirby, E. D., Mirescu, C., Guo, F.,…Kaufer, D. (2014). Stress and glucocorticoids promote oligodendrogenesis in the adult hippocampus. *Molecular Psychiatry, 19,* 1275–1283. doi:10.1038/mp.2013.190

Christianson, J. P., Paul, E. D., Irani, M., Thompson, B. M., Kubala, K. H., Yirmiya, R.,…Maier, S. F. (2008). The role of prior stressor controllability and the dorsal raphe nucleus in sucrose preference and social exploration. *Behavioural Brain Research, 193*(1), 87–93.

Christianson, J. P., Ragole, T., Amat, J., Greenwood, B. N., Strong, P. V., Paul, E. D.,…Maier, S. F. (2010). 5-Hydroxytryptamine 2C receptors in the basolateral amygdala are involved in the expression of anxiety after uncontrollable traumatic stress. *Biological Psychiatry, 67*(4), 339–345.

Civai, C., Crescentini, C., Rustichini, A., & Rumiati, R. I. (2012). Equality versus self-interest in the brain: Differential roles of anterior insula and medical prefrontal cortex. *NeuroImage, 62,* 102–112.

Coifman, K. G., Bonanno, G. A., Ray, R. D., & Gross, J. J. (2007). Does repressive coping promote resilience? Affective-autonomic response discrepancy during bereavement. *Journal of Personality and Social Psychology, 92*(4), 745–758.

Craig, A. D. (2002). How do you feel? Interoception: The sense of the physiological condition of the body. *Nature Reviews Neuroscience, 3*(8), 655–666.

Critchley, H. D., Mathias, C. J., Josephs, O., O'Doherty, J., Zanini, S., Dewar, B. K.,...Dolan, R. J. (2003). Human cingulate cortex and autonomic control: Converging neuroimaging and clinical evidence. *Brain, 126*(Pt. 10), 2139–2152.

Davidson, R. J. (1998). Affective style and affective disorders: Perspectives from affective neuroscience. *Cognition and Emotion, 12*(3), 307–330.

Davidson, R. J., & Fox, N. A. (1989). Frontal brain asymmetry predicts infants' response to maternal separation. *Journal of Abnormal Psychology, 98*(2), 127–131.

Davidson, R. J., & Irwin, W. (1999). The functional neuroanatomy of emotion and affective style. *Trends in Cognitive Sciences, 3*(1), 11–21.

Davidson, R. J., Pizzagalli, D., Nitschke, J. B., & Putnam, K. (2002). Depression: Perspectives from affective neuroscience. *Annual Review of Psychology, 53,* 545–574.

Davidson, R. J., Putnam, K. M., & Larson, C. L. (2000). Dysfunction in the neural circuitry of emotion regulation—A possible prelude to violence. *Science, 289*(5479), 591–594.

Davis, M., Walker, D. L., Miles, L., & Grillon, C. (2010). Phasic vs sustained fear in rats and humans: Role of the extended amygdala in fear vs anxiety. *Neuropsychopharmacology, 35*(1), 105–135.

Decety, J., & Lamm, C. (2006). Human empathy through the lens of social neuroscience. *Science World Journal, 6,* 1146–1163.

Decety, J. L., & Meyer, M. (2008). From emotional resonance to understanding: A social developmental neuroscience account. *Development and Psychopathology, 20,* 1053–1080.

De Dreu, C. K. (2012). Oxytocin modulates cooperation within and competition between groups: An integrative review and research agenda. *Hormones and Behavior, 61*(3), 419–428.

Der-Avakian, A., & Markou, A. (2012). The neurobiology of anhedonia and other reward-related deficits. *Trends in Neuroscience, 35*(1), 68–77.

DeWalls, F. (2014). *The bonobo and the atheist: In search of humanism among primates.* New York, NY: W. W. Norton.

Dias, B. G., & Ressler, K. J. (2014). Parental olfactory experience influences behavior and neural structure in subsequent generations. *Nature Neuroscience, 17*(1), 89–96.

Diekhof, E. K., & Gruber, O. (2010). When desire collides with reason: Functional interactions between anteroventral prefrontal cortex and nucleus accumbens underlie the human ability to resist impulsive desires. *Journal of Neuroscience, 30*(4), 1488–1493.

Diekhof, E. K., Nerenberg, L., Falkai, P., Dechent, P., Baudewig, J., & Gruber, O. (2011). Impulsive personality and the ability to resist immediate reward: An fMRI study examining interindividual differences in the neural mechanisms underlying self-control. *Human Brain Mapping, 33*, 2768–2784.

Duclos, S. E., Laird, J. D., Schneider, E., Sexter, M., Stern, L., & van Lighten, O. (1989). Emotion-specific effects of facial expression and postures on emotional experience. *Journal of Personality and Social Psychology , 57*(1), 100–108.

Dunlop, B. W., & Nemeroff, C. B. (2007). The role of dopamine in the pathophysiology of depression. *Archives of General Psychiatry, 64*(3), 327–337.

Eigste, I.-M., Zayas, V., Mischel, W., Shoda, Y., Ayduk, O., Dadlani, M. B., ... Casey, B. J. (2006). Predicting cognitive control from preschool to late adolescence and young adulthood. *Psychological Science, 17*(6), 478–484.

Eippert, F., Veit, R., Weiskopf, N., Erb, M., Birbaumer, N., & Anders, S. (2007). Regulation of emotional responses elicited by threat-related stimuli. *Human Brain Mapping, 28*, 409–423.

Eisenberg, N., & Eggum, N. D. (2009). Sympathy and personal distress. In J. Decety & W. Ickes (Eds.), *The social neuroscience of empathy* (pp. 71–83). Cambridge, MA: MIT Press.

Eisenberger, N. I. (2012). Broken hearts and broken bones: A neural perspective on the similarities between social and physical pain. *Current Directions in Psychological Science, 21*(1), 42–47.

Eisenberger, N. I., Taylor, S. E., Gable, S. L., Hilmert, C. J., & Lieberman, M. D. (2007). Neural pathways link social support to attenuated neuroendocrine stress responses. *NeuroImage, 35*(4), 1601–1612.

Epel, E. S., Blackburn, E. H., Lin, J., Dhabhar, F. S., Adler, N. E., Morrow, J. D., & Cawthon, R. M. (2004). Accelerated telomere shortening in response to life stress. *Proceedings of the National Academy of Sciences of the United States of America, 101*(49), 17312–17315.

Fabes, R. A., Eisenberg, N., & Eisenbud, L. (1993). Behavioral and physiological correlates of children's reactions to others in distress. *Developmental Psychology, 29*, 655–663.

Farook, M. M., Wang, Q., Moochhala, S. M., Zhu, Z. Y., Lee, L., & Wong, P. T.-H. (2004). Distinct regions of the periaqueductal gray (PAG) are involved in freezing behavior in hooded PVG rats on the cat-freezing test apparatus. *Neuroscience Letters, 354*, 139–149.

Faure, A., Reynolds, S. M., Richard, J. M., & Berridge, K. C. (2008). Mesolimbic dopamine in desire and dread: Enabling motivation to be generated by localized glutamate disruptions in nucleus accumbens. *Journal of Neuroscience, 28*(28), 7184–7192.

Fleshner, M., Nguyen, K. T., Cotter, C. S., Watkins, L. R., & Maier, S. F. (1998). Acute stressor exposure both suppresses acquired immunity and potentiates innate immunity. *American Journal of Physiology, 275*(3, Pt. 2), R870–878.

Forgeard, M. J. C., Haigh, E. A. P., Beck, A. T., Davidson, R. J., Henn, F. A., Maier, S. F.,...Seligman, M. E. P. (2011). Beyond depression: Towards a process-based approach to research, diagnosis, and treatment. *Clinical Psychology, 18*(4), 275–299.

Friedman, B. H. (2010). Feelings and the body: The Jamesian perspective on autonomic specificity of emotion. *Biological Psychology, 84*(3), 383–393.

Gallese, V., & Goldman, A. (1998). Mirror neurons and the simulation theory of mind-reading. *Trends in Cognitive Sciences, 2*(12), 493–501.

Goel, V. D., & Dolan, R. J. (2003). Explaining modulation of reasoning by belief. *Cognition, 87,* B11–B22.

Gouin, J.-P., Carter, C. S., Pournajafi-Nazarloo, H., Glaser, R., Malarkey, W. B., Loving, T. J.,...Kiecolt-Glaser, J. K. (2010). Marital behavior, oxytocin, vasopressin, and wound healing. *Psychoneuroendocrinology, 35*(7), 1082–1090.

Greenwood, B. N., Foley, T. E., Le, T. V., Strong, P. V., Loughridge, A. B., Day, H. E., & Fleshner, M. (2011). Long-term voluntary wheel running is rewarding and produces plasticity in the mesolimbic reward pathway. *Behavioural Brain Research, 217*(2), 354–362.

Greenwood, B. N., Strong, P. V., Loughridge, A. B., Day, H. E., Clark, P. J., Mika, A.,...Fleshner, M. (2012). 5-HT2C receptors in the basolateral amygdala and dorsal striatum are a novel target for the anxiolytic and antidepressant effects of exercise. *PLoS ONE, 7*(9), e46118.

Gusnard, D. A., Ollinger, J. M., Shulman, G. L., Cloninger, C. R., Price, J. L., Van Essen, D. C., & Raichle, M. E. (2003). Persistence and brain circuitry. *Proceedings of the National Academy of Sciences of the United States of America, 100*(6), 3479–3484.

Hale, M. W., & Lowry, C. A. (2011). Functional topography of midbrain and pontine serotonergic systems: Implications for synaptic regulation of serotonergic circuits. *Psychopharmacology (Berlin), 213*(2–3), 243–264.

Hale, M. W., Raison, C. L., & Lowry, C. A. (2013). Integrative physiology of depression and antidepressant drug action: Implications for serotonergic mechanisms of action and novel therapeutic strategies for treatment of depression. *Pharmacology & Therapeutics, 137*(1), 108–118.

Hale, M. W., Shekhar, A., & Lowry, C. A. (2012). Stress-related serotonergic systems: Implications for symptomatology of anxiety and affective disorders. *Cellular and Molecular Neurobiology, 32*(5), 695–708.

Hammack, S. E., Richey, K. J., Watkins, L. R., & Maier, S. F. (2004). Chemical lesion of the bed nucleus of the stria terminalis blocks the behavioral consequences of uncontrollable stress. *Behavioral Neuroscience, 118*(2), 443–448.

Hanusch, K. U., Janssen, C. H., Billheimer, D., Jenkins, I., Spurgeon, E., Lowry, C. A., & Raison, C. L. (2013). Whole-body hyperthermia for the treatment of major depression: Associations with thermoregulatory cooling. *American Journal of Psychiatry, 170*(7), 802–804.

Hariri, A. R., Mattay, V. S., Tessitore, A., Fera, F., & Weinberger, D. R. (2003). Neocortical modulation of the amygdala response to fearful stimuli. *Biological Psychiatry, 53*, 494–501.

Harmon-Jones, E., Lueck, L., Fearn, M., & Harmon-Jones, C. (2006). The effect of personal relevance and approach-related action expectation on relative left frontal cortical activity. *Psychological Science, 17*(5), 434–440.

Harmon-Jones, E., & Sigelman, J. (2001). State anger and prefrontal brain activity: Evidence that insult-related relative left-prefrontal activation is associated with experienced anger and aggression. *Journal of Personality and Social Psychology, 80*(5), 797–803.

Hartley, C. A., & Phelps, E. A. (2010). Changing fear: The neruocircuitry of emotion regulation. *Neuropsychopharmacology, 35*, 136–146.

Heatherton, T. F., & Wagner, D. D. (2011). Cognitive neuroscience of self-regulation failure. *Trends in Cognitive Science, 15*(3), 132–139.

Heim, C., Young, L. J., Newport, D. J., Mletzko, T., Miller, A. H., & Nemeroff, C. B. (2009). Lower CSF oxytocin concentrations in women with a history of childhood abuse. *Molecular Psychiatry, 14*, 954–958.

Herring, M. P., O'Connor, P. J., & Dishman, R. K. (2010). The effect of exercise training on anxiety symptoms among patients: A systematic review. *Archives of Internal Medicine, 170*(4), 321–331.

Hikosaka, O. (2007; modified 2011). Habenula. *Scholarpedia, 2*(6), 2703.

Hikosaka, O. (2010). The habenula: From stress evasion to value-based decision-making. *Nature Reviews Neuroscience, 11*(7), 503–513.

Hikosaka, O. (2011). *Habenula.* Retrieved July 7, 2014, from Scholarpedia.org/article/habenula

Hong, S., Jhou, T. C., Smith, M., Saleem, K. S., & Hikosaka, O. (2011). Negative reward signals from lateral habenula to dopamine neurons are mediated by rostromedial tegmental nucleus in primates. *Journal of Neuroscience, 31*(32), 11457–11471.

Hyman, S. E., Malenka, R. C., & Nestler, E. J. (2006). Neural mechanisms of addiction: The role of reward-related learning and memory. *Annual Review of Neuroscience, 29*, 565–598.

Jacobs, T. L., Epel, E. S., Lin, J., Blackburn, E. H., Wolkowitz, O. M., Bridwell, D. A.,…Saron, C. D. (2011). Intensive meditation training, immune cell telomerase activity, and psychological mediators. *Psychoneuroendocrinology, 36*(5), 664–681.

Jovanovic, T., & Norrholm, S. D. (2011). Neural mechanisms of impaired fear inhibition in posttraumatic stress disorder. *Frontiers in Behavioral Neuroscience, 5*, 44. doi:10.3389/fnbeh.2011.00044

Kalinin, S., Polak, P. E., Lin, S. X., Sakharkar, A. J., Pandey, S. C., & Feinstein, D. L. (2012). The noradrenaline precursor L-DOPS reduces pathology in a mouse model of Alzheimer's disease. *Neurobiology of Aging, 33*(8), 1651–1663.

Kemp, A. H., Quintana, D. S., Kuhnert, R. L., Griffiths, K., Hickie, I. B., & Guastella, A. J. (2012). Oxytocin increases heart rate variability in humans at rest: Implications for social approach-related motivation and capacity for social engagement. *PLoS ONE, 7*(8), e44014. doi:10.1371/journal.pone.0044014

Kettenmann, H., Kirchhoff, F., & Verkhratsky, A. (2013). Microglia: New roles for the synaptic stripper. *Neuron, 77*, 10–18.

Kiecolt-Glaser, J. K., Epel, E. S., Belury, M. A., Andridge, R., Lin, J., Glaser, R.,...Blackburn, E. (2013). Omega-3 fatty acids, oxidative stress, and leukocyte telomere length: A randomized controlled trial. *Brain Behavior and Immununity, 28*, 16–24.

Killeen, P. R., Russell, V. A., & Sergeant, J. A. (2013). A behavioral neuroenergetics theory of ADHD. *Neuroscience & Biobehavioral Reviews, 37*(4), 625–657. doi:10.1016/j.neubiorev.2013.02.011

Koob, G. F. (2013). Addiction is a reward deficit and stress surfeit disorder. *Frontiers in Psychiatry, 4*, article 72, 1–18.

Korte, S. M., Koolhaas, J. M., Wingfield, J. C., & McEwen, B. S. (2005). The Darwinian concept of stress: Benefits of allostasis and costs of allostatic load and the trade-offs in health and disease. *Neuroscience and Biobehavioral Reviews, 29*(1), 3–38.

Kringelbach, M. L. (2010). The hedoni brain: A functional neuroanatomy of human pleasure. In M. L. Kringelbach & K. C. Berridge (Eds.), *Pleasures of the brain* (pp. 202–221). New York, NY: Oxford.

Kringelbach, M. L., & Berridge, K. C. (2009). Towards a functional neuroanatomy of pleasure and happiness. *Trends in Cognitive Science, 13*(11), 479–487.

Kringelbach, M. L., & Berridge, K. C. (2012). The joyful mind. *Scientific American, 307*(2), 40–45.

Kroes, R. A., Burgdorf, J., Otto, N. J., Panksepp, J., & Moskal, J. R. (2007). Social defeat, a paradigm of depression in rats that elicits 22-kHz vocalizations, preferentially activates the cholinergic signaling pathway to the periaqueductal grey. *Behavioral Brain Research, 18*(220), 290–300.

Lammel, S., Lim, B. K., Ran, C., Huang, K. W., Betley, M. J., Tye, K. M.,...Malenka, R. C. (2012). Input-specific control of reward and aversion in the ventral tegmental area. *Nature, 491*(7423), 212–217.

Lane, R. D., McRae, K., Reiman, E. M., Chen, K., Ahern, G. L., & Thayer, J. F. (2009a). Neural correlates of heart rate variability during emotion. *NeuroImage, 44*(1), 213–222.

Lane, R. D., Waldstein, S. R., Chesney, M. A., Jennings, J. R., Lovallo, W. R., Kozel, P. J., . . . Cameron, O. G. (2009b). The rebirth of neuroscience in psychosomatic medicine, Part I: Historical context, methods, and relevant basic science. *Psychosomatic Medicine, 71*(2), 117–134.

Lang, P. J., & Bradley, M. M. (2010). Emotion and the motivational brain. *Biological Psychology, 84*(3), 437–450.

LeDoux, J. (2012). Rethinking the emotional brain. In J. Debiec, M. Heller, B. Brożek, & J. LeDoux (Eds.), *The emotional brain revisited* (pp. 7–12). Kraków: Copernicus Center Press.

LeDoux, J. (2014). *The synaptic self: How our brains become who we are.* New York, NY: Penguin Group.

Levey, A. (2014, May 28). *New targets for Alzheimer's disease.* Grand rounds presentation at Department of Psychiatry, Emory University School of Medicine, Atlanta, GA.

Li, B., Piriz, J., Mirrione, M., Chung, C., Proulx, C. D., Schulz, D., . . . Malinow, R. (2011). Synaptic potentiation onto habenula neurons in the learned helplessness model of depression. *Nature, 470*(7335), 535–539.

Li, Y., Meloni, E. G., Carlezon, W. A., Jr., Milad, M. R., Pitman, R. K., Nader, K., & Bolshakov, V. Y. (2013). Learning and reconsolidation implicate different synaptic mechanisms. *Proceedings of the National Academy of Sciences of the United States of America, 110*(12), 4798–4803.

Liddell, B. J., Brown, K. J., Kemp, A. H., Barton, M. J., Das, P., Peduto, A., . . . Williams, L. M. (2005). A direct brainstem-amygdala-cortical "alarm" system for subliminal signals of fear. *NeuroImage, 24*(1), 235–243.

Lieberman, M., & Eisenberger, N. I. (2009). The pain and pleasures of social life: A social cognitive neuroscience approach. *Science, 323,* 890–891.

Lieberman, M. D. (2013). *Social: Why our brains are wired to connect.* New York, NY: Crown.

Littrell, J. (2008a). The mind–body connection: Not just a theory anymore. *Social Work in Health Care, 46,* 17–38.

Littrell, J. (2008b). New developments in understanding of cardiovascular disease and the implications for social work. *Social Work in Health Care, 46,* 35–49.

Littrell, J. (2012). Taking the perspective that a depressive state reflects inflammation: Implications for the use of antidepressant medications. *Frontiers in Psychology.* Retrieved from http://www.frontiers.org/Journal/Abstract .aspx?s=944&name=psychology_for_clinical_settings&ART_DOI=10.3389/ fpsyg.2012.00297

Lowe, C. J., Hall, P. A., & Staines, W. R. (2014). The effects of continuous theta burst stimulation to the left dorsolateral prefrontal cortex on executive function, food cravings, and snack food conumption. *Psychosomatic Medicine, 76,* 503–511.

Lüscher, C. (2013). Drugs of abuse. In B. G. Katzung, S. B. Masters, & A. J. Trevor (Eds.), *Basic and clinical pharmacology* (12th ed., pp. 565–580). New York, NY: McGraw Hill.

Maier, S. F., & Watkins, L. R. (2005). Stressor controllability and learned helplessness: The roles of the dorsal raphe nucleus, serotonin, and corticotropin-releasing factor. *Neuroscience and Biobehavioral Reviews, 29*(4–5), 829–841.

Maier, S. F., & Watkins, L. R. (2010). Role of the medial prefrontal cortex in coping and resilience. *Brain Research, 1355,* 52–60.

Mantovani, A. (2010). Molecular pathways linking inflammation and cancer. *Current Molecular Medicine, 10*(4), 369–373.

Marco, E. M., Garcia-Gutierrez, M. S., Bermudez-Silva, F. J., Moreira, F. A., Guimaraes, F., Manzanares, J., & Viveros, M. P. (2011). Endocannabinoid system and psychiatry: In search of a neurobiological basis for detrimental and potential therapeutic effects. *Frontiers in Behavioral Neuroscience, 5,* 63. doi:10.3389/fnbeh.2011.00063

McEwen, B. S., & Milner, T. A. (2007). Hippocampal formation: Shedding light on the influence of sex and stress on the brain. *Brain Research Reviews, 55*(2), 343–355.

McGowan, P. O., Meaney, M. J., & Szyf, M. (2008). Diet and the epigenetic (re)programming of phenotypic differences in behavior. *Brain Research, 1237,* 12–24.

Mischel, W., Ebbeson, E. B., & Raskoff-Zeiss, A. (1972). Cognitive and attentional mechanisms in delay of gratification. *Journal of Personality and Social Pscyhology, 21*(2), 204–218.

Murphy, K. (2012). *Janeway's immunobiology* (6th ed.). New York, NY: Garland Science.

Nadeau, S. E., Ferguson, T. S., Valenstein, E., Vierck, C. J., Petruska, J. C., Streit, W. J., & Ritz, L. A. (2004). *Medical neuroscience.* Philadelphia, PA: Saunders.

Nestler, E. J., & Carlezon, W. A., Jr. (2006). The mesolimbic dopamine reward circuit in depression. *Biological Psychiatry, 59*(12), 1151–1159.

Nolte, J. (2009). *The human brain: An introduction to its functional anatomy* (6th ed.). New York, NY: Elsevier.

Ochsner, K. N., Bunge, S. A., Gross, J. J., & Gabrieli, J. D. (2002). Rethinking feelings: An fMRI study of the cognitive regulation of emotion. *Journal of Cognitive Neuroscience, 14,* 1215–1229.

Ochsner, K. N., Silvers, J. A., & Buhle, J. T. (2012). Functional imaging studies of emotion regulation: A synthetic review and evolving model of the cognitive control of emotion. *Annals of the New York Academy of Sciences, 1251,* E1–24. doi:10.1111/j.1749–6632.2012.06751.x

O'Connor, M. F., Schultze-Florey, C. R., Irwin, M. R., Arevalo, J. M. G., & Cole, S. W. (2014). Divergent gene expression to complicated grief and non-complicated grief. *Brain, Behavior, & Immunity, 37,* 78–83.

O'Connor, M. F., Wellisch, D. K., Stanton, A. L., Eisenberger, N. I., Irwin, M. R., & Lieberman, M. D. (2008). Craving love? Enduring grief activates brain's reward center. *NeuroImage, 42*(2), 969–972.

O'Connor, M. F., Wellisch, D. K., Stanton, A. L., Olmstead, R., & Irwin, M. R. (2012). Diurnal cortisol in complicated and non-complicated grief: Slope differences across the day. *Psychoneuroendocrinology, 37*(5), 725–728.

O'Doherty, J., Dayan, P., Schultz, J., Deichmann, R., Friston, K., & Dolan, R. J. (2004). Dissociable roles of ventral and dorsal striatum in instrumental conditioning. *Science, 304*(5669), 452–454.

Pace, T. W., & Miller, A. H. (2009). Cytokines and glucocorticoid receptor signaling. Relevance to major depression. *Annals of the New York Academy of Sciences, 1179,* 86–105.

Panksepp, J., Wright, J. S., Döbrössy, M. D., Schlaepfer, T. E., & Coenen, V. A. (2014). Affective neurosience strategies for understanding and treating depression: From preclinial models to three novel therapeutics. *Clinical Psychological Science, 2*(Suppl. 2), 472–494. Retrieved from http://cpx.sagepub.com/content/by/supplemental-data

Parkhurst, C. N., Yang, G., Ninan, I., Savas, J. N., Yates, J.R. III, Lafaille, J. J., . . . Gan, W.-B. (2013). Microglia promote learning-dependent synapse formation through brain-derived-neurotrophic factor. *Cell, 155,* 1596–1690.

Paul, E. D., Johnson, P. L., Shekhar, A., & Lowry, C. A. (2014). The Deakin/Graeff hypothesis: Focus on serotonergic inhibition of panic. *Neuroscience and Biobehavioral Reviews, 46*(Pt. 3), 379–396.

Paulmann, S., Pell, M. D., & Kotz, S. A. (2009). Comparative processing of emotional prosody and semantics following basal ganglia infarcts: ERP evidence of selective impairments for disgust and fear. *Brain Research, 1295,* 159–169.

Paus, T. (2001). Primate anterior cingulate cortex: Where motor control, drive, and cognition interface. *Nature Reviews Neuroscience, 2,* 417–424.

Phelps, E. A. (2006). Emotion and cognition: Insights from studies of the human amygdala. *Annual Review of Psychology, 57,* 27–53.

Porges, S. W. (2007). The polyvagal perspective. *Biological Psychology, 74*(2), 116–143.

Porges, S. W. (2011). *The polyvagal theory: Neurophysiological foundations of emotions, attachment, communication, and self-regulation.* New York, NY: Norton.

Pruessner, J. C., Champagne, F., Meaney, M. J., & Dagher, A. (2004). Dopamine release in response to a psychological stress in humans and its relationship to early life maternal care: A positron emission tomography study using [11C] raclopride. *Journal of Neuroscience, 24*(11), 2825–2831.

Purves, D., Augstine, G. J., Fitzpatrick, D., Hall, W. C., LaMantia, A. S., & White, L. E. (2012). *Neuroscience* (5th ed.). Sunderland, MA: Sinauer Associates.

Rash, J. A., & Campbell, T. S. (2014). The effect of intranasal oxytocin administration on acute cold pressor pain: A placebo-controlled, double-blind, within-participant crossover investigation. *Psychosomatic Medicine, 76,* 422–429.

Rilling, J. K., Sanfey, A. G., Aronson, J. A., Nystrom, L. E., & Cohen, J. D. (2004). Opposing BOLD responses to reciprocated and unreciprocated altruism in putative reward pathways. *Neuroreport, 15*(16), 2539–2543.

Rizzolatti, G., Fogassi, L., & Gallese, V. (2001). Neurophysiological mechanisms underlying the understanding and imitation of action. *Nature Reviews Neuroscience, 2*(9), 661–670.

Robinson, T. E., & Berridge, K. C. (2008). Review. The incentive sensitization theory of addiction: Some current issues. *Philosophical Transactions of the Royal Society of London. Series B: Biological Sciences, 363*(1507), 3137–3146.

Roth, T. L., Lubin, F. D., Funk, A. J., & Sweatt, J. D. (2009). Lasting epigenetic influence of early-life adversity on the BDNF gene. *Biological Psychiatry, 65*(9), 760–769.

Saar, D., Reuveni, I., & Barkai, E. (2012). Mechanisms underlying rule learning-induced enhancement of excitatory and inhibitory synaptic transmission. *Journal of Neurophysiology, 107*(4), 1222–1229.

Saeed, S. A., Antonacci, D. J., & Bloch, R. M. (2010). Exercise, yoga, and meditation for depressive and anxiety disorders. *American Family Physician, 81*(8), 981–986.

Salamone, J. D., Correa, M., Farrar, A., & Mingote, S. M. (2007). Effort-related functions of nucleus accumbens dopamine and associated forebrain circuits. *Psychopharmacology (Berlin), 191*(3), 461–482.

Schaaf, C. P., Zschocke, J., & Potocki, L. (2012). *Human genetics: From molecules to medicine.* New York, NY: Wolters Kluwer: Lippincott Williams & Wilkins.

Schooler, J. W., & Mauss, I. B. (2010). To be happy and to know it: The experience and meta-awareness of pleasure. In K. C. Berridge & M. L. Kringelbach (Eds.), *Pleasures of the brain* (pp. 244–254). New York, NY: Oxford.

Sgoifo, A., Braglia, F., Costoli, T., Musso, E., Meerlo, P., Ceresini, G., & Troisi, A. (2003). Cardiac autonomic reactivity and salivary cortisol in men and women exposed to social stressors: Relationship with individual ethological profile. *Neuroscience and Biobehavioral Reviews, 27,* 179–188.

Shin, L. M., & Liberzon, I. (2010). The neurocircuitry of fear, stress, and anxiety disorders. *Neuropsychopharmacology, 35*(1), 169–191.

Slavich, G. M., & Irwin, M. R. (2014). From stress to inflammation and major depressive disorder: A social signal transduction theory of depression. *Psychological Bulletin, 140*(3), 774–815.

Sokol-Hessner, P., Camerer, C. F., & Phelps, E. A. (2013). Emotion regulation reduces loss aversion and decreases amygdala responses to losses. *Social Cognitive and Affective Neuroscience, 8,* 341–350. doi:10.1093/scan/nss002

Stamatakis, A. M., Jennings, J. H., Ung, R. L., Blair, G. A., Weinberg, R. J., Neve, R. L.,...Stuber, G. D. (2013). A unique population of ventral tegmental area neurons inhibits the lateral habenula to promote reward. *Neuron, 80*(4), 1039–1053.

Strohle, A. (2009). Physical activity, exercise, depression and anxiety disorders. *Journal of Neural Transmission, 116*(6), 777–784.

Strong, P. V., Christianson, J. P., Loughridge, A. B., Amat, J., Maier, S. F., Fleshner, M., & Greenwood, B. N. (2011). 5-hydroxytryptamine 2C receptors in the dorsal striatum mediate stress-induced interference with negatively reinforced instrumental escape behavior. *Neuroscience, 197,* 132–144.

Suderman, M., McGowan, P. O., Sasaki, A., Huang, T. C., Hallett, M. T., Meaney, M. J.,...Szyf, M. (2012). Conserved epigenetic sensitivity to early life experience in the rat and human hippocampus. *Proceedings of the National Academy of Sciences of the United States of America, 109*(Suppl. 2), 17266–17272.

Sullivan, R. M., & Dufresne, M. M. (2006). Mesocortical dopamine and HPA axis regulation: Role of laterality and early environment. *Brain Research, 1076*(1), 49–59.

Sütterlin, S., Anderson, S., & Vögele, C. (2011). Inhibition in action—Inhibitory components in the behavioral activation system. *Journal of Behavioral and Brain Science, 1,* 160–166.

Sutton, S. K. W. T., Larson, C. L., Holden, J. E., Perlman, S. B., & Davidson, R. J. (1997). Assymetry in prefrontal cortex metabolism during appetive and aversive emotional states: An FDG-PET study. *Psychophysiology, 34,* S89.

Szyf, M. (2014). Lamarck revisited: Epigenetic inheritance of ancestral odor fear conditioning. *Nature Neuroscience, 17*(1), 2–4.

Tabibnai, G., Monterosso, J. R., Baicy, K., Aron, A. R., Poldrack, R. A., Chakrapani, S.,...London, E. D. (2011). Different forms of self-control share a neurocognitive substrate. *Journal of Neuroscience, 31*(13), 4805–4810.

Takahashi, H., Kato, M., Matsuura, M., Mobbs, D., Suhura, T., & Okubo, Y. (2009). When your pain is my gain: Neural correlates of envy and schadenfreude. *Science, 323,* 937–939.

Tang, Y. P., Shimizu, E., Dube, G. R., Rampon, C., Kerchner, G. A., Zhuo, M.,...Tsien, J. Z. (1999). Genetic enhancement of learning and memory in mice. *Nature, 401*(6748), 63–69.

Thayer, J. F., & Lane, R. D. (2009). Claude Bernard and the heart–brain connection: Further elaboration of a model of neurovisceral integration. *Neuroscience Biobehavioral Review, 33*(2), 81–88.

Thayer, J. F., Hansen, A. L., Saus-Rose, E., & Johnsen, B. H. (2009). Heart rate variability, prefrontal neural function, and cognitive performance: The neurovisceral integration perspective of self-regulation, adaptation, and health. *Annals of Behavioral Medicine, 37*(2), 141–153.

Tomarken, A. J., & Davidson, R. J. (1994). Frontal brain activation in repressors and nonrepressors. *Journal of Abnormal Psychology, 103*(2), 339–349.

Tomarken, A. J., & Keener, A. D. (1998). Frontal brain assymetry and depression: A self-regulatory perspective. *Cognition and Emotion, 12*(3), 387–420.

Treadway, M. T., & Zald, D. H. (2011). Reconsidering anhedonia in depression: Lessons from translational neuroscience. *Neuroscience and Biobehavioral Review, 35*(3), 537–555.

Trezza, V., Baarendse, P. J. J., & Vanderschuren, L. J. M. J. (2010). The pleasure of play: Pharmacological insights into social reward mechanisms. *Trends in Pharmacological Science, 31*(10), 463–469.

Trezza, V., Damsteegt, R., Manduca, A., Petrosino, S., VanKerkhof, L. W. M., Pasterkamp, R. J.,...Vanderschuren, L. J. J. (2012). Endocannabinoids in amgydala and nucleus accumbens mediate social play reward in adolescent rats. *Journal of Neuroscience, 32*(43), 14899–14908.

Tricomi, E., Rangel, A., Camerer, C. F., & O'Doherty, J. P. (2010). Neural evidence for inequality-averse social preferences. *Nature, 46*, 1089–1092.

Urry, H. L., van Reekum, C. M., Johnstone, T., Kalin, N. H., Thurow, M. E., Schaefer, H. S.,...Davidson, R. J. (2006). Amygdala and ventromedial prefrontal cortex are inversely coupled during regulation of negative affect and predict the diurnal pattern of cortisol secretion among older adults. *Journal of Neuroscience, 26*(16), 4415–4425.

Verbruggen, F., Aron, A. R., Stevens, M. A., & Chambers, C. D. (2010). Theta burst stimulation dissociates attention and action updating in human inferior frontal cortex. *Proceedings of the National Academy of Sciences of the United States of America, 107*(31), 13966–13971.

Wacker, J., Mueller, E. M., Pizzagalli, D. A., Henning, J., & Stemmier, G. (2013). Dopamine-D2-receptor blockage reverses the association between trait approach motivation and frontal asymmetry in an approach-motivation context. *Psychological Science, 24*(4), 1–9.

Wagner, T. D., Davidson, M. L., Hughes, B. L., Lindquist, M. A., & Ochsner, K. N. (2008). Prefrontal–subcortical pathways mediating successful emotion regulation. *Neuron, 59*(6), 1037–1050.

Way, B. M., Taylor, S. E., & Eisenberger, N. I. (2009). Variation in the mu-opioid receptor gene (OPRM1) is associated with dispositional and neural sensitivity to social rejection. *Proceedings of the National Academy of Sciences of the United States of America, 106*(35), 15079–15084.

Weaver, I. C., D'Alessio, A. C., Brown, S. E., Hellstrom, I. C., Dymov, S., Sharma, S.,...Meaney, M. J. (2007). The transcription factor nerve growth factor-inducible protein A mediates epigenetic programming: Altering epigenetic marks by immediate-early genes. *Journal of Neuroscience, 27*(7), 1756–1768.

Wicker, B., Keysers, C., Plailly, J., Royet, J. -P., Gallese, V., & Rizzolatti, G. (2003). Both of us disgusted in *My* insula: The common neural basis of seeing and feeling disgust. *Neuron, 40*(3), 655–664.

Wolkowitz, O. M., Mellon, S. H., Epel, E. S., Lin, J., Dhabhar, F. S., Su, Y.,...Blackburn, E. H. (2011). Leukocyte telomere length in major depression: Correlations with chronicity, inflammation and oxidative stress—preliminary findings. *PLoS ONE, 6*(3), e17837. doi:10.1371/journal.pone.0117837

Young, L., & Alexander, B. (2014). *The chemistry between us: Love, sex, and the science of attraction.* New York, NY: Penguin.

Zak, P. J., Kurzban, R., & Matzner, W. T. (2004). The neurobiology of trust. *Annals of the New York Academy of Sciences, 1032*, 224–227.

EXERCISES TO REHEARSE THE VOCABULARY USED IN SUBSEQUENT CHAPTERS

1. Nucleotides comprised of a base, sugar, and phosphate group that are found on chromosomes are called _____.

2. A _____ is comprised of three nucleotides and specifies which amino acid should be added to an emerging peptide chain.

3. A _____ factor moves to a promoter site at the beginning of a gene and brings in the machinery for producing messenger RNA from a DNA template.

4. _____ provides the instructions for transcription of a peptide chain.

5. An _____ is a particular version of a polymorphic gene.

6. _____ can be enzymes or structural factors such as collagen or keratin.

7. Humans have 23 pairs of _____, which are comprised of DNA wound around proteins.

8. Variation in the _____ region of a gene determines how frequently a protein is made from the gene.

9. The field focused on the packing up, the unpacking, and opening of DNA so that it can be copied into making mRNA is called _____.

10. _____ are at the ends of chromosomes. They shorten with each duplication. Their length reflects the level of stress the organism has experienced.

11. A _____ is the chemical mechanism through which one neuron communicates with another.

12. A _____ is the space between the axon terminal of one neuron and the dendrite of another neuron.

13. The axon of a neuron delivers its chemical message to a _____ for a particular neurotransmitter that is found on the dendrites of the receiving neuron.

14. Some neurotransmitters (norepinephrine, serotonin, and dopamine) are returned to the presynaptic neuron by a protein, called a _____.

15. _____ are exogenous chemicals that increase the message delivered by a neurotransmitter.

16. _____ are exogenous chemicals that decrease the message delivered by a neurotransmitter.

17. _____, _____, and _____ are neurotransmitters referred to as monoamines.

18. Serotonin neurons are clustered in an area of the brain stem called the _____.

19. Norepinephrine neurons are clustered in an area of the brain stem called the _____.

20. Dopamine neurons are clustered in four primary pathways of the brain: _____, _____, _____, and _____.

21. _____ is the neurotransmitter released from the caudal dorsal raphe in an animal experiencing uncontrollable shock.

22. An animal whose neurons in the ventral tegmental area have been ablated will no longer work for food, although the animal may display signs of enjoyment. The missing neurotransmitter is _____.

23. The dopaminergic _____ pathway is implicated in Parkinson's disease.

24. _____ is the brain's major excitatory neurotransmitter.

25. _____ is the brain's major inhibitory neurotransmitter.
26. The dorsal anterior cingulate cortex contains many receptors for opiates and has been characterized as an _____.
27. The two major arms of the immune system are the _____ system and the _____ system.
28. The _____ system is involved in patrolling for particular amino acid targets and is induced by vaccination.
29. The _____ system will attack foreign-appearing pathogens and results in systemic inflammation.
30. _____ are hormones that are released by white blood cells and serve as the mechanism of communication between the leukocytes and between the leukocytes and other cells of the body.
31. There are three types of _____ cells in brain: astrocytes, microglia, and oligodendrocytes.
32. _____ direct blood flow to active areas of the brain.
33. _____ are the brain's resident macrophages, a type of white blood cell.
34. _____ is the neurotransmitter of wanting but not necessarily liking.
35. The dopaminergic neurons of the ventral tegmental area project to the _____, an area in the ventral striatum.
36. The _____ plays a strong role in inhibiting neurons in the ventral tegmental area that project to the nucleus accumbens.
37. The _____ also projects to the caudal part of the dorsal raphe.
38. The _____ is an output structure of the amygdala, which if lesioned will preclude learned helplessness.
39. Areas of the _____ constitute brain areas for emotional and impulse regulation.
40. More activity on the left cortex versus the right identifies a person as having a strong _____.
41. The autonomic nervous system is comprised of the _____ system and the _____ system.
42. The vagus nerve is part of the _____.
43. The _____ of the parasympathetic nervous system inhibits inflammation and enhances regulatory capacity.
44. _____ is a measure of vagal tone or strength of the vagus nerve.

45. All kinds of stress, including running and starvation, will elevate the hormone: _____.
46. _____ is the hormone involved in social connection.
47. The axis controlling the release of cortisol from the adrenal glands by the hypothalamus and the pituitary gland is called the _____.

Answers

1. DNA; 2. Codon; 3. Transcription; 4. Messenger RNA; 5. Allele;
6. Proteins; 7. Chromosomes; 8. Promoter; 9. Epigenetics; 10. Telomere;
11. Neurotransmitter; 12. Synaptic cleft; 13. Receptor; 14. Transporter;
15. Agonist; 16. Antagonist; 17. Dopamine, norepinephrine, serotonin;
18. Raphe; 19. Locus coeruleus; 20. Tuberoinfundibular, nigrostriatal, mesolimbic, mesocortical; 21. Serotonin; 22. Dopamine;
23. Nigrostriatal; 24. Glutamate; 25. GABA; 26. Alarm center;
27. Adaptive innate; 28. Adaptive; 29. Innate; 30. Cytokines; 31. Glial;
32. Astrocytes; 33. Microglia; 34. Dopamine; 35. Nucleus accumbens;
36. Habenula; 37. Habenula; 38. Bed nucleus of the stria terminalis;
39. Prefrontal cortex; 40. Behavioral activation system;
41. Parasympathetic nervous system, sympathetic nervous system;
42. PNS; 43. Vagus nerve; 44. Heart rate variability; 45. Cortisol;
46. Oxytocin; 47. HPA or hypothalamic–pituitary–adrenal axis.

3

Psychopharmacology

This chapter covers information about psychopharmacology for the behavioral health clinician. The chapter begins by offering some basic information about drugs: how drugs enter the system, how they are cleared from the body, and how they are distributed. The concepts of tolerance and withdrawal are explained. The purpose is to provide the background necessary for understanding what might be read in the *Physicians' Desk Reference* (*PDR*), a manual issued annually by pharmaceutical houses in collaboration with the Food and Drug Administration (FDA) and published by PDR Network providing information regarding side effects, FDA-approved indications, and half-lives of each drug currently available in the market. Following this, the major categories of psychotropic agents available in the United States are covered. The presumed mechanisms of action are reviewed. Information regarding efficacy and side effects is presented in the other chapters covering specific disorders. Following the presentation of the major categories of pharmaceutical medications, the mechanisms of action of addicting drugs are presented.

The second section of the chapter provides information regarding how drugs are discovered and how the FDA evaluates them. Consideration of why pharmaceuticals are so expensive is presented. Problems with the way the FDA carries out its mission are discussed. In the third section of the chapter, the issues regarding potential roles for behavioral health clinicians with respect to medications are considered. Issues regarding informed consent are discussed and the imperative of providing information regarding pharmaceutical options is covered. The distinction between practicing medicine and offering information is reviewed.

PHARMACOKINETICS AND PHARMACODYNAMICS

Drugs are defined as chemicals that influence physiological functions. Psychotropic drugs are chemicals that influence mood and behavior. Although alcohol certainly fits this definition, unlike other psychotropics, alcohol contains calories and can be utilized to produce energy for cellular processes. Thus, alcohol is not considered a drug by the FDA. Before they can influence function, drugs must be ingested and delivered to target organs. Pharmacokinetics is the study of absorption, distribution, and drug elimination. Pharmacodynamics is the study of dose–response relationships and how a drug produces its effects (Holford, 2013).

Ways to Ingest Drugs

Many drugs are delivered to the body through oral ingestion (per os [PO], which is Latin for "by mouth"). The pKa of the drug, that is, the degree to which the drug is ionized into positive and negative particles, influences whether the drug will be efficiently absorbed in the small intestine. For absorption through the gut, the drug cannot be too lipophilic (fat loving) or too lipophobic. A reverse transporter in the cells of the gut will kick some drugs back out into the cavity of the gut. Grapefruit inhibits this reverse transporter, thereby increasing the absorption of many drugs (Holford, 2013).

Drugs that are lipid (fat) soluble can be delivered through the skin (transdermal). Hormones and nicotine are delivered through patches worn on the skin, for example. Some drugs are absorbed through the mucous lining in the lung when the drug is inhaled. Street drugs (marijuana, heroin, and cocaine) and nicotine can be smoked, although pharmaceuticals are not generally smoked. However, narcan–naloxone, a chemical with higher affinity to opiate receptors than heroin, can be administered by spraying it into the nose. Narcan can rapidly reverse respiratory depression, which results in death attributable to an overdose of opiates. Drugs can also be delivered into the body by injection using a needle. Injections can be given into a vein (intravenous [IV]), into a muscle (intramuscular [IM]), or under the skin (subcutaneous [SC]).

Once the drug is brought into the body, it is delivered to the rest of the body through the bloodstream. Some drugs can be bound to proteins in the bloodstream. Distribution mechanisms must be understood in order to determine availability of the drug to target tissues. For psychotropic drugs, a big hurdle is the blood–brain barrier (BBB). The BBB refers to the layers of lipid bilayer insulation around blood vessels in the brain created by the astrocyte cells. The BBB prevents large, nonlipid-soluble molecules from diffusing into the tissues of the brain. Many drugs cannot traverse the BBB and, therefore, cannot influence the neurons. Psychotropic drugs are capable of traversing the BBB. However, the BBB prevents some molecules, for example, dopamine, a molecule deficient in those with Parkinson's disease, from being directly administered. Therefore, the precursor to dopamine, L-dopa, is prescribed for Parkinson's patients instead.

Ways in Which Drugs Are Eliminated From the Body

Drugs do not stay in the body forever. Drugs such as alcohol, which is highly lipid soluble, can be eliminated through the lungs and thus the concentration of the alcohol in the body can be measured with a breathalyzer. Most drugs are altered in the liver so that they will be eliminated from the body by the kidney. In the liver, enzymes of the P450 system metabolize drugs (Correia, 2013). These enzymes can be inhibited by grapefruit.

Most drugs follow first-order kinetics, which means that the amount of the drug eliminated decreases as a function of time. Drugs that follow first-order kinetics have half-lives. A half-life is the time it takes to eliminate half of the dosage of the drug ingested. To determine how much of the drug is left in the body at a particular number of half-lives, one computes the reciprocal of two taken to a power representing the number of half-lives. Thus, if the half-life is 4 hours, then at three half-lives (12 hours), $(1/2)^3 = 1/8$ of the amount of drug initially taken into the body is eliminated. The half-life of a drug is related to the frequency with which a drug needs to be taken in order to achieve a steady state in the bloodstream. In contrast to drugs with half-lives, alcohol follows zero-order kinetics. A given amount of alcohol is metabolized at a constant rate regardless of the concentration of the chemical in the body. Alcohol is eliminated by the liver at approximately the rate of one drink per hour (a drink is 1.25 oz. of 80-proof whiskey, 12 oz. of 4% beer, or 4 oz. of 12%-alcohol wine). For all drugs regardless of the kinetics they follow, general rules for adults may not apply when determining how long the drug remains in the body of small children and elderly. Small children, because their liver enzymes have not been stimulated by exposure to various compounds as in adults, may not eliminate drugs as rapidly as adults. Older people may have compromised liver and kidney function and, thus, will not clear drugs as rapidly as healthy younger adults (McKim, 1990).

After drugs are ingested, some drugs get distributed to particular tissues and are slowly released from these tissues into the bloodstream over time. Cannabinoids are highly lipid soluble. They are effectively stored in fat. For persons who regularly smoke marijuana, the drug is slowly released over time into their systems. If they exercise, marijuana is released from fat stores and can then impact their brains (Gunasekaran et al., 2009). They can be high again. Acutely, marijuana can dilate the blood vessels in the eyes, so they appear bloodshot. The eyes of one of my clients being treated for marijuana dependence did not look clear until about a month after abstinence.

If consumed in high concentration, some drugs can be lethal. The effective dose 50 (ED50) is the concentration of the drug required to achieve the desired effect in 50% of the animals tested. The lethal dose 50 (LD50) is the dose at which 50% of the animals died. The difference between the ED50 and the LD50 is the drug's safety margin. Barbiturates, which at one time were used to treat anxiety or insomnia, have narrow safety margins and have been replaced by benzodiazepines, which have much better safety margins. Alcohol can depress respiration and can be lethal. Nicotine does have a lethal dose and injecting victims with nicotinic acid is a method for murder that shows up in murder mysteries, although this dose is never reached through smoking (Hart, Ksir, & Ray, 2009). Opiates can depress the breathing centers in the brain stem. Opiate (oxycodone, heroin, methadone) overdoses are common. The older tricyclic antidepressants can induce lethal cardiac arrhythmias (Olson, 2013), with a 10-day supply being sufficient to induce death. The older tricyclics have been replaced by the far less dangerous selective serotonin reuptake inhibitors (SSRIs).

The delivery mechanism for getting the drug into the body will affect how rapidly the drug influences the brain (Mathias & Swan, 1995). IV injections and inhalation are generally fast-acting delivery mechanisms; drugs reach the brain before they are broken down by the liver. Oral ingestion and transdermal, subcutaneous, and muscular delivery are slow. Transdermal (through the skin) and oral absorption may result in incomplete absorption. Moreover, drugs that are orally administered will be delivered to the liver, where they are broken down before they can reach the brain. Drugs that are ingested through the gastrointestinal track generally do not reach the brain in high concentration (Holford, 2013).

The rule of thumb for addiction is that the higher the concentration of the drug delivered, the faster the development of compulsive drug taking (Mathias & Swan, 1995). Thus, stimulants (including amphetamine) taken as oral medication for attention deficit hyperactivity disorder (ADHD) are less addictive than smoking methamphetamine.

Drug Dependence

For pharmacologists, the terms *addiction* or *drug dependence* used to mean that the drug was associated with tolerance and withdrawal. Tolerance means that when ingested regularly over a period of time, the individual's body adjusts so that a higher dosage of the drug is required to achieve the desired effect. Withdrawal implies that if the drug is abruptly discontinued, then symptoms that are the opposite of the effect of the drug are observed. The body's homeostatic mechanism was imputed to explain both tolerance and withdrawal. According to theory, when a drug is ingested, the body attempts to return the body to baseline to achieve homeostasis. Thus, more of the drug is required to induce the desired effect. If the drug is abruptly withdrawn, the body's homeostatic adjustment still operates, producing effects to counteract the drug. Without the restraining influence of the drug, the homeostatic mechanisms are unopposed and a withdrawal phenomenon is observed (McKim, 1990).

The homeostatic mechanism explanation has been challenged for many drugs. For example, for alcohol, a lack of correlation between the severity of withdrawal symptoms and the severity of tolerance has been observed. Moreover, some dimensions of tolerance to alcohol are attributable to repeatedly performing behaviors (practicing) with high levels of alcohol in the system. If the animal is not allowed to practice on a running wheel, then tolerance to alcohol, measured by the ability to maintain balance on the running wheel, is not observed (Littrell, 1991). With regard to withdrawal phenomena, explanations that are chemically specific have been advanced for a number of drugs.

At an earlier time, drug dependence was invoked to explain why some people develop compulsive-use patterns of drugs (Hart et al., 2009). As is discussed in Chapter 8, contemporary views of addiction no longer include drug dependence as the mechanism for explaining compulsive-use patterns. Many pharmaceutical drugs (antidepressants, lithium, valproate, and antipsychotics) are associated with withdrawal symptoms. These drugs are not associated with compulsive drug taking (Haddad, 2001). The concept of tolerance has been parsed. Tolerance can develop to some of the effects of the drug but not others. Thus, although some drugs do create symptoms if abruptly stopped and while tolerance does build, the explanations for these phenomena may differ for each particular drug.

General Concepts

The mechanism of action of various psychotropic drugs generally involves a particular neurotransmitter. As pointed out in Chapter 2, the term *agonist* refers to the property of potentiating the action of a particular neurotransmitter. The term *antagonist* refers to the property of blocking the action of a particular neurotransmitter. Most psychotropic drugs are anticholinergic, meaning that they are antagonists for acetylcholine. Anticholinergics dilate the pupils, decrease the output of the salivary glands, decrease heat loss due to an inability to perspire, and create confusion. Hence the mnemonics for excessive anticholinergic action, "red as a beat" (skin flushed), "dry as a bone" (dry mucous membranes and no sweat), "hot as a hare" (hyperthermia), "mad as a hatter" (confusion and delirium), and "blind as a stone" (blurred vision) (Olson, 2013).

Pharmaceutical drugs have many names. There is the chemical name, which follows organic chemistry molecular nomenclature rules, the generic compound name, and the brand or trade label. In the medical literature, usually the generic compound label is used to identify the drug.

MAJOR CLASSES OF PSYCHOTROPIC DRUGS

The side effects and efficacy of various drugs will be covered in the chapters discussing the particular conditions for which they are used. In this chapter, the mechanism of action is presented along with the names (generic name and trade name) of the major drugs available in the market in each category. The *PDR* lists all drugs on the market included along with FDA-approved uses, side effects, and recommended dosing. The same information is available online from PDR.net or by visiting the FDA website.

Legend drugs are drugs that require a prescription as opposed to being sold over the counter (OTC). Some drugs are scheduled, meaning that they are covered under the Controlled Substances Act of 1970. Scheduled drugs are limited to the number of refills available and have criminal penalties associated with trafficking. Some drugs carry black-box warnings when side effects are severe.

Stimulants

Amphetamine, dextroamphetamine (Dexedrine), methylphenidate (Ritalin, Metadate, and Concerta), Adderall (a mixture of various amphetamine preparations, which has a longer half-life), and lisdexamfetamine (Vyvanse) are all classified as stimulants. Their mechanism of action is to operate on catecholamine (dopamine, norepinephrine, and epinephrine) transporters to block uptake of the neurotransmitter and to get the transporter to run in reverse, releasing the catecholamine. Although stimulants were used during the 1920s in inhalants to relieve nasal congestion, they have been replaced for the most part. In the 1950s, stimulants were used for weight control, but were discontinued because of the building of rapid tolerance. They are still occasionally used for narcolepsy, although modafinil is presently more likely to be prescribed. Currently, a stimulant's primary use is the treatment of attention deficit hyperactivity disorder (ADHD) in children and adults (Biaggioni & Robertson, 2013; Howland & Mycek, 2006; McKim, 1990).

Antipsychotics

All antipsychotics, whether the older neuroleptics or the new atypicals, have a high affinity for dopamine D2 receptors. They sit on the D2 receptor and are basically inert, preventing dopamine signaling. They will block the action of dopamine in the nucleus accumbens. The newer atypicals also are serotonin antagonists. Because all antipsychotics can inhibit dopamine function in the basal ganglia, they can induce Parkinson's-type symptoms (called extrapyramidal effects). Sometimes, anticholinergic drugs, such as benzatropine (Cogentin), are given along with antipsychotics to relieve the effects on muscles so that the extrapyramidal effects are attenuated (Howland & Mycek, 2006). The new atypicals have less severe extrapyramidal symptoms, although the Clinical Antipsychotic Trials of Intervention Effectiveness (CATIE) trial established that they also produce movement problems (see Chapter 6, Side Effects With Current Treatments section). Some antipsychotics, such as haloperidol (Haldol), fluphenazine (Prolixin Decanoate), risperidone (Risperdal Consta), olanzapine (Zyprexa Relprevv), paliperidone (Invega Sustenna), and aripiprazole (Abilify Maintena), can be injected into a muscle so that the drug is active for a longer period of time (Meltzer, 2013). There are racial differences in the capacity for metabolizing antipsychotics. Asian Americans tend to run higher blood levels on antipsychotics and thus do not require as high a dose as Caucasians. African Americans are also more likely to carry slower metabolizing enzymes (Burroughs, Maxey, & Levy, 2002; Gaedigk, Bradford, Marcucci, & Leeder, 2002).

Neuroleptics

The older antipsychotics are sometimes referred to as neuroleptics. Many of the old neuroleptics belonged to either the phenothiazine category or the butyrophenone category, which classified the dopamine antagonist according to the shape of its molecular structure.

Atypicals

The atypicals were introduced in the 1990s and were supposed to be associated with attenuated extrapyramidal symptoms. However, the CATIE trial found that the atypicals are also associated with movement problems (see Chapter 6, Side Effects With Current Treatments section). Besides their disappointment on the movement dimension, the atypicals are associated with weight gain that fails to plateau, diabetes, and high levels of fats (dyslipidemia) in the bloodstream. Ziprasidone (Geodon) is less problematic than the other atypicals with regard to weight gain (Stahl,

2013). Atypicals are also used to treat bipolar disorders. Several have been approved for unremitting depression. They are also used for sleep and anxiety. Although only 1% of the population carries a diagnosis of schizophrenia, Abilify and Seroquel are the fifth and sixth best-selling prescription drugs (Friedman, 2012). As discussed in Chapter 6, Side Effects of Current Treatments section, they have been shown to reduce cortex volume in people, and the volume reduction is about 11% in animals when taken over a 2-year period. Animal research employing random assignment confirmed the causal role of these drugs in cortex volume reduction.

Clozaril was the first "atypical" introduced to the market. Unique to clozapine (Clozaril) is the 1% to 2% possibility of agranulocytosis, that is, a failure of the bone marrow to produce a particular type of white blood cell (WBC; Howland & Mycek, 2006; Meltzer, 2013). Because agranulocytosis is life-threatening, frequent monitoring of blood is required for those taking Clozaril.

Antidepressants

We pointed out that the antipsychotics are antagonists for dopamine (a type of monoamine). In contrast, all of the antidepressants are agonists for one or another of the monoamines (dopamine, serotonin, or norepinephrine). There are two types of antidepressants in the market: monoamine oxidase inhibitors (MAOIs) and neurotransmitter uptake inhibitors.

Within the class of neurotransmitter reuptake inhibitors, there are the old tricyclics, the heterocyclics, and reuptake inhibitors that are more specific for a particular monoamine. Selective serotonergic reuptake inhibitor (SSRI) is now a common term. All of the reuptake inhibitors have the property of allowing the neurotransmitter to remain in the synapse for a longer period of time. Reuptake inhibitor antidepressants have many uses in addition to treatment of depression. They are used to treat obsessive-compulsive disorder (OCD) and anxiety. Some of them block rapid eye movement (REM) sleep and because people wake up more easily, they have been used to treat children with enuresis.

MAOIs work by inhibiting monoamine oxidase (MAO), the enzyme that breaks down norepinephrine, dopamine, and serotonin. Unfortunately, MAO also breaks down tyramine, a molecule found in many foods. When tyramine is not metabolized, it causes a life-threatening increase in sympathetic activity. Patients taking MAOIs must refrain from taking many OTC medications, eating aged cheeses, herring, and many other common dietary items, and drinking wine. For this reason, MAOIs have fallen out of use, despite the fact that they have the desirable property of more rapidly providing remission of depression (DeBattista, 2013; Howland & Mycek, 2006).

Sedative-Hypnotic Agents

The sedative-hypnotics, including barbiturates, benzodiazepine, and sleep agents, all act as gamma-aminobutyric acid type A (GABAA) receptors. The GABAA receptor comprises five subunits with various versions of proteins (alpha, beta, gamma, delta, epsilon, etc.) constituting the subunits at particular locations. Various classes of sedative-hypnotics differ in the particular subunits to which they will bind.

Barbiturates were synthesized by Dr. Adolf von Baeyer in the late 1800s. They were used to treat anxiety and to induce sleep. They still are used in surgery. They do, however, have a very narrow safety margin with the potential for causing respiratory depression, coma, and death. When bound to the GABAA receptor, barbiturates increase the duration of opening of the chloride channel so that the neuron is hyperpolarized (very depressed) and is less likely to generate an action potential ("fire"). Benzodiazepines are anxiolytics (anxiety reducers) that were brought on the market in the 1950s. They have a much better safety margin, and are rarely lethal unless combined with alcohol. They are "allosteric regulators" at the gamma-aminobutyric acid (GABA) receptor. They do not open the chloride channel but do increase the probability that GABA, the real neurotransmitter, will open the chloride channel. Benzodiazepines are commonly prescribed for anxiety, panic disorder, and sleep. They can cause dependence and are associated with lethal withdrawal symptoms, including anxiety, insomnia, and life-threatening seizures. Because some have long half-lives, withdrawal symptoms can occur days after drug discontinuation. Various withdrawal symptoms may not be attributed to drug withdrawal because of the lag time, and an individual may not seek appropriate treatment (Howland & Mycek, 2006; McKim, 1990; Trevor & Way, 2013).

Most sedative-hypnotics are either schedule III or IV drugs. They are used to treat alcohol withdrawal and are good for decreasing involuntary muscle spasms. They can induce blackouts (failure to encode memories for a duration of time) and should not be used if one is driving or operating machinery (Howland & Mycek, 2006; McKim, 1990; Trevor & Way, 2013).

Sleep agents, such as zolpidem (Ambien, Intermezzo), zaleplon (Sonata), and eszopiclone (Lunesta), are not benzodiazepines. They also potentiate GABA but bind at GABA receptors with differing subunits than benzodiazepine drugs. They are less likely to cause slurred speech and staggering (ataxia). With increasing use, these drugs seem to maintain their efficacy; that is, minimal tolerance has been reported (Trevor & Way, 2013). However, they are associated with blackouts wherein people get up in the middle of the night and drive their cars or fix meals without any memory of what they did. Accidents have been reported. The FDA has issued warnings for sleep driving and has recommended lower dosages for women (Associated Press, 2007; FDA, 2013a). Zolpidem is associated with an increased risk of Parkinson's disease (Yang et al., 2014).

Mood Stabilizers

Mood stabilizers are used for the treatment of bipolar disorders. Lithium is the oldest drug in use for bipolar disorders. Although there is speculation about the impact of lithium on intracellular function, there is no certainty as to its mechanism of action (Meltzer, 2013). Anticonvulsants are used in the treatment of epilepsy. They are also used in the treatment of bipolar disorder, although the mechanism of action is unknown (Meltzer, 2013).

MAJOR CLASSES OF DRUGS OF ABUSE

Cocaine and amphetamine are both stimulant drugs. The amphetamine sold on the streets is also sold as a pharmaceutical for the treatment of ADHD. Both cocaine and amphetamine have similar mechanisms of action, either releasing catecholamines directly or blocking reuptake so that the neurotransmitter remains in the synaptic cleft for a longer period of time.

Both amphetamine and cocaine can be smoked, snorted, or injected. Amphetamine can be taken orally. Cocaine, like other "caine" drugs (lidocaine, novocaine), blocks nerve conduction in pain fibers as well as acting as a vasoconstrictor. Cocaine is used in oral and optical surgery because it blocks pain transmission and stops bleeding at the site of the incision (Drasner, 2013).

Marijuana

Marijuana (tetrahydrocannabinol) can be smoked or consumed orally, usually included in baked goods. Many states have legalized medical marijuana, and Colorado, Washington, Oregon, and Alaska have legalized recreational marijuana for adults. Medically, marijuana is used for chronic pain, for the nausea associated with chemotherapy, to decrease intraocular pressure in glaucoma, as a muscle relaxant for conditions associated with muscle spasms, to decrease anxiety, and to increase appetite in those with HIV. There are receptors for cannabinoids in the amygdala, where marijuana decreases anxiety. Cannabinoid receptors can inhibit the GABAergic neurons in the ventral tegmental area (VTA), which would otherwise limit dopamine release in the nucleus accumbens; thus cannabinoids are dopamine agonists. Marijuana can also create a dysphoric state associated with depersonalization and psychotic symptoms. Marijuana withdrawal symptoms include insomnia, cramping, nausea, and anxiety. Because tetrahydrocannabinol is fat soluble, it can be stored in adipose tissue for an extended period of time. Thus, drug testing will be positive for a long period after discontinuation (Lüscher, 2013; McKim, 1990; Welch, 2011).

Opioids

Opioids do lead to compulsive drug use. Like all addictive drugs they increase dopamine release from VTA neurons into the nucleus accumbens. In the VTA, opioid receptors are located on GABAergic neurons. The GABA neurons inhibit dopamine release from the dopaminergic neuron. However, the opioid receptors inhibit the GABAergic neurons. Opioids put a break on a break, so to speak. Thus, opioids will increase dopamine release (Mazei-Robison & Nestler, 2012).

In addition to the VTA, opioid receptors are found in many areas, such as in the dorsal anterior cingulate cortex (dACC). Recall that the dACC is an alarm and anxiety center. Opioids inhibit the dACC and decrease anxiety.

They are also found in the spinal cord where they can inhibit pain transmission (Mazei-Robison & Nestler, 2012; Schumacher, Basbaum, & Way, 2013).

There are many opiate agonist drugs. Heroin is a schedule I drug, with no approved medical use. Medicinal opioids include morphine, oxycodone, codeine, meperidine (Demerol), Darvocet, oxycodone (Percocet), methadone, and many others. Buprenorphine functions as a partial agonist at opiate receptors (Schumacher et al., 2013).

The nonsynthetic opioids, that is, opioids that derive from the poppy rather than from the chemistry set, do result in pinpoint pupils. When taken in heavy doses, opioids can rapidly induce sleep; however, at low doses, they can exert a stimulant effect. Lethal overdose is attributable to respiratory depression, which can be rapidly reversed with naloxone. (Naloxone displaces other opiates from their receptors and does not have any effect of its own.) Naloxone can be injected, swallowed, or delivered through a nasal spray. In fact, paramedics sometimes carry naloxone for fast delivery to reverse opioid overdoses in patients (Schumacher et al., 2013).

The agony of heroin withdrawal is legendary. Withdrawal symptoms include intense dysphoria, nausea and vomiting, muscle aches, lacrimation (tearing), rhinorrhea (runny nose), mydriasis (enlarged pupil), piloerection (goose bumps), sweating, diarrhea, yawning, fever (Lüscher, 2013), and spontaneous ejaculations (Redmond, Kosten, & Reiser, 1983). Clonidine (a blood pressure medication) and codeine syrup can be administered to relieve withdrawal symptoms. For nonsynthetics, opiate withdrawal is not life-threatening (Tetrault & O'Connor, 2011).

In the United States, opiate agonist pharmaceuticals are promoted by the federal government as an alternative to street heroin. Methadone and buprenorphine are the heroin substitutes. Methadone comes as a syrup in orange and cherry flavor and is taken only once per day (see Chapter 8, "Addictions"). Buprenorphine is combined with naloxone and is sold as Suboxone or Bunavail. Bunavail is administered as a film on the gum (RxList Inc., 2015).

The pharmaceutical houses have devised a clever packaging strategy to prevent IV injection of buprenorphine. Suboxone, a mixture of buprenorphine and naloxone, is administered under the tongue. When Suboxone is administered under the tongue, only the buprenorphine is absorbed. However, if persons crush their Suboxone pill and try to inject, the naloxone will go to the receptor before the buprenorphine. The naloxone effects predominate, making Suboxone a safe preparation (drugs.fda).

Nicotine

Approximately 24% of Americans are current smokers and tobacco-related disease is responsible for 440,000 deaths annually (Fowler, Arends, & Kenny, 2008). Nicotine binds to the nicotinic acetylcholine receptors in the brain. Agonists at nicotinic acetylcholine receptors increase the release of glutamate such that the excitatory input to dopaminergic neurons in the VTA is increased (Mao, Gallagher, & McGehee, 2011). Thus, nicotine enhances the release of dopamine from VTA neurons into the nucleus accumbens (see Chapter 8). There are also nicotinic acetylcholine receptors in areas of the brain where they enhance cognitive performance.

There are receptors where nicotine will bind outside the brain. Nicotinic acetylcholine receptors are found on the neurons in the ganglion of both the parasympathetic nervous system and sympathetic nervous system. Nicotinic acetylcholine receptors are also found at the neuromuscular junction. Nicotine can thus improve cognitive performance, increase arousal, and increase muscle tone (Lüscher, 2013; Nolte, 2009).

Nicotine is one of the most rapidly addictive drugs in the formulary. Withdrawal symptoms include irritability, restlessness, mouth sores, insomnia, difficulty concentrating, and dizziness (Hughes, 2007). An increased metabolic rate is an acute effect of nicotine and after discontinuation many people gain weight (Filozof, Fernández Pinilla, & Fernández-Cruz, 2004).

The antidepressants, Wellbutrin (bupropion) and Chantix (varenicline) have been approved to decrease nicotine withdrawal distress. Varenicline has been associated with suicidal ideation induction, violence, and impaired driving ability (Lüscher, 2013). For smoking cessation, supplying nicotine using methods other than smoking is a strategy. Nicotine is available in patches and in chewing gum. Stead et al. (2012) concluded that nicotine replacement in the form of patches and gum was as effective as bupropion. There was no evidence that nicotine replacement strategies increased heart attack risk.

Currently, nicotine is available as a spray. Questions regarding extended use of nicotine spray remain. Although the long-term effects of tobacco (cardiovascular disease, cancer, and emphysema) are very grave, it is unclear whether the long-term profile of nicotine administered in spray atomizers will be as grave (Palazzolo, 2013; Shahab, Brose, & West, 2013). Presently, nicotine is being investigated as a treatment for ulcerative colitis, Parkinson's disease, Alzheimer's disease, ADHD, schizophrenia, anxiety, depression, obesity, sleep apnea, and Tourette's syndrome (Dani, Kosten, & Benowitz, 2011). It may be that the negative effects of nicotine in cigarettes are largely attributable to the delivery mechanism.

Alcohol

About 10% of the population exhibits problems attributable to excessive consumption of alcohol. Detectable signs of excessive alcohol intake include elevations in liver enzyme scores or a palpable fatty liver. Excessive alcohol use can also result in detectable changes in red blood cells (RBC: e.g., megaloblastic anemia, sideroblastic anemia; Littrell, 1991; Masters, 2013; O'Shea, Dasarathy, & McCullough, 2010; Rehm, 2011). Alcohol is an addictive drug and as with other addictive drugs it increases dopamine release into the nucleus accumbens. However, in the amygdala, alcohol is also a GABA agonist (Di Chiara, 1997; Gilpin & Koob, 2008; Paul, 2006). Although excessive alcohol use has very negative effects, drinking in moderation has salubrious effects. Alcohol will increase production of high-density lipoproteins, which reduces the probability of cardiovascular disease (De Oliveira e Silva et al., 2000).

Hangovers resulting from alcohol ingestion do impair function, although the effects are not dramatic (Kim, Yoon, Lee, Choi, & Go, 2003; Ling, Stephens, & Heffernan, 2010). Alcohol withdrawal is potentially lethal. Symptoms of alcohol withdrawal are apparent 6 to 12 hours after alcohol cessation. Symptoms include an intentional tremor, visible when a person reaches for some object. Other symptoms include vomiting, excessive sweating, agitation, and anxiety (Littrell, 1991). Severity of distress correlates with increase in blood pressure. At 12 to 24 hours, some individuals progress to visual, tactile, and auditory hallucinations. Generalized seizures can occur at 24 to 48 hours. Delirium tremens, with a mortality rate of 5% to 15%, can occur at 48 to 72 hours following a decrease in blood alcohol levels, consisting of hallucinations, disorientation, and autonomic instability (Lüscher, 2013).

Although extreme withdrawal can occur after alcohol discontinuation, the occurrence is rare. Most individuals do not require hospitalization. Oxazepam or lorazepam, benzodiazepines that are not dependent on liver metabolism, is often used for withdrawal treatment (Lüscher, 2013).

Table 3.1 provides a list of some of the drugs available on the market organized by class and mechanism of action.

TABLE 3.1
Generic and Trade Names for Major Drugs on the Market
Organized by Class

Class	Subclass	Generic Name	Trade Name	Comments
Stimulant	Relatively short acting	Methampheta-mine	Dexoxyn	
		Methylphenidate	Ritalin, Metadate, Concerta	
		Dexmethyl-phenidate	Focalin	
		Dextroampheta-mine	Dexedrine	
		Lisdexa-mfetamine-dimesylate	Vyvanse	
Stimulant norepine-phrine reuptake blocker		Atomoxetine	Strattera	
Nonstimulant alpha-2A receptor agonist for ADHD		Guanfacine	Intuniv	
Stimulant	Relatively long acting	Amphetamine	Adderall XR	
		Methylphenidate	Concerta	
		Methylphenidate patch	Daytrana	
Antipsychotic	Neuroleptic phenothia-zine	Chlorpromazine	Thorazine	
		Fluphenazine	Prolixin	
		Trifluoperazine	Stelazine	
		Thioridazine	Mellaril	
	Neuroleptic butyro-phenone	Haloperidol	Haldol	
Antipsychotic	Atypical	Aripiprazole	Abilify	
		Clozapine	Clozaril	
		Iloperidone	Fanapt	
		Lurasidone	Latuda	
		Loxapine	Loxitane	
		Olanzapine	Zyprexa	
		Paliperidone	Invega	
		Quetiapine	Seroquel	

(continued)

TABLE 3.1 (*continued*)

Class	Subclass	Generic Name	Trade Name	Comments
		Risperidone	Risperdal	
		Ziprasidone	Geodon, Zeldox, Zipwell	
Antidepressant	MAOI	Phenelzine	Nardil	
		Tranylcypromine	Parnate	
		Selegiline	Emsam	Does not require as much food restriction
		Isocarboxazid	Marplan	
Antidepressant	Tricyclic	Amitriptyline	Elavil	
		Clomipramine	Anafranil	Only for OCD
		Nortriptyline	Aventyl, Pamelor	
		Maprotiline	Ludiomil	
		Doxepin	Sinequan	
		Imipramine	Tofranil	
		Desipramine	Norpramin	
		Doxepin	Sinequan	
		Protriptyline	Vivactil	
		Trimipramine	Surmontil	
		Amoxapine	Asendin	
Antidepressant	Atypical	Bupropion	Wellbutrin	
		Mirtazapine	Remeron	
Antidepressant	SSRI	Citalopram	Celexa	
		Escitalopram	Lexapro	
		Fluoxetine	Prozac, Sarafem	
		Fluvoxamine	Luvox	
		Paroxetine	Paxil, Pexeva	
		Sertraline	Zoloft	
		Vilazodone	Viibryd	
		Vortioxetine	Brintellix	
		Fluvoxamine	Luvox	Only for OCD
Antidepressant	Both SSRI and SNRI	Duloxetine	Cymbalta	
		Desvenlafaxine	Pristiq	
		Venlafaxine	Effexor	
	5-HT2 antagonists	Trazodone	Desyrel	
Tranquilizer	Benzodiazepine	Alprazolam	Xanax	
		Chlordiazepoxide	Librium	
		Clonazepam	Klonopin	
		Clorazepate	Tranxene	

(*continued*)

TABLE 3.1 (*continued*)
**Generic and Trade Names for Major Drugs on the Market
Organized by Class**

Class	Subclass	Generic Name	Trade Name	Comments
		Diazepam	Valium	
		Estazolam	Prosom	
		Flurazepam	Dalmane	
		Lorazepam	Ativan	
		Temazepam	Restoril	Short half-life
		Triazolam	Halcion	Short half-life
Tranquilizer	Unknown mechanism of action	Buspirone	BuSpar	
Tranquilizer	Barbiturate	Amobarbital	Amytal	
		Mephobarbital	Mebaral	
		Phenobarbital	Luminal sodium	
		Secobarbital	Seconal	
Sleep agent	Nonbenzo-diazepine	Eszopiclone	Lunesta	
	Pyrazolo-pyrimidine	Zaleplon	Sonata	
	Imidazo-pyridine	Zolpidem	Ambien, Intermezzo	
Mood stabilizer	Lithium	Lithium carbonate	Eskalith, Lithobid	
Mood stabilizer	Anticonvul-sants	Valproic acid	Depakote, Epilium	
		Carbamazepine	Tegretol	
		Lamotrigine	Lamictal	
		Topiramate	Topamax	
		Oxcarbazepine	Trileptal	
Strong opioid agonist		Alfentanil	Alfenta	Short acting
		Buprenorphine	Suboxone Buprenex	
		Dolophine	Methadone	
		Fentanyl	Duragesic	
		Hydrocodone	Norco, Vicodin	
		Hydromorphone	Dilaudid, Exalgo	
		Meperidine	Demerol	
		Morphine	Avinza, Astra-morph	

(continued)

TABLE 3.1 (*continued*)

Class	Subclass	Generic Name	Trade Name	Comments
		Oxycodone	OxyContin, Percocet	
		Reminfentanil	Ultiva	Very short acting
		Sufentanil	Sufenta	More potent than fentanyl
Less strong opioid agonist		Codeine	Not potent; often in cough medicine	
		Tramadol	Ultram	
		Propoxyphene	Darvon	
Pure antagonists for opioids	Short acting	Naloxone	Narcan	
	Long acting	Naltrexone	Revia, Depade	
		Naltrexone	Vivitrol	Extended-release injectable

ADHD, attention deficit hyperactivity disorder; MAOIs, monoamine oxidase inhibitors; OCD, obsessive-compulsive disorder; SNRI, serotonin–norepinephrine reuptake inhibitor; SSRI, selective serotonin reuptake inhibitor.

MARKETING OF DRUGS IN THE UNITED STATES

Katzung (2013) explains the process of how drugs are developed. When a disease process is understood and the target for changing the process is clear, molecules can be screened for their impact on particular cell functions. This is the process for discovering novel interventions. However, only 10% to 12% of new drugs are for novel intervention strategies. Most newly marketed drugs are not novel interventions for treating disease. Rather, older approved chemicals are tweaked, for example, by adding a side chain to the molecule. These are called "me too" drugs. Although the "me too" drugs are usually not any more efficacious than the drugs already on the market, advertising efforts are mounted to capture market share for the drug.

After a chemical has been screened for its impact on various cells, it is tested in animals. When there is an animal model for a disorder, then the candidate molecule will be screened for its capacity to alter the disorder. For example, a drug might be tested for its ability to reduce signs of distress after exposure to uncontrollable shock. When initially screening drugs as potential antidepressants, the forced swim test or the tail suspension test can be used. If the drug under evaluation results in an animal struggling for a longer period of time in an uncontrollable situation, then the drug is considered a good candidate for further testing. Before being tested on humans, the lethal dose in animals is established. The drug is tested for toxicity in two species for 3 months. If the drug will be taken for extended periods of time by people, then it is tested in animals for more than 6 months. Tests are conducted to determine carcinogenesis during a 2-year period as well as impact on reproduction in rodents and rabbits. After the animal toxicity tests, the drug is ready for testing in humans. Patent applications, which are filed at this point, can be made either for the novel compound or for a new use of a drug that is already on the market.

In Phase 1, the drug is tested in healthy volunteers (20 to 100) to identify the maximum dose tolerated. Phase 1 trials are usually not blinded. Measurements of absorption, half-life, and metabolism are often done. Phase 2 trials are conducted to determine efficacy. The drug is tested against placebo and sometimes against a known efficacious drug. Phase 2 has the highest rate of drug failures with only 25% of tested molecules moving to Phase 3. In Phase 3, the drug is tested in clinical settings against a placebo with double blinding. Then an application for market approval is made to the FDA. In 2007, the median approval time was 10.2 months for drugs that are similar to those already on the market. For drugs with urgent need (HIV treatments and cancer), the review process may be accelerated and occasionally permission is granted to make the drug available even before Phase 2 studies have been completed. After the drug reaches the market, Phase 4 begins. Adverse drug effects are expected to be reported to the FDA (Katzung, 2013). In fact, it is estimated that less than 1% to 10% of adverse effects are reported (Gøtzsche, 2013, p. 122; Hawthorne, 2005) and only 14% of adverse drug events are reported when they occur in institutional settings (Alsumidaie, 2014). Sidney Wolfe (2014) published an article in *JAMA Internal Medicine* objecting to liberal FDA policies on how pharmaceutical houses inform physicians of drug-associated risks. It should be noted that during Phases 2 and 3, drugs are evaluated individually. In the real world, patients are often treated with multiple chemicals at one time. There are no drug-combination trials.

The pharmaceutical house has exclusive patent rights to market a drug for a 20-year period, and because the patent is filed prior to the human testing, most drugs are sold under exclusive patent for about 11 years. Following patent expiration any company, after establishing with the FDA that they can produce an equivalent product, can produce the drug as a generic. Currently, 67% of prescriptions are for generics (Katzung, 2013).

Elliott (2010) has criticized the American system for conducting Phase 1 trials. Immigrants often serve as the research participants in these trials. Some people, struggling artists or the chronically unemployed, become professional guinea pigs who volunteer to participate in these trials. An industry has developed around Phase 3 trials. Companies, such as SFBC International, Inc., organize their own "Institutional Review Boards" to approve studies. Companies pay doctors in private practice to enroll subjects while company representatives collect the data. The pharmaceutical houses then analyze the data (Fisher, 2009). Approximately 70% of clinical trials on drugs are funded by the industry (Mello, Clarridge, & Studdert, 2005) and 74% of Phase 3 trials are conducted outside of academic centers (Brody, 2007; Fisher, 2009; Gøtzsche, 2013). Industry trial studies are four times more likely to be positive than National Institutes of Health (NIH) trials (Lexchin, Bero, Djulbegovic, & Clark, 2003). Cohen (2013, p. 1) interviewed an FDA employee, Thomas Marcinjak, who suggested that the "clinical trial system is broken," referring to the many missing cases that were unaccounted for in the data from various drug trials.

In 1992, the Prescription Drug User Fee Act was passed by Congress and was reauthorized in 2007 (Prescription Drug User Fee Act, 1992). This act requires pharmaceutical houses to pay the FDA for processing their drug applications (Bass, 2008). The rationale for the legislation was to expand the FDA capacity to quickly approve new applications and speed the delivery of drugs to market.

The FDA faces new challenges with the development of biological products. Biological products refer to proteins made from human-engineered sequences of DNA grown in bacteria among other things. Hawthorne (2005) has suggested that with limited funds, the FDA resources will be severely stretched.

Concerns About Threats to Health

In the last 10 years, many books have been published by doctors who have witnessed changes in their profession attributable to the influence of pharmaceutical companies. Gøtzsche (2013), a cofounder of the prestigious Cochrane Reviews, which publishes meta-analyses on treatments for various conditions, characterizes "big pharma" as organized crime. The pharmaceutical companies are driven by profit motives and Gøtzsche charges that pharmaceutical houses are largely indifferent to the safety or efficacy of their products. Other doctors are similarly critical of the influence of the pharmaceutical industry. Possibly, the first public note of concern over pharmaceutical house influence on the practice of medicine came from Arnold Relman, an editor of the *New England Journal of Medicine* (Angell, 2004). Other voices followed. Otis Brawley, the medical director of the American Cancer Society (Brawley & Goldberg, 2012), wrote about the drug industry's promotion of a drug for increasing the production of RBCs with the rationale that the drug would decrease fatigue in those receiving chemotherapy. In 2003, reports that the drug promotes tumor growth began to appear. Drug companies continued with aggressive marketing and the FDA held hearings in 2007 (Brawley & Goldberg, 2012). Amgen, the manufacturer, pled guilty and was fined $760 million for misbranding, which included activities to encourage off-label marketing for the treatment of cancer patients who were not receiving chemotherapy (Department of Justice, 2012).

In addition to Otis Brawley, other doctors have criticized the pharmaceutical houses. Doug Bremner (2011) ran a study finding that Accutane, a drug used to treat acne, causes suicidal ideation. He was later sued by the drug manufacturer and discouraged from publicizing his findings by the medical school that employed him. A similar story of legal harassment by a drug company is told about Martin Teicher, who was the first to publish about SSRIs inducing suicidal ideation (Bass, 2008). Richard Smith, a former *British Medical Journal* editor, in the introduction to Peter Gøtzsche's book, acknowledges that Gøtzsche's style is inflammatory, but he largely agrees with Gøtzsche's conclusions. Pharmed Out, an organization of faculty and medical students at Georgetown University, has been holding annual conferences attempting to devise ways to limit the impact of money-driven medicine. They have an interesting website. An alarming fact attests to the legitimacy of all the concerns. Adverse prescription drug reactions are the fourth leading cause of death in the United States (Katzung, 2013).

Concerns Over Cost

Americans pay more for their health care than any other nation in the world. Despite spending more than any other nation in the world, America is nowhere near the top on health care outcomes such as mortality (Relman, 2014). Presently, the United States is in the 50th place on health care outcomes (Brawley & Goldberg, 2012). Canada, which spends half of what the United States spends on health care per capita, is in the seventh place in health care outcomes (Brawley & Goldberg, 2012). Switzerland is in the second place on spending on health care, with costs that are 50% less than those in the United States (Brawley & Goldberg, 2012).

Everyone is alarmed by the rising percentage of the economy dedicated to health care. In 2009, health care consumed 17.3% of the gross domestic product. From 1999 to 2009, health care spending has doubled from $1.3 trillion to $2.5 trillion (Blow, 2011). A contributor to the high cost of health care is the cost of drugs, which accounts for 10% to 12% of each health care dollar (Katzung, 2013; Reich, 2014). Canadians, in a country where the government negotiates the price of drugs, pay 70% less than the United States for their drugs (Hawthorne, 2005). Under the Patient Protection and Affordable Care Act, the government (Medicare and Medicaid) is forbidden from negotiating the price of drugs (Reich, 2014). According to Reich (2014), Big Pharma spent more on political campaigns ($36 billion in 2012) than any other industry.

Rather than being an inevitable rising cost of medical progress, drugs should not be as expensive as they are. Pharmaceutical houses spend about 13% of their budget on research and 25% on marketing (Brody, 2007). The majority of new drugs are discovered in public institutions. The Bayh–Dole Act of 1980 allows universities and pharmaceutical companies to patent drug discoveries made at publicly funded institutions (Angell, 2004, p. 7). According to the Bayh–Dole and the Stevenson–Wydler Acts, the FDA is allowed to set a reasonable price for any drug whose discovery is funded by the public dollar (Stevenson–Wydler Technology Innovation Act, 1980). However, this is rarely done (Angell, 2004).

There are other practices that contribute to the high cost of drugs. Pharmaceutical houses often get patent extensions for new formulations of the same drug. This practice restricts competition (Angell, 2004). Large pharmaceutical houses also pay other manufacturers not to market a generic (called "pay for delay"; Federal Trade Commission, 2010).

There is concern that the FDA is under the influence of the pharmaceutical industry. There is a high turnover rate at the FDA and many former FDA employees go to work in the industry (Brody, 2007; Hawthorne, 2005). Since 2002, for 91% of the panels advising on drug approval by the FDA, at least one person has a conflict of interest. For half of the panels, 55% of its members have conflicts of interest (Angell, 2004). This may well be a low estimate. The FDA does not require the report of compensation from the industry below $25,000 and equity interest in stock below $50,000 (FDA, 2013b). The FDA Amendments Act of 2007 requires the FDA to report the number of advisory panel members with conflict of interest. According to the 2009 report to Congress, 27.27% of the advisory panel members making recommendations on psychopharmacological drugs had ties to the industry but were given waivers (Food and Drug Administration Report to Congress, 2009). In 2009, nine FDA scientists wrote to President Obama alleging widespread corruption in the agency. The FDA retaliated by installing spyware on the scientists' computers (Gøtzsche, 2013, p. 111).

This is not just the appearance of a loss of function in protecting the public interest by the FDA's employees. Since pharmaceutical houses began paying for drug reviews, the numbers of black-box warnings and drug withdrawals from the market have increased from 21.2% to 26.7%. Currently, new drugs stand a 26.7% chance of either receiving a black-box warning or being withdrawn for safety reasons within 25 years of approval (Frank et al., 2014). Cases in which harmful drugs were marketed and resulted in death have been documented. Richard Horton, editor for the prestigious British journal, *The Lancet*, characterized the FDA as suffering "a fatal erosion of integrity." Horton (2001) published an editorial in *The Lancet* with a scathing criticism of the FDA's handling of a drug for irritable bowel syndrome, Glaxo-Welcome's Lotronex (alosetron hydrochloride). Several FDA investigators who raised criticisms of the safety of Lotronex were excluded from further discussion on the drug. Horton told Reuters (2001, as quoted in *Wired*), "the FDA is not only compromised because it receives so much of its funding from industry but because it comes under incredible Congressional pressure to be favorable to industry. That has led to deaths." The case of Lotronex is not an isolated case. Steven Nissen, cardiologist at the Cleveland Clinic, tells a similar story about Avandia, a drug for type 2 diabetes. In a Democracy Now (2012) video about the documentary film *Escape Fire*, which can be viewed online, Nissen discussed Avandia with Amy Goodman. (*Escape Fire* is about what needs to change in medicine.) GlaxoSmithKline pleaded guilty to criminal misconduct for concealing the hazards associated with Avandia. Nissen views the FDA as an accomplice in this concealment (Herper, 2013).

The FDA is not the only institution compromised by industry funding. Only 15% of states have a policy banning consultants to industry from membership on boards making decisions about drugs for state-run Medicaid programs (Nguyen & Bero, 2013).

Where Does the Pharmaceutical Industry Spend Its Money?

As stated previously, only 10% to 15% of the drugs on the market are new discoveries (Katzung, 2013). Most are "me-too" drugs, which were developed by tweaking a prior chemical already on the market. Millions are spent on studies, which Marcia Angell characterizes as marketing devices, to advertise the "me-too" drugs in an attempt to capture more market share. In drug trials, drugs are often tested against placebo rather than against drugs that are already on the market. In a study (Antihypertensive and Lipid-Lowering Treatment to Prevent Heart Attack Trial [ALLHAT] study) in which various blood pressure medications were compared for efficacy, diuretics, the cheapest drugs on the market, were found to be superior (Angell, 2004). It is also the case that older drugs have the advantage of having Phase 4 information on adverse effects.

The pharmaceutical industry also relies on direct marketing to the public, which is legal only in New Zealand and the United States (Berndt, 2007). As previously mentioned, pharmaceutical houses spend 1.5 times more of their budget on marketing than on research and development (Angell, 2004; Maher, 2006).

Another fact attests to the high cost of drugs not being an inevitable result of medical progress. Drug industry profits are among the highest of any industry and accounted for $712 billion in 2007 (Katzung, 2013). Profits in the drug industry are only exceeded by profits in commercial banking and the oil industry (Maher, 2006). In 2002, profits of the pharmaceutical houses were higher than all of the other Fortune 500 industries combined (Angell, 2004; Gøtzsche, 2013).

Mechanisms for Controlling Medical Practice

The process by which information about drugs is publicized has also been criticized (Goldacre, 2012a; Seife, 2012; Whoriskey, 2012). Drug companies pay key opinion leaders at medical schools to lecture on their newer products to convince doctors that their patented medications are superior. Pharmaceutical houses fund 60% of the continuing-education events for practicing doctors (Gøtzsche, 2013). Arnold Relman pointed out that half of the members of the body making decisions about accrediting continuing-education events were connected to the industry (Brody, 2007). *Ghostwriting* is the term for academic physicians allowing their names to be attached to articles and books written by pharmaceutical houses for large sums of money. Ghostwriting is common. Moreover, physicians rely on treatment guidelines developed by panels of experts. Panel experts issuing guidelines are often industry funded (Gøtzsche, 2013).

The FDA requires two positive trials to approve a drug. All of the negative trials are ignored by the FDA (1998; Gøtzsche, 2013). Pharmaceutical houses fund 70% of the drug trials, designing the studies and choosing the outcome measures (Mello et al., 2005). In terms of publications, the positive studies are published but the negative trials are less often made public (Turner, Matthews, Linardatos, Tell, & Rosenthal, 2008). Moreover, when a study is conducted by a researcher with financial ties to the pharmaceutical house, negative findings are less likely to be reported (Friedman & Richter, 2004). Thus, doctors reading medical journals get a distorted evaluation of the efficacy of any particular drug. Another industry trick utilized when the planned drug trial yields negative results has been to scan the data for a point in time when results favor the drug. The time point at which the drug looks like it is effective becomes the end point that is published in a journal (Brody, 2007).

All drug trials are now required to be registered before they are conducted so that the chicanery of capitalizing on chance cannot occur. According to the FDA Amendments Act of 2007 to the Food and Drug Administration Modernization Act of 1997, a summary of results of trials is to be provided within a year of completion. Moreover, the International Committee of Medical Journal Editors vowed that they would not publish studies that had not complied with the registration of their drug trials (Bass, 2008). However, medical journal editors rarely insist on the observation of these standards (Goldacre, 2012b, 2013). Not only do journals sometimes fail to ensure that publications reflect results from the studies as planned, but journal editors do not always ensure that article abstracts reflect the actual findings from studies (Gøtzsche, 2013). Abramson (2013) discusses the fact that the abstracts of articles on drug trials have failed to report the more negative details that are buried in the article. Vedula, Li, and Dickerson (2013) document the discrepancies between actual study findings on Neurontin (gabapentin, which is a drug for epilepsy and other uses) and industry advertisements. The establishment of the Cochrane Reviews was an attempt to provide doctors with more honest evaluations of the efficacy of particular interventions (Avorn, 2013).

Medical journals are compromised by their financial dependence on pharmaceutical houses. Many medical journals rely on advertising revenue from the pharmaceutical industry or large article reprint orders from the pharmaceutical houses to cover costs (Gøtzsche, 2013). A study by Wilkes, Doblin, and Shapiro (1992) published in *Annals of Internal Medicine* reported that expert panels found many advertisements to be unbalanced and misleading. The industry response to the article by Wilkes et al. was to pull its advertisements from *Annals of Internal Medicine*, subsequent to which the journal editors resigned (Brody, 2007).

In addition to controlling much of the information that physicians rely on, pharmaceutical houses have additional mechanisms for influencing physicians. Physicians are bombarded by free gifts from pharmaceutical houses. In fact, the Physician Payment Sunshine Act, part of the Patient Protection and Affordable Care Act (2010), was passed to limit this practice. Under this law, pharmaceutical houses must report their gifts to physicians (Rodwin, 2013). Pharmaceutical companies and device makers paid doctors $380 million over a 5-month period in 2013 (Reich, 2014). Although doctors may believe that they are not influenced by free gifts, they are (Elliott, 2010; Sah & Fugh-Berman, 2013).

Off-Label Promotion

When drug companies suspect that their drug will not prove efficacious in a drug trial, they often stop testing and promote "off-label" use of the drug. Off-label marketing is illegal, but drug representatives are allowed to discuss studies of off-label use with doctors and to respond to a doctor's questions. Prior to the FDA Amendments Act of 2007, if a company did not bring its product to market, the data regarding efficacy were not in the public record (Hawthorne, 2005). Title VIII of the FDA Amendments Act of 2007 leaves the decision of whether the information is publicly available up to the discretion of the NIH.

Physicians are allowed to prescribe any drug on the market to treat any condition regardless of whether the drug has been approved by the FDA for the particular age group or the particular use. When physicians engage in "off-label" prescribing, the physician, rather than the drug company, assumes liability for any untoward effects; that is, the physician and not the company can be sued. In fact, half of all the prescriptions billed to Medicare and Medicaid are for off-label uses (Angell, 2004). Off-label use is common in insurance-funded medicine (Mojtabai & Olfson, 2010), and in the Veterans Administration (VA) system (Leslie, Mohamed, & Rosenheck, 2009).

Drug companies have been sued for off-label promotion of atypical antipsychotics for the elderly and for small children. When Eliot Spitzer was attorney general for the state of New York, his office sued GlaxoSmithKline for misleading doctors about the efficacy and safety of paroxetine for adolescents. Internal company memos showed that the company knew paroxetine was associated with suicidal ideation in controlled studies. (According to Eliot Spitzer, the FDA was also aware [Harris, 2004].) Moreover, in a ghostwritten publication by psychiatrist Martin Keller, the abstract indicated that the drug was effective although the data in the article failed to find a difference between placebo and drug. In fact, GlaxoSmithKline settled with Spitzer's office, agreeing to register its trials and paying $2.5 million for repeated and persistent consumer fraud in concealing the harms of paroxetine (Bass, 2008; Hawthorne, 2005).

Even for drugs that are on the market, side effects identified during a trial of the drug for a new indication are usually not made part of the public record unless the drug is finally approved for the new indication. Cymbalta, an antidepressant, was tested for urinary incontinence in adults. None of the subjects in the urinary incontinence trial was depressed. The study was negative for improvement of urinary incontinence but did find that Cymbalta was associated with a significant increase in suicide attempt rates (400/100,000 on Cymbalta vs. 160/100,000 on placebo). Because the Cymbalta was not approved for urinary incontinence, the study's findings were not made public (Gøtzsche, 2013). Recently, however, Cymbalta did get approved for urinary incontinence and Cymbalta now has a warning for suicidal ideation in children and adults (Lenzer, 2005).

Psychiatric Medications

Medications for psychiatric disorders are particularly vulnerable to criticism. The drug industry supplies one third of the American Psychiatric Association's budget (Gøtzsche, 2013). Ghostwriting is especially prevalent in psychiatry (Leo, Lacasse, & Cimino, 2011). For those issuing treatment guidelines for bipolar disorder, schizophrenia, and depression, more than 90% had financial ties to pharmaceutical houses (Cosgrove, Bursztajn, Krimsky, Anaya, & Walker, 2009). The reader might wonder, given their professional stakes and the professional pride of members of the psychiatric profession, how money could play a truly influential role. An answer might lie in just what is on offer to those who might be vulnerable. The individual compensation packages from the pharmaceutical companies for their top industry consultants and speakers topped $550,000. Half of those receiving that level of compensation were psychiatrists (Weber & Ornstein, 2013).

It should be noted that most psychiatrists are not responsible for the current state of affairs. Most are hardworking and well meaning. However, as Ben Goldacre (2012a) points out in his TED (technology, education, and design) Talk, "What Doctors Don't Know About the Drugs They Prescribe" well-meaning doctors are limited by the information that is available to them. Evidence-based practice is based on evidence. What can be done when the evidence is tainted?

Antidepressants and antipsychotic drugs are among the highest grossing drugs for the pharmaceutical industry (Gøtzsche, 2013). In fact, 20% of Americans are prescribed psychotropic medications (Friedman, 2013). In *Anatomy of an Epidemic*, journalist Robert Whitaker (2010), compared the outcomes for various conditions in the era before psychiatric drugs to outcomes after their availability. For all categories of disorder, outcomes have deteriorated since the advent of modern treatments. In fact, Whitaker argues that the expansion of persons on disability in the United States is attributable to drug-induced disability. Marcia Angell (2011a, 2011b, 2011c) reviewed Whitaker's book in *The New York Review of Books*. She did not disagree with Whitaker and, in fact, recognized that diagnosis in psychiatry is much more subjectively based than in other areas of medicine. A fierce debate ensued in subsequent issues of the *The New York Review of Books* between Angell and several prominent psychiatrists. This was not the first occasion when Marcia Angell was openly critical of psychiatry. In her role as an editor of the *New England Journal of Medicine*, Angell (2000) wrote an editorial regarding a major study evaluating antidepressants and talk therapy published by Keller et al. (2000). Angell indicated that it was the policy of the journal to publish the ties to industry of all authors as well as to have a disinterested party write an editorial regarding the findings of major studies. Angell indicated that Keller's ties to pharmaceutical houses were longer than the article. Moreover, Angell had to go to Britain to locate a psychiatrist without ties to pharmaceutical houses to write the editorial.

Others have also criticized the "psych" medication industry. After public outcry on induced suicidal ideation in teens by antidepressants, a hearing was held in September of 2004. Even though the FDA information was not shared with the members of the FDA panel, black-box warnings were placed on SSRIs for children and young adults (Bass, 2008; Hawthorne, 2005).

There have been no useful novel biochemical approaches to psychiatric treatment in the last 50 years; new pharmaceuticals have been "me-too" chemicals (Friedman, 2013). It is notable that the pharmaceutical houses have largely abandoned the search for new psychotropic medications (Friedman, 2013). Tom Insel (2011), director of the National Institute of Mental Health (NIMH), attributes this departure to "the absence of biomarkers, the lack of valid diagnostic categories, and our limited understanding of the biology of these illnesses."

Both Panksepp (2004) and Insel (2011) have noted that most psych drugs were discovered before any understanding of the physiology involved in the behavioral manifestation. According to Panksepp (2004), behaviorists went to work for pharmaceutical houses. Inspired by B. F. Skinner, the emphasis was on behavior and not what was happening inside the "black box" of the brain. The behaviorists screened molecules for their impact on behavior with little regard for examining the pathway in the brain explaining how the molecule altered overt behavior. Drugs were often discovered through serendipity. For example, people noticed that chlorpromazine (Thorazine) produced a calming effect on animals and it had been used to sedate individuals for surgery. It was therefore tried out for its impact on the agitation of psychosis. John Cade noted that lithium seemed to decrease aggression and excitement in animals. It was given to those with mania. MAOIs, used to treat tuberculosis, seemed to energize patients; hence, it was adapted for the treatment of depression. Insel (2014) characterizes the pharmaceutical industry's approach to psychiatric medications in the following way, "We've studied drugs, not disorders—if you throw something at the wall, and the P is less than 0.05, you win."

The NIMH has instituted new policies for receipt of funding for testing new drugs. The NIMH is pledged to limit funding of drug trials to those occasions when there is a rationale for how the drug targets a basic physiological pathway assumed to give rise to the disorder (Reardon, 2014). The NIMH also has committed itself to observing the rules on the registration of drug trials.

THE ROLE OF BEHAVIORAL HEALTH CLINICIANS WITH REGARD TO PHARMACEUTICALS

Bentley and Walsh's (2013) *The Social Worker and Psychotropic Medication* and Dziegielewski's (2009) *Social Work Practice and Psychopharmacology: A Person-in-Environment Approach* are texts written to prepare behavioral health clinicians to work with medications. The aforementioned texts were written primarily for social workers working with persons receiving services for the chronically mentally ill. In working with those deemed to be chronically mental ill, behavioral health clinicians may have responsibilities for monitoring side effects of pharmaceuticals. Additionally, master's-level behavioral health clinicians are often hired to provide psychoeducation for those with chronic mental illness and their family members. Psychoeducation consists of encouraging compliance with physician recommendations and providing rationales for medication compliance.

In their books, Bentley, Walsh, and Dziegielewski have been favorable to the expansion of social work roles. In some states, clinical psychologists with additional training have acquired prescription privileges. Dziegielewski advocates for social workers seeking these privileges as well.

In this section, some caveats in taking on responsibilities for monitoring side effects are provided. The last segment of this section considers issues that arise for behavioral health clinicians who work independently, as occurs in private practice settings. In these settings, behavioral health clinicians do not have specific obligations with regard to medications. However, they do have responsibility for securing informed consent for whatever treatment they intend to provide. In this section, obligations for discussing medications in the context of securing informed consent are considered as well as the issue of what nonmedical professionals can say with regard to medications.

Obligations in Assuming Responsibilities for Monitoring Side Effects

When a profession assumes responsibility for medications, not only is the prescribing physician named in the lawsuit but others with responsibility (e.g., the pharmacist and the nurse) can also be sued (Littrell & Ashford, 1995). The responsibility for monitoring side effects is heavy. The range of adverse events that regularly occur with prescription drugs is far-reaching. Psychiatric drugs are responsible for 9.6% of medication adverse drug events seen in emergency rooms (Hampton, Daubresse, Chang, Alexander, & Budnitz, 2014). When I worked in the Alcohol and Drug Dependency department at a health maintenance organization, sometimes alcoholics were prescribed the more fast-acting MAOI antidepressants to treat their depression. Recovering alcoholics do relapse. Drinking on an MAOI can result in stroke. Antidepressants can result in orthostatic hypotension, that is, dizziness that occurs if someone stands up too quickly. This is a particular problem in the elderly. SSRI antidepressants can induce serotonin syndrome, which is rare but serious. The serotonin syndrome includes delirium, muscle convulsions, and can be lethal. Antipsychotics can induce neuromalignant syndrome, which is also rare, but equally serious. Neuromalignant syndrome is associated with muscle convulsions, high temperature, delirium, and death. SSRIs have black-box warnings for suicidal ideation in teens and young adults. The antipsychotic drugs can induce irreversible tardive dyskinesia, a severe movement disorder. Trazodone (Desyrel, an antidepressant) can result in an erection of extended duration, for which surgical intervention may be necessary. Antipsychotic drugs interfere with the body's ability to regulate temperature and, given physical exertion or high ambient temperatures, heat stroke can occur (Charder & Knoll, 2014). None of these possible occurrences are trivial. Taking responsibility for monitoring side effects may entail the obligation for noticing these occurrences before it is too late to prevent irreversible damage.

Although few behavioral health clinicians have been involved in litigation regarding adverse medication reactions, it has occurred. In his blog " 'I Was Just Following Orders': a Seroquel Suicide, a Study Coordinator, and a 'Corrective Action' " on November 12, 2012, on the Mad in America website (www.madinamerica.com), Carl Elliott discusses the legal proceedings against social worker Jean Kenny. Kenny was the study coordinator for the Cancer, Lifestyle & Evaluation of Risk (CLEAR) study and the CATIE study at the University of Minnesota. Kenny's job included obtaining informed consent, administering prescription drugs, monitoring side effects, and making judgments about akathisia (movement problem induced by antipsychotic medication). Dan Markingson was enrolled in the trial evaluating an antipsychotic medication, perhaps without having consented. Markingson's mother made many calls to Kenny reporting that her son was deteriorating. Eventually, Markingson did commit suicide in a particularly gruesome way. Markingson's mother sued the university and later made complaints to the board about Jean Kenny. The board took corrective action against Kenny requiring her to take 18 hours worth of continuing education. The case illustrates the liability that taking responsibility for the impact of medications confers.

Clinicians Functioning Independently

Many mental health clinicians are therapists. Often they function independently without being members of a team, which would systematically review how clients are progressing. In 1994, José Ashford and I conducted a study in which fieldwork supervisors were the research participants (Littrell & Ashford, 1994). (Fieldwork supervisors provide instructions to social work students in internship settings.) We provided scenarios of a man and his wife who sought counseling for marital problems. In the scenario, a description of the husband portrayed many symptoms of depression. We varied the setting in which the couple was seen: using either a family service agency or a community mental health center. We asked fieldwork supervisors whether they would consider the possibility of a referral for medication. What our results showed was that the setting in which the client was seen had an impact on what clinicians said they would do. If the man was seen in a community mental health center, he would be referred. If he was seen in a family service agency, fieldwork supervisors were less likely to say they would raise the medication issue. Our study suggested that the setting determined what the fieldwork supervisors construed to be their responsibilities. The study raises an issue regarding the absence of clarity on whether a profession has a responsibility for assessing *International Classification of Diseases-10 (ICD-10)* (WHO, 2015) criteria and assuming the responsibilities of a mental health professional in the diverse settings in which they might be working.

Informed-Consent Duties of Clinicians in Clear Mental Health Professional Roles

According to Appelbaum, Lidz, and Meisel (1987), lawyers with expertise in mental health law, informed-consent statutes have been passed in almost all states. Colorado, Ohio, and Washington have passed informed-consent legislation for mental health counselors (Handelsman, 2001). Informed consent requires that clinicians inform clients of the risk and benefits associated with proposed treatments as well as the risk and benefits of procedures for particular conditions that the clinician does not intend to provide. Assuming that informed-consent statutes extend to all mental health clinicians, behavioral health clinicians may be bound by the same standards.

The case of Osheroff versus Chestnut Lodge may have precedent-setting implications regarding the duty to discuss medication options for various *ICD-10* conditions. Chestnut Lodge was a residential treatment center known for its psychoanalytic approach. Chestnut Lodge treated Osheroff with talk therapy for his depression. When he failed to improve, Osheroff sued Chestnut Lodge for failure to provide the option of medication. The case was settled out of court. Although a precedent was not established, the imperative of exploring a range of options with clients is consistent with most mental health professional codes of ethics. Thus, if a client clearly meets criteria for an *ICD-10* disorder, a discussion regarding a medication option should occur and be documented (Littrell & Ashford, 1995).

With regard to informed consent, written agreements are now preferred, with a copy of the agreement provided to the client (Bennett, Wise, Johnson-Greene, & Bucky, 2007; Littrell & Ashford, 1995). The written agreement should inform the client of avenues available to redress concerns about the therapist. The document should be written at a level consistent with the client's level of educational attainment (Welfel, 2012).

What Can Nonmedical Clinicians Say About Medications?

Informing of a medication option is advisable when a client clearly meets criteria for an *ICD-10* disorder. In the context of considering options for a client who is not currently taking medication, the nonmedical clinician can provide information. However, the information should be current and accurate. Clinicians who regularly have such conversations with clients about medications should probably have references ready to support whatever information they offer. Conversations should be documented along with the client's decision.

With regard to clients who are on medication, the issue of what nonphysicians can say has arisen. Tuma was a nurse working with cancer patients. After Tuma advised a particular patient on the benefits of Laetrile, the attending physician contacted the nursing board asserting that the nurse had acted improperly. The nursing board tried to revoke Tuma's license, but Tuma appealed. The administrative law judge ruled for Tuma, indicating that the nursing board had the prerogative to establish whatever rules the board deemed appropriate, however, it violated the due process to punish someone for breaking a rule that was never stated. Since the Tuma case, rather than nonphysicians being further constrained regarding what they can say about medications, job descriptions with respect to medications for nonphysicians have expanded. In the courts, the duty to catch medication errors has been imposed on pharmacists. Nurse practitioners and psychologists have prescription privileges in many states. However, discussion about the actions of another profession's treatment of a client is a gray area without many legal precedents (Littrell & Ashford, 1995). Professional codes, except for comments on promoting harmonious collegial relationships, are vague (Ingersoll, 2001). State licensing statutes should certainly be consulted.

It is unwise to encourage clients to quit taking their medication. As discussed in subsequent chapters, all psychotropic medications have relatively severe withdrawal symptoms. Withdrawal from benzodiazepines can even be lethal. Antipsychotic medications create receptor sensitivity to dopamine and induce expression of greater numbers of receptors. When the medication is abruptly withdrawn, psychosis might emerge in persons who were taking antipsychotics for treatment of a nonpsychotic condition. Antidepressant medication withdrawal is rather severe. Thus, clients should be warned about abrupt discontinuation of any medication.

Recent evidence suggests that in only a very small minority of cases do physicians discuss potential adverse effects of antidepressants with clients (Gopal et al., 2012). (Side effects of various medications are covered throughout this book.) Clients who are currently on medication may be experiencing side effects that they are misattributing. It may be helpful to inform clients regarding which symptoms may be side effects of their drugs. Providing general information about a drug does not constitute practicing medicine. Encouraging clients to inform their physicians about side effects is good practice. Encouraging clients to inform physicians about any supplements they are taking is good practice as supplements may be contraindicated with particular medications (Ingersoll, 2001). Helping clients who are dissatisfied with the approach of their physicians to find another doctor is an alternative.

WEBSITES FOR INFORMATION REGARDING DRUGS

EROWID.org provides useful information on street drugs and pharmaceutics.
The U.S. FDA website drugs@FDA has a link to "dailymeds" another FDA website.
The NIMH website www.nimh.nih.gov/health/publications/mental-health-medications/index.shtml lists side effects and black-box warnings.
US.DoJ.gov gives Drug Enforcement Administration (DEA) information on street drugs. http://www.dea.gov/index.shtml
Agency for Healthcare Research and Quality National Guideline Clearing House: www.healthfinder.gov
National Institute on Drug Abuse: www.drugabuse.gov
Pharmedout.org
An online version of the *Physicians' Desk Reference* can be found at www.pdr.net

REFERENCES

Abramson, J. (2013). *Overdosed America: The broken promise of American medicine.* New York, NY: HarperCollins.
Alsumidaie, M. (2014). *FDA sentinel: Catching biopharmaceutical sponsors by surprise.* Retrieved from http://www.appliedclinicaltrialsonline.com/

appliedcliinicaltrials/Blogs/FDA-Sentinel-cathing-biopharmaceutical-sponsors-by-surprise

Angell, M. (2000). Is academic medicine for sale? *New England Journal of Medicine, 342*(20), 1516–1518.

Angell, M. (2004). *The truth about drug companies: How they deceive us and what to do about it.* New York, NY: Random House.

Angell, M. (2011a). Why there is an epidemic of mental illness. *New York Review of Books, 58*(11), 20–22.

Angell, M. (2011b). The illusion of psychiatry. *New York Review of Books, 58*(12), 20–22.

Angell, M. (2011c). The illusion of psychiatry: An exchange. *New York Review of Books, 58*(13), 82–84.

Appelbaum, P. S., Lidz, C. W., & Meisel, A. (1987). *Informed consent: Legal theory and clinical practice.* New York, NY: Oxford University Press.

Associated Press. (2007). *FDA says pills can cause "sleep-driving."* Retrieved from http://www.washingtonpost.com/wp-dyn/content/article/2007/03/14/AR2007031401027.html

Avorn, J. (2013, June 11). Healing the overwhelmed physician. *The New York Times,* p. A25.

Bass, A. (2008). *Side effects: A prosecutor, a whistleblower, and a bestselling antidepressant on trial.* New York, NY: Algonquin Books.

Bayh-Dole. *Patent and Trademark Amendments Act* of 1980, Pub. L. No. 96–517 (December 12, 1980).

Bennett, J. E., Wise, E. H., Johnson-Greene, D., & Bucky, S. F. (2007). Informed consent: Too much of a good thing or not enough? *Professional Psychology: Research and Practice, 38,* 179–186.

Bentley, K., & Walsh, J. (2013). *The social worker and psychotropic medication* (4th ed.). New York, NY: Brooks/Cole/Cengage.

Berndt, E. R. (2007). *The United States' experiences with direct-to-consumer advertising of prescription drugs: What have we learned?* Unpublished manuscript, Massachusetts Institute of Technology, Cambridge, Massachusetts.

Biaggioni, I., & Robertson, D. (2013). Adrenoceptor agonists and sympathomimetic drugs. In B. G. Katzung, S. B. Masters, & A. J. Trevor (Eds.), *Basic and clinical pharmacology* (12th ed., pp. 129–150). New York, NY: McGraw Hill.

Blow, C. (2011, September 17). For jobs, it's war. *The New York Times,* p. A21.

Brawley, O., & Goldberg, P. (2012). *How we do harm: A doctor breaks rank about being sick in America.* New York, NY: St. Martin's Press.

Bremner, J. D. (2011). *The goose that laid the golden egg.* New York, NY: That Right Publishing.

Brody, H. (2007). *Hooked: Ethics, the medical profession, and the pharmaceutical industry.* New York, NY: Rowman & Littlefield.

Burroughs, V. J., Maxey, R. W., & Levy, R. A. (2002). Racial and ethnic differences in response to medicines: Towards individualized pharmaceutical treatment. *Journal of the National Medical Association, 94*(10, Suppl.), 1–26.

Charder, N., & Knoll, J. L. (2014). Heatstroke and psychiatric patients. *Psychiatric Times, 31*(7), 1, 12–13, 20.

Cohen, D. (2013). FDA official: "Clinical trial system is broken." *British Medical Journal, 347,* 16980.

Controlled Substances Act of 1970, Pub. L. No. 91–513, 84 Stat. 1236 aka 84 Stat. 1242 (1970).

Correia, M. A. (2013). Drug biotransformation. In B. G. Katzung, S. B. Masters, & A. J. Trevor (Eds.), *Basic and clinical pharmacology* (12th ed., pp. 53–68). New York, NY: McGraw Hill.

Cosgrove, L., Bursztajn, H. J., Krimsky, S., Anaya, M., & Walker, J. (2009). Conflicts of interest and disclosure in the American Psychiatric Association's clinical practice guidelines. *Psychotherapy and Psychosomatics, 78*(4), 228–232.

Dani, J. A., Kosten, T. R., & Benowitz, N. L. (2011). The pharmacology of nicotine and tobacco. In C. A. Cavacuiti (Ed.), *Principles of addiction medicine: The essentials.* New York, NY: Lippincott Williams & Wilkins.

DeBattista, C. (2013). Antidepressant agents. In B. G. Katzung, S. B. Masters, & A. J. Trevor (Eds.), *Basic and clinical pharmacology* (12th ed., pp. 521–540). New York, NY: McGraw Hill.

Democracy Now. (2012). *Medical whistleblower Dr. Steven Nissen on "Escape Fire: The Fight to Rescue American Healthcare."* Retrieved from http:www.democracynow.org

De Oliveira e Silva, E. R., Foster, D., Harper, M. M., Seidman, C. E., Smith, J. D., Breslow, J. L., & Brinton, E. A. (2000). Alcohol consumption raises HDL cholesterol levels by increasing the transport rate of apolipoproteins A-1 and A-II. *Circulation, 102,* 2347–2352.

Department of Justice. (2012). *Amgen Inc. pleads guilty to federal charge in Brooklyn, NY; pays $762 million to resolve criminal liability and False Claims Act allegations. Office of Public Affairs.* Retrieved from www.justice.gov/opa/pr/2012/december/12-civ-1523.html

Di Chiara, G. (1997). Alcohol and dopamine. *Alcohol Health and Research World, 21*(2), 108–114.

Drasner, K. (2013). Local anesthetics. In B. G. Katzung, S. B. Masters, & A. J. Trevor (Eds.), *Basic and clinical pharmacology* (12th ed., pp. 449–463). New York, NY: McGraw Hill.

Dziegielewski, S. (2009). *Social work practice and psychopharmacology: A person-in-environment approach* (2nd ed.). New York, NY: Springer Publishing Company.

Elliott, C. (2010). *White coat, black hat: Adventures on the dark side of medicine.* Boston, MA: Beacon Press.

Federal Trade Commission. (2010). *Pay-for-delay: When drug companies agree not to compete.* Retrieved July 1, 2014, from http://www.ftc.gov/news-events/media-resources/mergers-and-competition/pay-delay

Filozof, C., Fernández Pinilla, M. C., & Fernández-Cruz, A. (2004). Smoking cessation and weight gain. *Obesity Reviews, 5*(2), 95–103.

Fisher, J. A. (2009). *Medical research for hire: The political economy of pharmaceutical clinical trials.* New Brunswick, NJ: Rutgers University Press.

Food and Drug Administration. (1998). *Guidance for industry: Providing clinical evidence of effectiveness for human drug and biological products.* Retrieved from http://www.fda.gov/downloads/Drugs/GuidanceComplianceRegulatory/Information/Guidance/UCI

Food and Drug Administration. (2009). *Fiscal year 2008 annual report on FDA advisory committee vacancies and public disclosures.* Retrieved from www.fda.gov/downloads/advisorycommittees/aboutadvisorycommittees/ucm179962.pdf

Food and Drug Administration. (2013a). *FDA safety communication: Risk of next-morning impairment after use of insomnia drugs: FDA requires lower recommended doses for certain drugs containing zolpidem (Ambien, Ambien CR, Euluar, and Zolpimist).* Retrieved from http://www.fda.gove/Drugs/DrugSafety?ucm334033.htm

Food and Drug Administration. (2013b). *Guidance for clinical investigators, industry, and FDA staff financial disclosures by clinical investigators.* Retrieved from http://www.fda.gov/downloads/RegulatoryInformation/Guidance/UMC341008.pdf

Food and Drug Administration Amendments Act, Pub. L. No. 110–85, 121 Stat. 823 (2007).

Food and Drug Administration Modernization Act of 1997, Pub. L. No. 105–115, 111 Stat. 2296 (1997).

Fowler, C. D., Arends, M. A., & Kenny, P. J. (2008). Subtypes of nicotinic acetylcholine receptors in nicotine reward, dependence, and withdrawal: Evidence from genetically modified mice. *Behavioural Pharmacology, 19*(5–6), 461–484.

Frank, C., Himmelstein, D. U., Woolhandler, S., Bor, D. H., Wolfe, S. M., Heymann, O.,...Lasser, K. E. (2014). Era of faster FDA drug approval has also seen increased black-box warnings and market withdrawals. *Health Affairs, 33*(8), 1453–1459.

Friedman, L. S., & Richter, E. D. (2004). Relationship between conflicts of interest and research results. *Journal of General Internal Medicine, 19*(1), 51–56.

Friedman, R. (2012, September 24). A call for caution on antipsychotic drugs. *The New York Times,* Health. Retrieved from www.nytimes.com/2012/09/25/health/a-call-for-caution-on-antipsychotic-drugs

Friedman, R. (2013, August 19). A dry pipeline for psychiatric drugs. *The New York Times,* Health. Retrieved from http:www.nytimes.com/2013/08/20/health/a-dry-pipeline-for-psychiatric-drugs

Gaedigk, A., Bradford, L. D., Marcucci, K. A., & Leeder, J. S. (2002). Unique CYP2D6 activity distribution and genotype-phenotype discordance in black Americans. *Clinical Pharmacology and Therapeutics, 72*(1), 76–89.

Gilpin, N. W., & Koob, G. F. (2008). Neurobiology of alcohol dependence: Focus on motivational mechanisms. *Alcohol Research & Health, 31*(3), 185–195.

Goldacre, B. (2012a). *What doctors don't know about the drugs they prescribe.* Retrieved from www.ted.com/talks/ben_goldacre_what_doctors_don't_know_about_the_ drugs_they_prescribe

Goldacre, B. (2012b). *Bad pharma: How drug companies mislead doctors and harm patients.* New York, NY: Faber & Faber.

Goldacre, B. (2013, February 2). Health care's trick coin. *The New York Times.* Retrieved from http:www.nytimes.com/2013/02/02/opinion/health-care's-trick-coin

Gopal, A. A., Cosgrove, L., Shuv-Ami, I., Wheeler, E. E., Yerganian, M. J., & Bursztajn, H. J. (2012). Dynamic informed consent processes vital for treatment with antidepressants. *International Journal of Law and Psychiatry, 35*(5–6), 392–397.

Gøtzsche, P. C. (2013). *Deadly medicines and organized crime: How big pharma has corrupted healthcare.* London: Radcliffe.

Gunasekaran, N., Long, L. E., Dawson, B. L., Hansen, G. H., Richardson, D. P., Li, K. M., ... McGregor, I. S. (2009). Reintoxication: The release of fat-stored delta(9)-tetrahydrocannabinol (THC) into blood is enhanced by food deprivation or ACTH exposure. *British Journal of Pharmacology, 158*(5), 1330–1337.

Haddad, P. M. (2001). Antidepressant discontinuation syndromes. *Drug Safety, 24*(3), 183–197.

Hampton, L. M., Daubresse, M., Chang, H. Y., Alexander, G. C., & Budnitz, D. S. (2014). Emergency department visits by adults for psychiatric medication adverse events. *JAMA Psychiatry, 71*(9), 1006–1014.

Handelsman, M. M. (2001). Accurate and effective informed consent. In E. R. Welfel & R. R. Ingersoll (Eds.), *The mental health desk reference: A practice-based guide to diagnosis, treatment, and professional ethics* (pp. 453–458). New York, NY: Wiley.

Harris, G. (2004, August 26). *Maker of Paxil to release trial results.* Retrieved July 14, 2014, from www.nytimes.com?2004/08/26/business/26CNF-Drugs.html

Hart, C. L., Ksir, C., & Ray, O. (2009). *Drugs, society, & human behavior* (13th ed.). New York, NY: McGraw Hill.

Hawthorne, F. (2005). *Inside the FDA: The business and politics behind the drugs we take and the food we eat.* New York, NY: John Wiley.

Herper, M. (2013, May 23). Steven Nissen: The hidden agenda behind the FDA's new Avandia hearings. *Forbes.* Retrieved from http://www.forbes.com/sites/ matthewherper/2013/05/23/steven-nissen-the-hidden-agenda-behind-the-fdas-avandia-hearings/

Holford, N. H. G. (2013). Pharmacokinetics & pharmacodynamics: Rational dosing & time course of drug action. In B. G. Katzung, S. B. Masters, & A. J.

Trevor (Eds.), *Basic and clinical pharmacology* (12th ed., pp. 37–52). New York, NY: McGraw Hill.

Horton, R. (2001). Lotronex and the FDA: A fatal erosion of integrity. *Lancet, 357*(9268), 1544–1545. Retrieved from http://www.wired.com/medtechhealth/news/2001/05/43891

Howland, R. D., & Mycek, M. J. (2006). *Pharmacology* (3rd ed.). Baltimore, MD: Lippincott Williams & Wilkins.

Hughes, J. R. (2007). Effects of abstinence from tobacco: Valid symptoms and time course. *Nicotine & Tobacco Research, 9*(3), 315–327.

Ingersoll, R. E. (2001). The nonmedical therapist's role in pharmacological interventions with adults. In E. R. Welfel & R. R. Ingersoll (Eds.), *The mental health desk reference: A practice-based guide to diagnosis, treatment, and professional ethics* (pp. 88–92). New York, NY: John Wiley.

Insel, T. R. (2011). *Mental illness defined as disruption in neural circuits.* Retrieved from http://www.nimh.nih.gov/about/director/2011/mental-illness-defined-as-disruption-in-neural-circuits.shtml

Insel, T. R. (2014). *Director's blog: A new approach to clinical trials.* Retrieved from http://www.nimh.nih.gov/about/director/2014/a-new-approach-to-clinical-trials.shtml

Katzung, B. G. (2013). Development and regulation of drugs. In B. G. Katzung, S. B. Masters, & A. J. Trevor (Eds.), *Basic and clinical pharmacology* (12th ed., pp. 69–78). New York, NY: McGraw Hill.

Keller, M. B., McCullouch, J. P., Klein, D. N., Arrow, B., Dunner, D. L., Gelenberg, A. J., ... Zajecka, J. (2000). A comparison of nefazodone, the cognitive behavioral-analysis system of psychotherapy, and their combination for the treatment of chronic depression. *New England Journal of Medicine, 324*(20), 1462–1470.

Kim, D. J., Yoon, S. J., Lee, H. P., Choi, B. M., & Go, H. J. (2003). The effects of alcohol hangover on cognitive functions in healthy subjects. *International Journal of Neuroscience, 113*(4), 581–594.

Lenzer, J. (2005). FDA warns that antidepressants may increase suicidality in adults. *British Medical Journal, 331*(7508), 70. doi: 10.1136/bmj.331.7508.70-b

Leslie, D. L., Mohamed, S., & Rosenheck, R. A. (2009). Off-label use of antipsychotic medications in the department of Veterans Affairs health care system. *Psychiatric Services, 60*(9), 1175–1181.

Leo, J., Lacasse, J. R., & Cimino, A. N. (2011). Why does academic medicine allow ghostwriting? A prescription for reform. *Society, 48,* 371–375.

Lexchin, J., Bero, L. A., Djulbegovic, B., & Clark, O. (2003). Pharmaceutical industry sponsorship and research outcome and quality: Systematic review. *British Medical Journal, 326*(7400), 1167–1170.

Ling, J., Stephens, R., & Heffernan, T. M. (2010). Cognitive and psychomotor performance during alcohol hangover. *Current Drug Abuse Reviews, 3*(2), 80–87.

Littrell, J. (1991). *Understanding and treating alcoholism: Biological, psychological and social aspects of alcohol consumption and abuse.* Hillsdale, NJ: LEA Press.

Littrell, J., & Ashford, J. B. (1994). The duty of social workers to refer for medications: A study of field instructors. *Social Work Research, 18*(2), 123–128.

Littrell, J., & Ashford, J. B. (1995). Is it proper for psychologists to discuss medications with clients? *Professional Psychology, Research and Practice, 26*(3), 238–244.

Lüscher, C. (2013). Drugs of abuse. In B. G. Katzung, S. B. Masters, & A. J. Trevor (Eds.), *Basic and clinical pharmacology* (12th ed., pp. 565–580). New York, NY: McGraw Hill.

Maher, M. (2006). *Money-driven medicine: The real reason health care costs so much.* New York, NY: Collins.

Mao, D., Gallagher, K., & McGehee, D. S. (2011). Nicotine potentiation of excitatory inputs to ventral tegmental area dopamine neurons. *Journal of Neuroscience, 31*(18), 6710–6720.

Masters, S. B. (2013). The alcohols. In B. G. Katzung, S. B. Masters, & A. J. Trevor (Eds.), *Basic and clinical pharmacology* (12th ed., pp. 389–402). New York, NY: McGraw Hill.

Mathias, R., & Swan, N. (1995). Studying the effects of drugs in humans. *NIDA Notes, 10*(6). Retrieved from http://archives.drugabsue.gov/NIDA_Notes/NNVol110N6/ARCClin.html

Mazei-Robison, M. S., & Nestler, E. J. (2012). Opiate-induced molecular and cellular plasticity of ventral tegmental area and locus coeruleus catecholamine neurons. *Cold Spring Harbor Perspectives in Medicine, 2*(7), a012070.

McKim, W. A. (1990). *Drugs and behavior: An introduction to behavioral pharmacology* (2nd ed.). Englewood Cliffs, NJ: Prentice Hall.

Mello, M. M., Clarridge, B. R., & Studdert, D. M. (2005). Academic medical centers' standards for clinical-trial agreements with industry. *New England Journal of Medicine, 352*(21), 2202–2210.

Meltzer, H. (2013). Antipsychotic agents and lithium. In B. G. Katzung, S. B. Masters, & A. J. Trevor (Eds.), *Basic and clinical pharmacology* (12th ed., pp. 501–520). New York, NY: McGraw Hill.

Mojtabai, R., & Olfson, M. (2010). National trends in psychotropic medication polypharmacy in office-based psychiatry. *Archives of General Psychiatry, 67*(1), 26–36.

Nguyen, N. Y., & Bero, L. (2013). Medicaid drug selection committees and inadequate management of conflicts of interest. *JAMA Internal Medicine, 173*(5), 338–343.

Nolte, J. (2009). *The human brain: An introduction to its functional anatomy.* New York, NY: Mosby, Elsevier.

Olson, K. R. (2013). Management of the poisoned patient. In B. G. Katzung, S. B. Masters, & A. J. Trevor (Eds.), *Basic and clinical pharmacology* (12th ed., pp. 1027–1038). New York, NY: McGraw Hill.

O'Shea, R. S., Dasarathy, S., & McCullough, A. J.; Practice Guideline Committee of the American Association for the Study of Liver Diseases; Practice Parameters Committee of the American College of Gastroenterology. (2010). Alcoholic liver disease. *Hepatology, 51*(1), 307–328.

Palazzolo, D. L. (2013). Electronic cigarettes and vaping: A new challenge in clinical medicine and public health: A literature review. *Frontiers in Public Health, 1*, 56. doi:10.3389/fpubh.2013.00056

Panksepp, J. (2004). Biological psychiatry sketched—Past, present, and future. In J. Panksepp (Ed.), *Biological psychiatry* (pp. 3–32). Hoboken, NJ: Wiley-Liss.

Patient Protection and Affordable Care Act of 2010, Pub. L. No. 11–148, 124 Stat. 1025, 111th U.S. Congress (2010).

Paul, S. M. (2006). Alcohol-sensitive GABA receptors and alcohol antagonists. *Proceedings of the National Academy of Sciences of the United States of America, 103*(22), 8307–8308.

PDR Network, LLC. (2015). *Physicians' desk reference* (69th ed.) Montvale, NJ: Author.

Prescription Drug User Fee Act, Pub. L. No. 102–571, 106 Stat. 4491 (1992).

Reardon, S. (2014). NIH rethinks psychiatry trials: Mental-health division will no longer fund research aiming to relieve symptoms without probing underlying causes. *Nature.* Retrieved from http://www.nature.com/news/nih-rethinks-psychiatry-trials-1.14877

Redmond, D. E., Kosten, T. R., & Reiser, M. F. (1983). Spontaneous ejaculation associated with anxiety: Psychophysiological considerations. *American Journal of Psychiatry, 140*(9), 1163–1166.

Rehm, J. (2011). The risks associated with alcohol use and alcoholism. *Alcohol Research & Health, 34*(2), 135–143.

Reich, R. (2014, October 6). The real reason big pharma rips us off. *AterNet.* Retrieved from www.alternet.org/corporate-accountability-and-work-place/robert-reich-real-reason-big-pharma-rips-us-off

Relman, A. (2014, August 14). A challenge to American doctors. *New York Review of Books, 61*(13), 32–33. Retrieved from http://www.nybooks.com/articles/archives/2014/aug/14/challenge-american-doctors/

Rodwin, M. A. (2013). *Institutional corruption & pharmaceutical policy.* Suffold University Law School. Legal studies research paper series, Research Paper 13–25. Retrieved from Social Science Research Network, http://ssrn.com/abstract=2298140

RxList Inc. (2015). *Bunavail.* Retrieved from http://www.rxlist.com/bunavail-drug/indications-dosage.html

Sah, S., & Fugh-Berman, A. (2013). Physicians under the influence: Social psychology and industry marketing strategies. *Journal of Law, Medicine, and Ethics, 41*(3). Retrieved from http://papers.ssrn.com/sol3/papers.cfm?abstract.id=2286433

Schumacher, M. A., Basbaum, A. I., & Way, W. L. (2013). Opioid analgesics & antagonists. In B. G. Katzung, S. B. Masters, & A. J. Trevor (Eds.), *Basic and clinical pharmacology* (12th ed., pp. 543–564). New York, NY: McGraw Hill.

Seife, C. (2012, November 13). How drug company money is undermining science. *Scientific American, 307*(6).

Shahab, L., Brose, L. S., & West, R. (2013). Novel delivery systems for nicotine replacement therapy as an aid to smoking cessation and for harm reduction: Rationale, and evidence for advantages over existing systems. *CNS Drugs, 27*(12), 1007–1019.

Stahl, S. M. (2013). *Stahl's essential psychopharmacology: Neuroscientific basis and practical applications* (4th ed.). Cambridge, UK: Cambridge University Press.

Stead, L. F., Perera, R., Bullen, C., Mant, D., Hartmann-Boyce, J. Cahill, K., & Lancaster, T. (2012). Nicotine replacement therapy for smoking cessation. *Cochrane Database Systems Review, 11,* CD000146. doi: 10.1002/14651858.C000146.pub4

Stevenson–Wydler Technology Innovation Act, Pub. L. No. 96–480, 94 Stat. 2311 (1980).

Tetrault, J. M., & O'Connor, P. G. (2011). Management of opioid intoxication and withdrawal. In C. A. Cavacuiti (Ed.), *Principles of addiction medicine: The essentials.* New York, NY: Lippincott Williams & Wilkins.

Trevor, A. J., & Way, W. L. (2013). Sedative-hypnotic drugs. In B. G. Katzung, S. B. Masters, & A. J. Trevor (Eds.), *Basic and clinical pharmacology* (12th ed., pp. 373–388). New York, NY: McGraw Hill.

Turner, E. H., Matthews, A. M., Linardatos, E., Tell, R. A., & Rosenthal, R. (2008). Selective publication of antidepressant trials and its influence on apparent efficacy. *New England Journal of Medicine, 358*(3), 252–260.

Vedula, S. S., Li, T., & Dickersin, K. (2013). Differences in reporting of analyses in internal company documents versus published trial reports: Comparisons in industry-sponsored trials in off-label uses of gabapentin. *PLoS Medicine, 10:* e1001378. doi:10.1371/journal.pmed.1001378

Weber, T., & Ornstein, C. (2013, March 11). *Dollars for docs mints a millionaire Propublica.* Retrieved from www.propublica.org/article/dollars-for-docs-mints-a-millionaire

Welch, S. P. (2011). The pharmacology of cannabinoids. In C. A. Cavacuiti (Ed.), *Principles of addiction medicine: The essentials.* New York, NY: Lippincott Williams & Wilkins.

Welfel, E. R. (2012). *Ethics in counseling and psychotherapy: Standards, research, and emerging issues* (5th ed.). Pacific Grove, CA: Brooks/Cole Cengage Learning.

Whitaker, R. (2010). *Anatomy of an epidemic: Magic bullets, psychiatric drugs, and the astonishing risk of mental illness in America.* New York, NY: Broadway Books.

Whoriskey, P. (2012, November 24). As drug industry's influence over research grows, so does the potential for bias. *Washington Post.* Retrieved from www .washingtonpost.com/business/economy/2012/11/24/bb64d596-1264-11e2-be82-c3411b7680a9_story.html

Wilkes, M. S., Doblin, B. H., & Shapiro, M. F. (1992). Pharmaceutical advertisements in leading medical journals: Experts' assessments. *Annals of Internal Medicine, 116*(11), 912–919.

Wired. (2001, May 17). Medical editor rips into FDA. Reuters. Retrieved from http://archive.wired.com/medtech/health/news/2011/05/43891

Wolfe, S. M. (2014). Proposed US Food and Drug Administration guidance for industry on distributing medical publications about the risks of prescription drugs and biological products: A misguided approach. *JAMA Internal Medicine, 174*(10), 1543–1544.

World Health Organization. (2015). *International classification of diseases and related health problems, 10th revision (ICD-10).* (2012). Geneva, Switzerland: Author. Retrieved from http://apps.who.int/classifications/icd10/browsee/2015

Yang, Y. W., Hsieh, T. F., Yu, C. H., Huang, Y. S., Lee, C. C., & Tsai, T. H. (2014). Zolpidem and the risk of Parkinson's disease: A nationwide population-based study. *Journal of Psychiatric Research, 58,* 84–88.

4

Depression

This chapter covers major depression. It begins with a discussion of the syndrome of depression as defined by criteria in the various versions of the *Diagnostic and Statistical Manuals (DSMs)* issued before the newly minted *DSM-5* (American Psychiatric Association [APA], 2013). The prevalence in time and across national boundaries will be considered. The role of events and genetics in bringing on depression is discussed. The link between depressive behaviors and systemic inflammation is considered. The efficacy, rationale, and side effects for various treatments are reviewed. A discussion about possible causes of the increasing rates of persons meeting the criteria for depression in the Western world is left for the final chapter of this book.

THE SYNDROME OF DEPRESSIVE BEHAVIORS

Major depression is a disorder that primarily relies on the subjective characterization by the client of his or her own behavior. The syndrome requires a self-report of negative mood, absence of enjoyment (anhedonia), lack of energy, thoughts of worthlessness or guilt, recurrent thoughts of death, and inability to concentrate. Several of the behaviors contributing to the criteria for a diagnosis of depression can be assessed through observation by another person: motoric agitation or motoric retardation, change in appetite, and change in sleeping. Ninety percent of those with depression are also anxious (Ressler & Mayberg, 2007).

Prevalence Over Time and Cultures

The lifetime probability of ever meeting the *DSM* criteria for depression is 25% for women in the United States and 7% to 12% for men in the

United States (Ressler & Mayberg, 2007). The rates of depression have increased steadily across the decades in the United States (Lambert, 2006). If you were a male born around the turn of the 20th century, you had a 1% probability of becoming depressed, whereas if you were born after 1960, your rate rises to 9% to 10%. If you were a female born around the turn of the 20th century, your rate of depression was 2%, whereas later rates rise to 25% (Klerman & Weissman, 1989; Wickramaratne, Weissman, Leaf, & Holford, 1989). Although the rates of depression have increased across cohorts born after World War II, suicide rates for men have remained relatively constant between 1940 and the 1980s (Maris, Berman, & Silverman, 2000). The rates of depression are particularly high in the United States and Europe as contrasted with developing countries. In China and Taiwan, less than 1% of persons ever suffer a mood disorder (Parker, Gladstone, & Chee, 2001). In Africa and in Mexico, the rates are low (Grant et al., 2004; Rook & Lowry, 2008).

Approximately, 88.1% of depressive episodes, whether a first or subsequent episode, occur in response to a life event (Keller, Neale, & Kendler, 2007). The onset of the first episode of major depression is preceded by the occurrence of a stressful life event in 70% to 82% of cases (Keller et al., 2007; Slavich, Monroe, & Gotlib, 2011; Slavich, O'Donovan, Epel, & Kemeny, 2010). Interpersonal loss is the most frequent type of stress associated with emergent depression, particularly when the loss involves rejection by another (Slavich, Thornton, Torres, Monroe, & Gotlib, 2009; Slavich et al., 2010, 2011). Those who have experienced early parental loss are more likely to become depressed after a stressor (Slavich et al., 2011). Clarifying the relationship between type of stressors and specific symptoms, Kendler, Hettema, Butera, Gardner, and Prescott (2003), in a sample of 7,322 individuals, found that events involving humiliation and loss were more likely to precipitate depression, whereas events associated with danger and loss were precipitants to anxiety.

FINDINGS IN THOSE WITH MAJOR DEPRESSION

Brain Imaging and EEG Findings

In imaging studies, those with depression display greater activity in those brain areas associated with conflict monitoring, such as the anterior cingulate gyrus (Davidson, Pizzagalli, Nitschke, & Putnam, 2002). Those with both depression and anxiety display increased activation of the amygdala in response to unpleasant imagery (Treadway & Zald, 2011). They display stronger activation of the anterior insular cortex and the subgenual anterior cingulate (Johansen-Berg et al., 2008; Ressler & Mayberg, 2007), two additional areas associated with conflict monitoring.

In depressed individuals, brain areas associated with response to reward and motivated behavior, which are strongly innervated by dopamine, tend to show lesser levels of activation. Brain imaging work finds lower levels of activation in both the ventral striatum and the orbitofrontal cortex (Der-Avakian & Markou, 2012). In response to rewarding stimuli, those with depression also fail to show strongly enhanced activity in the nucleus accumbens (Pizzagalli et al., 2009). Consistent with lower dopamine tone, those with depression have lower levels of dopamine metabolites in the cerebrospinal fluid (CSF; Dunlop & Nemeroff, 2007).

In Chapter 2, the habenula's role in learned helplessness was reviewed. After exposure to uncontrollable shock, the habenula activates the raphe to increase anxiety and inactivates appetitive structures (the ventral tegmental area and the nucleus accumbens). In fact, greater activity in the habenula has been noted in persons with depression and in healthy people receiving failure feedback (Hikosaka, 2010, 2011). Fritz Henn (Forgeard et al., 2011) has noted that rats bred for susceptibility toward learned helpless induction show enhanced activation of the lateral habenula.

In Chapter 2, Davidson's theory regarding the behavioral activation/approach system versus the behavioral inhibition/withdrawal system was reviewed. In fact, greater activity on the left cortex of the brain is associated with greater blood flow to the ventral striatum (where the nucleus accumbens is located; Davidson & Irwin, 1999). Davidson's theories concerning greater activity on the right side of the cortex versus the left side have been borne out. Those with depression do show more right-side versus left-side activity on EEG measurements, which is consistent with findings from glucose utilization and blood flow studies (Tomarken & Keener, 1998). Moreover, the children of depressed parents, who are not currently depressed, also show lower levels of activation in the left prefrontal cortex (PFC) (Tomakren & Keener, 1998).

There is reason to suspect that activity in the alarm or conflict management areas and the dopamine behavioral-activation-system regions may be related. Diffusion tensor imaging is a brain imaging technique that allows researchers to see the density of axon fibers connecting one area of the brain to another. This imaging work established that the subgenual anterior cingulate cortex (ACC) is strongly connected to the nucleus accumbens (associated with more active behavior), as well as other structures involved in mediating anxiety (the amygdala, the hypothalamus; Johansen-Berg et al., 2008). Helen Mayberg has used electrical stimulation of Brodmann's area 25 (the subgenual anterior cingulate) to turn off activity in this conflict-monitoring area. After brain regions associated with conflict-monitoring are turned off, people reported that "the curtain has lifted." The appetitive or approach system comes online with more activity in the nucleus accumbens. Rather than reporting euphoria, they want to engage with their environment. For example, one man said he felt like cleaning out the garage (Mayberg, 2007).

Hormonal Findings

Across studies, between 50% and 70% of depressed individuals display elevations in cortisol, the stress hormone (M. B. Müller & Holsboer, 2006; Pace & Miller, 2009). Persons with depression are also likely to be dexamethasone nonsuppressors (see Chapter 2, section on hormonal activity, for explanation), and they more often fail to show the expected fluctuations in cortisol release associated with circadian rhythms (Dunlop & Nemeroff, 2007). Oxytocin levels also tend to be lower in those with depression (Yuen et al., 2014).

Thinking Styles

Depression has been characterized by Aaron Beck as a pessimistic view of the self, the world, and the future. Research suggests that depressed individuals do exhibit negative automatic thoughts (Forgeard et al., 2011). Depressed individuals view negative events as more likely to occur and they are more likely to blame themselves for these events (Forgeard et al., 2011). They attend to negative stimuli and recall negative stimuli to a greater extent than do persons without depression (Gotlib & Joormann, 2010). Susan Nolen-Hoeksema (E. R. Watkins & Nolen-Hoeksema, 2014) has argued that persons with depression ruminate about negative events. When they have a stressful day, they ask themselves "why does this happen to me?" and "how long will this last?" In contrast, those who are not depressed are more likely to engage in physical activity after a stressful day.

Emotional Control or Regulation

Gotlib and Joormann (2010) place emphasis on an inability to regulate emotion in the development of a depressed mood. They showed that persons with depression are less adept at focusing on a target and ignoring distracting negative stimuli. Task performance of those with depression is particularly impaired after commission of a mistake (Pizzagalli, 2011). Sheline et al. (2009) showed that depressed people were unable to down-regulate activity in the alarm area (anterior cingulate) when asked to reappraise negative imagery.

Emotional control refers not only to the capacity for inhibiting attention to negative stimuli but also the capacity to sustain positive focus. Tomarken and Keener (1998) have questioned whether those with depression have difficulty sustaining positive affect. A number of studies offer data consistent with an inability to sustain positive emotions. Heller et al. (2009) compared the responses in persons instructed to enhance, suppress, or attend to positive and negative stimuli over a 37-minute time period. Although there were no differences initially in activity in the nucleus accumbens between depressed and nondepressed individuals to the positive imagery in the enhance condition, during the latter half of the time period, the depressed individuals could not sustain the activity in the nucleus accumbens to the positive imagery; those without depression could sustain activity in the nucleus accumbens.

The idea that depressed individuals have problems with emotional regulation is also consistent with findings from examination of the startle response. A startle response to an aversive noise is modulated by a prior presentation of positive or negative images. In nondepressed individuals, startle reflex is attenuated by positive imagery and enhanced by negative imagery. Dichter, Tomarken, Shelton, and Sutton (2004) showed that depressed individuals were unaffected by the pictures. On first viewing neutral images, they startled as readily to the aversive noise as the controls viewing the negative pictures. However, the startle response of depressed individuals was not diminished by the positive imagery. Thus, prior context did not alter the startle response of the depressed persons.

In Chapter 2, in the section on regulation of impulses, motor activity, and emotions, the areas of the brain involved in restraining impulses, delaying a prepotent response, restraining the amygdala after extinction, and regulating mood were reviewed. These areas include the dorsolateral PFC and the ventromedial PFC (Hartley & Phelps, 2010). There are findings with regard to these structures in persons with depression. In fact, those with depression show less activity in the dorsolateral PFC and dorsomedial PFC (Davidson et al., 2002). Those with depression, when asked to inhibit negative affect in response to negative imagery, show less activation of the left ventral lateral PFC and less diminution in amygdala activity (Johnstone, van Reekum, Urry, Kalin, & Davidson, 2007). Heart rate variability (HRV; vagal tone) is associated with better capacity to regulate behavior (see Chapter 8 and Chapter 2, section on polyvagal theory). Depressed persons exhibit lower levels of HRV (Chang et al., 2013; Kemp, Quintana, Felmingham, Matthews, & Jelinek, 2012).

Brain-Derived Neurotrophic Factor

Stressed animals exhibit low levels of brain-derived neurotrophic factor (BDNF) in the hippocampus (Lakshminarasimhan & Chattarji, 2012). There has been speculation that BDNF might play a causal role in creating symptoms of depression (Sheline, 2000). However, the story on BDNF is brain-region specific. In the nucleus accumbens, BDNF levels are increased by stress and depressed persons exhibit more BDNF in this brain area (Feder, Nestler, & Charney, 2009).

THEORIES

Learned Helplessness

In the 1970s, the learned-helplessness paradigm was introduced. Maier, Overmier, and Seligman exposed animals to uncontrollable shock. Control-group animals received the same level of shock as the animals that could not influence their fate; however, the control-group animals were able to escape their shock by pressing a lever. Both groups of rodents exhibited raised levels of cortisol. However, when an opportunity was later provided to escape an aversive stimulus, the learned-helplessness animals were passive. They also exhibited less activity on a forced-swim task.

As discussed in Chapter 2, the brain circuitry resulting in learned-helpless behavior has been identified. Uncontrollability of the shock is detected by the lateral habenula. The lateral habenula projects to the caudal dorsal raphe nucleus, which in turn projects to the amygdala to initiate anxiety-associated behaviors. The lateral habenula also projects to the ventral tegmental area (VTA) to inhibit cells in this area that project to the nucleus accumbens. The net result is lowered release of dopamine from the neurons in the VTA to the nucleus accumbens (Balcita-Pedicino, Omelchenko, Bell, & Sesack, 2011; Friedman et al., 2011; Omelchenko, Bell, & Sesack, 2009). Although the loss of dopamine is not a loss of pleasure per se, it does mean a loss of interest in and a loss of motivation for responding to both positive and negative stimuli. Thus, there will be a failure of activation of the ventral striatum (the projection area of the VTA) in response to rewards. Moreover, an inability to mount an enthusiastic response is observed (Der-Avakian & Markou, 2012; Treadway, Bossaller, Shelton, & Zald, 2012).

The lateral habenula is in the area of the brain that sets up circadian rhythms and sleep–wake cycles. The increased activity in the habenula may explain the sleep disruption that is frequently seen in those with depression (Aizawa, Cui, Tanaka, & Okamoto, 2013).

Inflammation

Manipulated Variable Research in Animals

Researchers have shown that exposure to uncontrollable shock will also increase the level of interleukin-1β (IL-1β), an inflammatory cytokine in the brain (Maier & Watkins, 1998). When an antagonist to IL-1β is placed into the hippocampi of the animals exposed to uncontrollable shock, the depressive behaviors (loss of exploration of novel stimuli, less moving around, and less drinking of sugar water) disappear. This finding suggested that inflammatory molecules in brain play a causal role in creating the depressive profile. Maier et al. also tested whether inflammation attributable to a response to a pathogen would also result in depressive behavior. They placed part of the cell wall of a bacterium, lipopolysaccharide (LPS), into the paw of the animal. This procedure raised the level of inflammatory cytokine in blood in peripheral regions. Subsequently, this led to more IL-1β in the brain. The animal exhibited depressive behaviors. Again, when an antagonist for IL-1β was placed into the hippocampus, the depressive behaviors disappeared (Maier & Watkins, 1998).

Others have manipulated peripheral inflammation either with LPS (the wall of a bacterium) or administration of an inflammatory cytokine. In animal work, after administration of LPS or administration of cytokines, inflammatory cytokines increase in the brain and the animal loses preference for formerly preferred foods and exhibits more social avoidance, less exploration, an increase in cortisol levels, and an increase in body temperature (Dantzer, O'Connor, Lawson, & Kelley, 2011; Nadjar, Bluthé, May, Dantzer, & Parnet, 2005). In terms of brain responsivity, the animals are less willing to work to apply electrical stimulation in areas associated with dopamine release (Borowski, Kokkinidis, Merali, & Anisman, 1998), and increased levels of activation in the bed nucleus of the stria terminalis in the amygdala (the anxiety region) are noted (Engler et al., 2011; Frenois et al., 2007).

Manipulated Variable Research in Humans

Findings from human work, in which inflammation is induced in the periphery, find both lower response in reward areas and stronger response in distress areas. The way in which peripheral inflammation is created has varied across studies. Eisenberger et al. (2011) noted that following LPS administration in the periphery, people displayed less activation in the ventral striatal area (where the nucleus accumbens is located) in response to monetary reward. In those females administered LPS in the periphery, greater activation of the dorsal anterior cingulate cortex (dACC; an alarm center) was found in response to social exclusion (Eisenberger, Inagaki, Rameson, Marshal, & Irwin, 2009) and higher activation was noted in the amygdala in response to fearful faces (Inagaki, Muscatell, Irwin, Cole, & Eisenberger, 2012). Harrison et al. inoculated research participants with nonharmful bacterial proteins to induce systemic inflammation. As predicted, the inoculated research participants displayed activation in the

ACC (Harrison et al., 2009). Inoculation with interferon-α (IFN-α), an inflammatory cytokine, is used to treat melanoma and hepatitis C. Patients treated with IFN-α show activation in the dorsal ACC (Capuron et al., 2005). Capuron et al. (2012) also noted less activity in the nucleus accumbens and other brain structures activated by dopamine after IFN-α treatment. In fact, the images looked almost identical to the images from Parkinson patients whose dopamine neurons die and who as a group show elevations in depressive symptoms (Miller, Haroon, Raison, & Felger, 2013).

Correlational Research in Depressed Persons

Many investigators have found that inflammatory markers are elevated in the blood of those with depression and anxiety. Elevated levels of interleukin 6 (IL-6), tumor necrosis factor alpha (TNF-α), C-reactive protein (CRP), intercellular adhesion molecule-1 (ICAM-1), and monocyte chemoattractant protein-1 (MCP-1) have been noted (Dowlati et al., 2010; Howren, Lamkin, & Suls, 2009; Rajagopalan et al., 2001; Raison, Capuron, & Miller, 2006; Schiepers. Wichers, & Maes, 2005; Zorrilla et al., 2001). There are false negatives as well, suggesting that depression is not always associated with inflammation (Musselman et al., 2001). However, the level of inflammatory cytokines does predict failure to respond to antidepressant medications (O'Brien, Scully, Fitzgerald, Scott, & Dinan, 2007; Yoshimura et al., 2009).

Stress and Inflammation

Researchers have also subjected study participants to stressful conditions, such as the Trier Social Stress Test. In this paradigm, research participants are assigned to give a speech about a painful subject (e.g., your most embarrassing moment) to a scowling audience. This procedure results in elevations in IL-6, with those who were already depressed exhibiting greater elevations in IL-6 (Pace et al., 2006). Other paradigms have been used to assess the link between stress and inflammation. In response to social rejection or a laboratory stressor, levels of inflammatory cytokines increase, which correlate with activation in the dorsal anterior cingulate cortex (Slavich, Way, Eisenberger, & Taylor, 2010).

Correlational findings are also available for persons undergoing particular types of stressors. Cole et al. (2007) examined levels of a transcription factor for inflammatory cytokines (nuclear factor-κB [NF-κB]). Cole et al. found that levels are elevated in lonely people. The spouses of persons with Alzheimer's disease have elevated IL-6 levels (Kiecolt-Glaser et al., 2003; von Känel et al., 2006). Those who are under stress in the work environment exhibit elevations in ICAM-1, inflammatory cytokines, and fibrinogen (a factor that will facilitate blood clotting; Hong, Nelesen, Krohn, Mills, & Dimsdale, 2006; Ramachandruni, Handberg, & Sheps, 2004; Steptoe et al., 2003; von Känel, Mills, Fainman, & Dimsdale, 2001). Slavich et al. (2010) noted that those with higher levels of TNF-α at baseline exhibited stronger activation of the dorsal anterior cingulate cortex in response to social rejection.

Anti-Inflammation Factors and the Hygiene Hypothesis

The studies in which inflammatory cytokines are increased either by a psychological stressor or by introducing a pathogen suggest that inflammation is a proximal cause of depression. The discussion has focused on inflammatory cytokines. However, the leukocytes also produce anti-inflammatory cytokines, such as interleukin 10 (IL-10) and transforming growth factor beta (TGF-β), following the clearance of a pathogen. Correlational findings suggest that depressed people also have lower levels of IL-10 along with their higher levels of inflammatory cytokines (Li et al., 2010).

The hygiene hypothesis has been proposed to explain why persons in developed countries have higher levels of depression, anxiety, inflammatory bowel disease, and asthma. Given environments where there is much exposure early in life to bacteria, such as *Mycobacterium vaccae* from animal feces, relatively high levels of IL-10 are induced. The elevations in anti-inflammatory cytokines will create resilience to the impact of later environmental stressors (Rook & Lowry, 2008, 2009).

Brain Mechanisms

The pathways through which brain inflammation and elevated cytokines can change behavior are beginning to be elucidated. Some new chemicals, neutrophil gelatinase-associated lipocalin (NGAL) and orexin, not previously introduced in this book may be relevant. Both NGAL and orexin may be proximal causes. NGAL is increased with inflammation and is relevant for hippocampal signaling (Naudé et al., 2014). Orexin is decreased with inflammation and is relevant for activation of appetitive structures (VTA and nucleus accumbens; Weymann, Wood, Zhu, & Marks, 2014). When inflammatory cytokines increase in the brain, the activity of the habenula is increased (Hikosaka, 2011). As previously discussed, habenula activity is increased in learned helplessness. Future work will no doubt provide greater specificity regarding the pathways through which inflammation influences behavior.

Heritability

Heritability for major depression is about 31% to 42% (Dunlop & Nemeroff, 2007). Alleles for proteins in the dopamine pathways do predispose for depression (Dunlop & Nemeroff, 2007). However, the most heavily studied allele for depression is the short promoter allele for the gene for making the serotonin transporter. The short transporter predisposes to depression. With the short transporter, lesser amounts of the serotonin transporter are produced. Presumably, serotonin remains in the synapse cleft for a longer period of time. In persons without a mood disorder, those with a short transporter display stronger amygdala response to frightening images (Hariri et al., 2002). In addition, those with short transporters display lower volume in brain areas that regulate emotions (Pezawas et al., 2005). Those with two short transporter alleles exhibit greater cortisol spikes following a stressor (Gotlib, Joormann, Minor, & Hallmayer, 2008). Those with a short transporter are also more likely to become depressed, given treatment with IFN-α (a cytokine used to treatment melanoma and hepatitis C; Miller et al., 2013).

Although most of the heritability studies have examined how those with the short transporter respond to negative stimuli, Way and Taylor (2010) examined response to positive stimuli. Those with the short transporter are more responsive to positive events. Indeed, Robert Levenson (reported in *APA Monitor* by Sleek, 2014) found that those with the short promoter for serotonin transporter were less happy in turbulent relationships but more happy than others in nurturing relationships. Thus, the allele for the short promoter seems to convey greater responsivity to the environment, rather than depression under all conditions.

Current research suggests that it is a genetic and environmental interaction that raises the risk for depression. Researchers often find that particular alleles only predispose to depression given a stressful environment. Uher et al. (2011) found that the short serotonin transporter only leads to depression given a stressful childhood environment. Moreover, social support can ameliorate the risk of increased depression of those with both the genetic predisposition and childhood maltreatment (Kaufman et al., 2004). Another genetic variation, which can predispose to depression given a bad early home environment, is the G allele for the oxytocin receptor. However, if an individual with one or two copies of the G allele has a happy childhood home environment, then the person rates higher on empathy, optimism, and trust (McQuaid, McInnis, Stead, Matheson, & Anisman, 2013). Again, the outcomes for various alleles, which increase the risk for depression, are heavily influenced by the environment. Given a supportive environment, risk alleles can promote positive outcomes.

DRUG TREATMENT

Presently, 11% of the population of the United States older than 12 years is taking an antidepressant. Of this 11%, 60% have been taking the antidepressant for more than 2 years and 14% have been taking the drug for more than a decade (Pratt, Brody, & Gu, 2011). Because many people are taking these drugs for decades, both the short-term and the long-term efficacy, as well as the side effects of these drugs, should be considered.

Efficacy

The predrug-era literature suggests that an untreated episode of depression will last on average about 2 to 6 months. Sixty-seven percent of patients will have recovered by 6 months and 89% will have recovered by the second year (Beck, 1967; Klein, Gittelman, Quitkin, & Rifkin, 1980; Lehman, 1983; Posternak & Miller, 2001; Posternak et al., 2006). Thus, the rates of spontaneous remission are high.

Typically, drug trials are conducted for an 8-week period (Thase et al., 2005). At 8 weeks, the average difference on a Hamilton Depression

Rating Scale (customary outcome measure) between the treatment group and placebo control is 1.8 points out of 56 (Kirsch, 2010). At 8 weeks, about two thirds of patients on the drug achieve a 50% reduction in symptoms, and about 33% to 40% achieve recovery such that they are no longer scoring in the depressed range (Nemeroff, 2001; Thase et al., 2005; Tranter, O'Donovan, Chandarana, & Kennedy, 2002). In an analysis of all the drug trials reported to the Food and Drug Administration (FDA) in which the dependent measure was assessed at 8 weeks, Kirsch (2010) found that antidepressants only achieved superior results over placebo for the extremely depressed (with a 4-point difference on the Hamilton Depression Rating Scale). Antidepressants failed to achieve better results than placebo for the mild and moderately depressed. In an analysis of the data from the National Institute of Mental Health Collaborative Depression Study, the remission rates broken down by disease severity are as follows: for very severe, 32% on drug versus 18% on placebo; for severe, 34% on drug versus 27% on placebo; and for mild and moderate, 45% on drug versus 44% on placebo (DeRubeis, Fournier, & Fawcett, 2010).

The question of outcome at 8 weeks does not capture long-term outcomes. Duration of wellness between episodes is a more meaningful outcome. In reviewing early predrug-era studies, Zis and Goodwin (1979) found that between 57% and 66% did not experience a second episode of depression ever. In another review of the predrug literature, H. E. Lehmann (1983) found that most individuals experienced remission for 2 to 3 years. The predrug long-term outcomes for sustained wellness are relatively positive. This can be contrasted with the literature on sustained recovery for those who continued on the drug. In a meta-analysis of those who continue on antidepressants, Williams, A. N. Simpson, K. Simpson, and Nahas (2009) report that 23% will relapse by 1 year, 34% will relapse by 2 years, and 45% will relapse by 3 years. Keller et al. (2007) examined a cohort of those with multiple episodes of depression who had responded to drugs and who remained well for 6 months. In the subsequent 6 months, 19% relapsed and another 19% had relapsed by 2 years. In summary, examining the outcomes from predrug to postdrug fails to suggest that pharmaceuticals have improved the duration of recovery.

Long-term outcomes on drugs are hard to evaluate. If antidepressant drugs are discontinued, a rather severe withdrawal syndrome ensues that includes both anxiety and dysphoria. Indeed, in studies comparing those who were recovered and then taken off drug versus those who maintained taking the drug, the differences in depression relapses are dramatic. It has been argued that because the relapse rates in those withdrawn (sometimes around 70%) are well above the rates of relapse in those never medicated, the difference is probably attributable to drug withdrawal (Littrell, 1994). Several other studies provide expectations of the outcome for those who continue on medications. Bockting et al. (2008) compared those who were not taking medications versus those who did. During the 2-year follow-up, 60% of the continuous users relapsed versus 46% of the nonusers. The Sequenced Treatment Alternatives to Relieve Depression (STAR*D) study conducted by the National Institute of Mental Health (NIMH), in which physicians could switch patients to various other antidepressants given a failure to respond, found that "the proportion that responded or remitted and stayed well for a year was estimated to be a disappointing 15%" (Nierenberg et al., 2008, p. 433). Examining the levels of wellness before the advent of antidepressants to levels of wellness in the medicated has led to the question of whether antidepressants convert a short-term episode into a chronic condition (Byrne & Rothschild, 1998; Fava & Offidani, 2011; Whitaker, 2010).

Withdrawal

When antidepressants are discontinued, dizziness, nausea, lethargy, headache, anxiety, tingling and burning sensations, confusion, tremor, sweating, insomnia, irritability, memory problems, anorexia, whooshing noises in the ear, muscle spasms, and protruding tongue movements have been observed (Ceccherini-Nelli et al., 1993; Haddad, 1997; Haddad & Dursun, 2008; Stoukides & Stoukides, 1991). Patients describe electric-shock sensations in the head along with visual flashes of light (Gotzsche, 2013; Haddad, 2001). Mania and hypomania have also been reported (Goldstein et al., 1999; Lejoyeux & Adès, 1997; McGrath, Stewart, Tricamo, Nunes, & Quitkin, 1993; Narayan & Haddad, 2011). Because these withdrawal symptoms are also reported in those who were prescribed antidepressants for anxiety (Pato, Zohar-Kadouch, Zohar, & Murphy, 1998), they cannot be attributed to "unmasking depression." Symptoms can persist as long as 13 weeks (Haddad, 2001).

Drug companies will not pay for studies regarding drug withdrawal. Therefore, we lack information about how long exposure to a drug is required for the body to become dependent on the drug. Also lacking are well-established protocols for withdrawal. Haddad (1997) reports that after the 8-week exposure, between 20% and 86% will exhibit withdrawal symptoms. Joseph Glenmullen (2005), in his book, *The Antidepressant Solution: A Step-by-Step Guide to Safely Overcoming Antidepressant Withdrawal, Dependence, and "Addiction,"* has provided instructions on how to taper drugs. However, long tapers will not always decrease the incidence of symptoms (Tint, Haddad, & Anderson, 2008). Frank, Kupfer, and Perel (1989) suggest that psychotherapy can decrease the risk of relapse during the withdrawal process.

In gathering material for this book, I requested that individuals send me their descriptions of coming off antidepressants. The subsequent paragraphs were contributed by an individual weaning her way off of an antidepressant. I think it is heuristic.

My story of withdrawal from Wellbutrin is not dramatic, but I think it is poignant. I'm happy to share it and you can decide whether it is a good fit for your book.

I have been on psychiatric medication since age 17 (I am now 36). Like many, I was told that I would be reliant on this medication for the rest of my life. I have tried almost every class of antidepressant, countless anti-psychotics, mood stabilizers, anti-anxiety medications…pretty much of a little bit of everything. At times, the medications were stabilizing, but at other times, the side effects greatly outweighed the benefits.

About a year ago, with my doctor I began decreasing my medication, but could only decrease it so much without "crashing." My doctor was not willing to weather the storm with me.

Six months ago I started seeing a practitioner from the Mad in America resource list with the same goal of discontinuing my medications. She and I were (and still are) determined to make this goal a reality.

At the time, I was only taking Wellbutrin, Lamictal, and Klonopin (I say only because, for me, this was nothing). I did not have a hard time coming off Klonopin as I have heard others describe. And I am not yet off Lamictal. However, I am off Wellbutrin, but the journey, though short, was my first personal experience with the true brain changing effects of psychiatric medication.

I had some typical side effects (nausea, dizziness) decreasing form 300 to 200 and then to 150, but coming off the 150 was torture. There is no extended-release dose below 150 and the smallest regular release dose is 75. Regardless of how I tried to taper, my body and mind were screaming.

I was exhausted and weighted down emotionally and physically and my mind was swimming in thoughts of suicide (which I have struggled with for nearly my entire life, but had been relatively absent for some time before stopping the Wellbutrin). Fearing my own impulsivity, I admitted myself to the hospital to restart the medication.

I was frustrated, but persistent. My doctor helped me transition to some natural supplements as I simultaneously tapered the Wellbutrin and eventually I was able to stop both the natural supplements and the Wellbutrin.

The process of coming off the Wellbutrin opened my eyes to the effect the Wellbutrin was having on my brain as well as the grip of the pharmaceutical industry. Given that now, not long after stopping all antidepressants, both natural and not, I am having a full range of natural emotional states, I do not believe I needed Wellbutrin any longer, yet it would have been easy to conclude otherwise given my reaction when I tried to stop it initially.

Good luck with you book!

Side Effects

Antidepressant drugs do have side effects. Dry mouth and nausea are the merely annoying side effects (*Physicians' Desk Reference*, 2015). In 80% of those taking selective serotonin reuptake inhibitors (SSRIs), sexual dysfunction, including anorgasmia, erectile dysfunction, diminished libido, and genital anesthesia, is reported (Rosen, Lane, & Menza, 1999). Sexual dysfunction can continue after drug discontinuation (Csoka, Csoka, Bahrick, & Mehtonen, 2008). Sperm production is also decreased (Akasheh, Sirati, Noshad Kamran, & Sepehrmanesh, 2014). There are serotonin transporters on platelets that are needed for blood clotting. SSRIs are associated with the risk of bleeding ulcers and stroke (Loke, Trivedi, & Singh, 2008; Serebruany, 2006; Wu, Wang, Cheng, & Gau, 2011). Serotonin transporters are also found on cells involved in bone turnover and SSRIs are associated with increased risk of osteoporosis (Bliziotes, 2010; Kawai & Rosen, 2010). In some, SSRIs can induce movement disorder, including lip smacking and dystonia (Leo, 1996; Zhou et al., 2005). A rare but potentially lethal side effect is the selective serotonin syndrome, which is characterized by tremor, muscular rigidity, high temperature, mental clouding or agitation, rapid heartbeat, and increased blood pressure (Boyer & Shannon, 2005).

Antidepressants do impact mental function. Cognitive dysfunction can occur such as poor memory (Damsa et al., 2004; Fava et al., 2006). Antidepressants can induce mania (Leverich et al., 2006; Post, Denicoff, Leverich & Frye, 1997), violence (Moore, Glenmullen, & Furberg, 2010), and suicidal ideation (Laje et al., 2007). They carry a black-box warning for suicide in young people. Cymbalta carries a warning for suicidal ideation in all ages (Lenzer, 2005). There are reports of emotional numbing. To further investigate emotional numbing, McCabe, Mishor, Cowen, and Harmer (2010) conducted an imaging study, comparing the brain scans of those on an SSRI (citalopram) with healthy individuals. Those on the drug exhibited diminished response to both negative and positive stimuli. Antidepressants can also lower seizure threshold (Haddad & Dursun, 2008).

In the long term, antidepressants may increase inflammation. Metabolic syndrome and obesity are associated with systemic inflammation. SSRIs increase risk of weight gain and metabolic syndrome (Dannon et al., 2007; Fava, 2000; Kivimäki et al., 2010; Raeder, Bjelland, Emil Vollset, & Steen, 2006; Serreti & Mandelli, 2010). Type 2 diabetes is another inflammatory condition and SSRIs increase the risk of type 2 diabetes (Andersohn, Schade, Suissa, & Garbe, 2009; Kivimäki et al., 2010; Rubin et al., 2010). Long-term antidepressant exposure is associated with higher levels of CRP (a marker for inflammation; Hamer, Batty, Marmot, Singh-Manoux, & Kivimäki, 2011) and with lower HRV (Dawood et al., 2007; Kemp et al., 2010; Licht et al., 2008).

Pregnancy

Thirteen percent of pregnant women are taking an antidepressant (Cooper, Willy, Pont, & Ray, 2007). Exposure to antidepressants increases the risk of preterm birth; low birth weight; pulmonary hypertension in the newborn; birth defects, such as heart malformations; lower Apgar scores in the newborn; and later developmental delays. Increased miscarriage and preeclampsia in the mother have been recognized (Chambers et al., 2006; Domar, Moragianni, Ryley, & Urato, 2013; Pedersen et al., 2009; Ross et al., 2013). Studies with a large number of patients have found that the risk of autism spectrum disorder is three to four times higher in mothers taking antidepressants (Croen, Grether, Yoshida, Odouli, & Hendrick, 2011; Rai et al., 2013; Sørensen et al., 2013).

Changing Recommendations

Examining the outcome studies for the antidepressants, the National Institute for Health and Clinical Excellence (NICE) in the United Kingdom has changed its guidelines for treating depression. The NICE guidelines recommend a stepped-care approach. For those with mild and moderate depression, psychotherapy and self-help strategies are recommended as the first line of treatment. Similar changes in strategy are recommended in the Netherlands (NICE, 2009; Sheldon, 2012).

Ketamine

A great deal of excitement has been generated in response to clinical trials using ketamine as an antidepressant. Ketamine has the reputation of providing rapid release of depressive symptoms. Ketamine is an N-methyl-d-aspartate (NMDA) receptor antagonist. Speculation regarding why ketamine might produce antidepressant effects ranges from increasing glutamate signaling at α-amino-3-hydroxy-5-methyl-4-isoxazolepropionic acid (AMPA) receptors, to increasing BDNF, and to increasing mammalian target of rapamycin (mTOR; a signaling protein induced by insulin). Regardless of the mechanism, it is good to remember that in animals, prolonged exposure to NMDA blockade with ketamine will destroy fast-spiking gamma-aminobutyric acid (GABA) interneurons, which is believed to be the culprit in schizophrenia (Woo, 2013). Indeed, Schatzberg (2014) cautions that the long-term dangers from ketamine are not yet known.

Novel Drugs

Consistent with inhibiting NMDA receptor function, as occurs with ketamine, both zinc and magnesium exert antidepressant effects, presumably by blocking NMDA signaling. However, N-acetylcysteine, which increases activity at the NMDA receptor, also exhibits antidepressant activity (Duman & Voleti, 2012; Murrough et al., 2013; Pilc, Wieronska, & Skolnick, 2013). GLYX-13 is a partial agonist at the NMDA receptor. It is a peptide comprised of four amino acids. It promotes playfulness in rats and is currently in clinical trials for depression (Burgdorf et al., 2013; Panksepp, Wright, Döbrössy, Schlaepfer, & Coenen, 2014).

With the recognition that the dorsal anterior cingulate cortex is involved in emotional pain and the finding that this region is replete with opioid receptors, Panksepp et al. (2014) have been testing the opioid partial agonist (buprenorphine) as a treatment for depression. Apparently, it did well in clinical trials in Israel. It is a legal drug. Caveats are needed here. There is a large literature contributed by people who work in of addictions. George Koob argues that, over time, the presence of external opiates will increase dynorphin (the discomfort opiate) in the brain (see Chapter 8, section on neuroscience of addiction). Thus, the duration of buprenorphine's long-term efficacy needs to be evaluated.

ELECTRICAL STIMULATION TREATMENT

Transcranial Magnetic Stimulation

Repetitive transcranial magnetic stimulation (TMS), which involves external application of an electrode, is an FDA-approved treatment for major depression. It is more effective than sham treatment (Ressler & Mayberg, 2007). In clinical trials, TMS is as effective as SSRIs with an effect size of 7.1 (George et al., 2010; Ressler & Mayberg, 2007) compared to an effect size of 0.67 for cognitive behavioral therapy (CBT) combined with antidepressant (Otto, Smits, & Reese, 2006). In those who are treatment resistant to antidepressant drugs, 36% recover following TMS (Demirtas-Tatlidede & Mechanic-Hamilton, 2006; Fitzgerald et al., 2006; O'Reardon et al., 2007). TMS increases activity in the dorsolateral PFC, an area that Davidson's work suggests regulates negative emotion (De Raedt et al., 2010). It normalizes the hypothalamic–pituitary–adrenal axis (Pridmore, 1999). It increases dopamine levels in the dorsal and ventral striatum (Dunlop & Nemeroff, 2007; Yadid & Friedman, 2008). The TMS stimulator is sold by Fisher Wallace for $700. It is FDA approved for depression. Unlike antidepressant drugs, it is not associated with weight gain, suicidal ideation, or sexual side effects. Cases of induction of mania have been reported (Dolberg, Schreiber, & Grunhaus, 2001). If used improperly, it can burn the face. Other reported side effects include soreness around the placement of the magnets but only 4% of those in trials drop out of treatment (O'Reardon et al., 2007).

Deep Brain Stimulation

Helen Mayberg targets the subgenual ACC for delivering electrical activity to reduce activation in this brain area. (The treatment does involve surgical intervention to implant the stimulator.) It does relieve depression. Rather than inducing euphoria, turning off the subgenual ACC allows patients to wish to engage with their environment. (Recall that one man said after brain stimulation that he wanted to clean out the garage; Panksepp et al., 2014; Ressler & Mayberg, 2007.) Other pioneers have targeted the lateral habenula for stimulation at levels that will downregulate activity with relative success (Sartorius et al., 2010). Additionally, increasing activity in the ventral striatum or nucleus accumbens has been targeted as offering relief of anhedonia (Der-Avakian & Markou, 2012).

Deep brain stimulation will probably be beyond what many people are willing to do. It is invasive, requiring insertion of the stimulator into the body. Mayberg reports that even though depression is relieved by the stimulator, patients opt for removal of the stimulator because they are reminded of their disorder when they look in the mirror.

ACTIVITIES TO INCREASE REGULATORY CAPACITY

Depressed people may have less developed areas in the brain for controlling or regulating both good and bad mood. Some have developed strategies for improving regulatory control. By using transcranial magnetic stimulation of the dorsolateral PFC over a series of days, deRaedt et al. (2010) were able to improve mood and enhance inhibitory control.

An approach called cognitive rehabilitation has been developed specifically to target the PFC in order to increase capacity for emotional regulation. According to Siegle, Shinassi, and Thase (2007), "cognitive rehabilitation begins by identifying affected cognitive functions and brain regions through neuropsychological assessment and neuroimaging"

(p. 236). Siegle et al.'s approach utilizes specific cognitive tasks to develop capacity through the PFC. Unlike traditional therapy, in which people talk about their problems (which can be a painful process), their approach focuses on clients externally. Siegle et al. utilized two tasks. In the first task, clients were instructed to distinguish a particular bird sound from white noise. The second task involved presentation of numbers, one at a time, on a computer screen. The client was asked to add the last two digits appearing on the screen. Thus, the client had to add, while keeping in short-term memory both the answer and the last digit presented, so that this digit could be summed with the next digit to appear on the screen. Following 2 weeks of training, depression and rumination had decreased more in the trained group than in the placebo group. Moreover, the amygdala displayed less activation in response to negative stimuli and there was an increase in PFC activity.

The research on using cognitive tasks to increase regulatory control is very consistent with animal work. Animals housed in enriched environments have stronger ventromedial PFC responses and are more resilient given social defeat (M. L. Lehmann & Herkenham, 2011).

As will be discussed in Chapter 8 and Chapter 2 in the section on polyvagal theory, vagal tone (more parasympathetic activity) is associated with better control over mood. HRV is an index of vagal tone. Ways to increase vagal tone are discussed in the section on decreasing inflammation, which follows on p. 164.

COGNITIVE BEHAVIORAL THERAPY

In the NIMH Collaborative Depression Study, antidepressant treatment was contrasted with CBT. Antidepressants were found to produce improvement faster, but by the end of the study outcomes equalized (Blackburn & Moore, 1997; Elkin et al., 1989; Shea et al., 1992, Simons, Murphy, Levine, & Wetzel, 1986; J. T. Watkins et al., 1993). Even for the severely depressed, outcomes for CBT and medications are equivalent, although CBT achieves a larger effect size in meta-analysis (DeRubeis, Gelfand, Tang, & Simons, 1999). In a particular study with random assignment to condition, for the moderately to severely depressed at 16 weeks, 58% achieve at least 50% reduction in symptoms in both the CBT and drug conditions. Forty-six percent were remitted in the antidepressant group and 40% were remitted in the CBT group (DeRubeis et al., 2005). Those treated with CBT show lower rates of relapse than those on drugs (Evans et al., 1992; Simons, Murphy, Levine, & Wetzel, 1986).

WAYS TO TARGET INFLAMMATION

Increasing HRV (Vagal Tone)

In Chapter 2 in the section on Polyvagal Theory, the concept of vagal tone, or more reliance on the parasympathetic nervous system, was reviewed. Vagal tone is measured by HRV. Greater HRV is anti-inflammatory as the lymph nodes receive input from the vagus nerve (Pavlov & Tracey, 2005; Rosas-Ballina & Tracey, 2009). There are a number of things one can do to increase vagal tone. Eating more omega-3s is associated with increases in HRV (Farooqui, Ong, Horrocks, Chen, & Farooqui, 2007). Electrical acupuncture will increase vagal tone (Oke & Tracey, 2009). Relatively cheap biofeedback equipment, including the cell phone "app" called Azumio, is available for improving vagal tone (Lehrer et al., 2003, 2006). (A clinical trial of this biofeedback method has been shown to decrease depression, Karavidas et al [2007].) Increasing time spent with trusted companions increases oxytocin levels, which will increase HRV (Grippo, Lamb, Carter, & Porges, 2007; Grippo, Trahanas, Zimmerman, Porges, & Carter, 2009; Kemp et al., 2012; Zak, Kurzban, & Matzner, 2005). Aerobic exercise increases HRV (Hansen, Johnsen, Sollers, Stenvik, & Thayer, 2004). Both meditation (Pace et al., 2009) and yoga (Bernardi et al., 2001; Kiecolt-Glaser, 2010) have been shown to decrease inflammation and to increase vagal tone or HRV.

Direct Anti-Inflammatories

As mentioned previously, higher levels of IL-6 have been noted in those who are treatment resistant to antidepressant drugs (O'Brien et al., 2007; Yoshimura et al., 2009). Raison et al. (2013) employed an antibody to TNF-α (called infliximab) to knock out a central inflammatory cytokine. They found that it did produce a treatment response in those who were elevated on inflammatory markers. However, those without inflammatory marker elevations fared better on placebo. Although this approach did achieve success for some, infliximab is a very strong disrupter of the immune system. Reports of neurological problems of the type associated with multiple sclerosis have been reported with these drugs (Fromont, DeSeze, Fleury, Maillefert, & Moreau, 2009; Mohan et al., 2001). They also carry a black-box warning for tuberculosis.

Aspirin inhibits cyclooxygenase (COX) enzymes so that the COX enzymes cannot produce prostaglandin E2, an inflammatory mediator. Aspirin does ameliorate negative mood in animals (Crestani, Seguy, & Dantzer, 1991; Dhir, Padi, Naidu, & Kulkarni, 2006; Teeling, Cunningham, Newman, & Perry, 2010). Aspirin as monotherapy has never been evaluated or compared to antidepressants in humans. The results on whether aspirin can augment the efficacy of antidepressants have been inconsistent. Müller et al. (2006) found that aspirin enhanced antidepressant efficacy; however, Warner-Schmidt et al. (2011) found that persons taking a COX inhibitor, such as aspirin, were less likely to respond to an SSRI.

In the social rejection paradigm used by Eisenberger et al., some subjects were pretreated with Tylenol (acetaminophen) prior to playing the rejection game. Those research participants receiving the Tylenol displayed much less activation in the dACC (an alarm center) in response to social exclusion (DeWall et al., 2010).

Diet

Omega-3 Fatty Acids

Fatty acids in which the first double bond is three carbons away from the end of the methyl end of the fatty acid chain are called omega-3s (Champe, Harvey, & Ferrier, 2008). Omega-3s include docosahexaenoic acid and eicosapentaenoic acid. Fish oil and walnuts are good sources of omega-3s. Omega-3s are noted for decreasing inflammation (Iwami, Nonomura, Shirasugi, & Niimi, 2011). They work through a variety of mechanisms.

As discussed in Chapter 2, the parasympathetic nervous system innervates the lymph nodes and decreases inflammation. HRV is a measure of vagal tone. Omega-3s increase HRV (Farooqui, Ong, Horrocks, Chen, & Farooqui, 2007) and consumption levels correlate with HRV in adults (Mozaffarian, Stein, Prineas, & Siscovick, 2008). Omega-3s get converted in the body to resolvins and protectins, which limit inflammation. In fact, there are receptors for resolvins and omega-3s on white blood cells (WBCs; Ji, Xu, Strichartz, & Serhan, 2011; Oh et al., 2010; Oh & Olefsky, 2012). When omega-3s bind to their receptors on WBCs (the GPR120 receptor) inflammation is inhibited and insulin sensitivity increases (Oh et al., 2010).

Omega-3s also skew the microbiota in the gut toward anti-inflammatory species (Forsythe, Sudo, Dinan, Taylor, & Bienenstock, 2010). In addition to having strong anti-inflammatory effects, there are receptors for omega-3 in the hypothalamus. When the omega-3s bind to these receptors, they increase metabolic rate and decrease appetite (Cintra et al., 2012; Lam et al., 2012).

The association of high levels of omega-3 consumption and a lower probability of experiencing depression has been noted (Kiecolt-Glaser, 2010). People whose diets are enriched with omega-3 experience less increase in inflammation under stress (Maes, Christophe, Bosmans, Lin, & Neels, 2000). They are also at lowered risk for the emergence of other inflammatory diseases, such as cardiovascular disease and type 2 diabetes (Arita et al., 2005). An initial test of omega-3s, specifically eicosapentaenoic acid, has shown promise as monotherapy in treating depression. Although the difference between placebo and omega-3 did not reach statistical significance in this small N study ($N = 35$; $p = .087$), there was a 45% response rate in those receiving omega-3s compared to a 23% response rate in the placebo group (Mischoulon et al., 2009). In a random assignment study, omega-3s did decrease the stress levels of medical students during examinations (Kiecolt-Glaser, Belury, Andridge, Malarkey, & Glaser, 2011). Further work with an adequately powered study is required before definitive conclusions can be made.

Mediterranean Diet

Mediterranean diets are associated with lower cytokine levels, less oxidative stress (i.e., presence of damaging molecules), and lower levels of depression (Dai et al., 2008; Luciano et al., 2012; Sánchez-Villegas et al., 2009). A particular protective effect has been noted for high consumption of fruits, nuts, and legumes, whereas consumption of whole-fat dairy and meat was deleterious (Sánchez-Villegas et al., 2009). Beyond the Mediterranean diet, curcumin, which is found in turmeric, is anti-inflammatory and suppresses the activation of NF-κB, a transcription factor inducing expression of many inflammatory cytokines (Aggarwal, 2010; Shehzad, Rehman, & Lee, 2013). Curcumin has been shown to produce antidepressant effects of comparable magnitude to fluoxetine in animals (R. Wang et al., 2008) and is better than placebo treatment in humans (Lopresti, Maes, Maker, Hood, & Drummond, 2014). Black pepper will facilitate the absorption of curcumin (Anand, Kunnumakkara, Newman, & Aggarwal, 2007).

Vitamin D

Vitamin D can facilitate the differentiation of T regulatory cells (the anti-inflammatory WBCs) as well as decreasing activation of NF-κB transcription factor activity in WBCs. (NF-κB increases many inflammatory cytokines). Vitamin D is associated with higher levels of IL-10 (the anti-inflammatory cytokines) and lower levels of inflammatory cytokines (Adler & Steinbrink, 2007; Adorini & Penna, 2009). Meta-analysis suggests that for those with clinically significant levels of depression, vitamin D supplementation has a moderate effect on decreasing symptoms; however, the number of studies is limited (Shaffer et al., 2014).

Folate, Vitamin B$_{12}$, and Homocysteine

Levels of folate, methionine, and homocysteine are connected. High levels of homocysteine suggest an inadequate conversion of homocysteine back to methionine. Thus, high levels of homocysteine signal low levels of methionine (an amino acid). The process of converting homocysteine to methionine requires 5-methyltetrahydrofolate. Several other enzymes are needed for maintaining adequate levels of 5-methyltetrahydrofolate. B vitamins are cofactors for enzymes in the conversion of homocysteine to methionine (Beydoun, Shroff, Beydoun, & Zonderman, 2010; Champe et al., 2008; Ye et al., 2011). Thus, both folate and B vitamins are needed for maintaining low levels of homocysteine and adequate levels of methionine.

Low folate levels have been observed in persons with major depression, as have high levels of homocysteine and low levels of B$_{12}$ and B$_6$ (Beydoun et al., 2010). Additionally, particular alleles for enzymes involved in processing these chemicals (folate hydrolase and methylenetetrahydrofolate reductase) are associated with higher levels of major depression (Ye et al., 2011).

Levels of homocysteine and methionine are related to depression through several pathways. High levels of homocysteine are bad because they cause inflammation (Alvarez-Maqueda et al., 2004; Siow, Au-Yeung, Woo, & O, 2006; G. Wang, Siow, & O, 2000). Adequate levels of methionine are needed to maintain good mental health because methionine is converted to S-adenosyl-methionine, which is required to make neurotransmitters, such as dopamine and norepinephrine (Beydoun et al., 2010; Ye et al., 2011).

Vitamin supplements and S-adenosyl-methionine (SAM) are readily available at health food stores. Folate and B vitamins can be consumed in green leafy vegetables, citrus fruits, peas, and beans. In clinical trials, response to SAM for decreasing depressive symptoms has been positive (Papakostas, Mischoulon, Shyu, Alpert, & Fava, 2010).

Avoid Inflammatory Factors

High levels of saturated fats in the diet enhance inflammation through a variety of avenues. In WBCs, there are receptors (toll-like receptors) to which saturated fats will bind with the result being activation of the WBC (Milanski et al., 2009). Particular proteins keep the cells lining the intestinal tract close together so that bacteria cannot enter the bloodstream. Saturated fats will disrupt these cell connectors so that bacteria can cross the barrier. Moreover, high saturated fats in the diet will change the composition of the microbes in the intestine toward more inflammatory species and decrease microbe species diversity (De La Serre et al., 2010; Lam et al., 2012; Wallis, 2014).

Gut microbiota have become a major focus of research. Stress will alter the gut microbiota (Y. Wang & Kasper, 2014). Microbiota are a factor in obesity. In animal research, if the feces of lean animals are implanted into the obese animals, the obese animals lose weight. The mechanisms through which bacteria influence hunger are complex. For example, *Helicobacter pylori* (bacteria associated with ulcers when present, but esophageal cancer when absent) decreases the release of ghrelin, a hunger-promoting hormone (Wallis, 2014). Thus, gut microbiota do influence health. Probiotics (found in yogurt) may aid in establishing proper bacterial colonies and may decrease both depression and anxiety (Y. Wang & Kasper, 2014). For extreme cases of inflammatory bowel disease, fecal transplants from a healthy donor are being done by some gastroenterologists.

Saturated fat also influences the neurons in the hypothalamus, which control hunger and metabolic rate. A high-fat diet induces stress in these cells. In the hypothalamus, brain glial cells also release more inflammatory factors given a high-saturated-fat diet (Maric, Woodside, & Luheshi, 2014; Schneeberger et al., 2013). A high-fat diet also increases the level of inflammatory cytokine production in the hippocampus in response to stress (Sobesky et al., 2014).

The sugar contained in fruit consists of sucrose, which is a glucose molecule linked to a fructose molecule. Sucrose is not inflammatory. However, the food industry now uses carbohydrates in corn to produce highly concentrated fructose, which is inflammatory (Ferder, Ferder, & Inserra, 2010; Tappy & Lê, 2010). High-fructose corn syrup is often added to fruit juices. Eliminating high-fructose corn syrup should further decrease inflammatory factors.

Preliminary evidence suggests that preservatives added to food (e.g., breads, ice cream) to increase shelf life change gut microbiota and contribute to gut inflammation and may be a factor in explaining the relatively high rates of inflammatory bowel disease in those eating a Western diet (Chassaing, 2013).

Obtaining Adequate Sleep

Sleep deprivation has inflammatory effects (Irwin, Wang, Campomayor, Callado-Hidalgo, & Cole, 2006; Lucassen et al., 2010; Redwine, Hauger, Gillin, & Irwin, 2000; Vgontzas et al., 2004). Thus, obtaining adequate levels of sleep can be expected to reduce risk of depression.

Exercise

Uncontrollable shock creates escape deficits, social avoidance, and an exaggerated fear response. Allowing an animal increased time on an exercise wheel will abrogate the impact of uncontrollable shock (Greenwood & Fleshner, 2011). Many findings suggest that exercise exerts salubrious effects by decreasing inflammation and associated phenomena (Cotman, Berchtold, &

Christie, 2007). Exercise decreases inflammatory cytokine response to stress (Hamer & Steptoe, 2007; Mathur & Pedersen, 2008). Exercise increases HRV (Coats et al., 1992), which dampens inflammation. Exercise influences immune system regulators. It decreases NF-κB activation, the transcription factor for inflammatory cytokines. Exercise decreases the expression of toll-like-receptor 4, which initiates an inflammatory response (Hamer & Steptoe, 2007). It improves the integrity of the gut intestinal barrier so the gut is less likely to allow entry of harmful bacteria (Luo, Xiang, Nieman, & Chen, 2014). In the brain, exercise is associated with increased BDNF in the hippocampus and with increased neurogenesis (Trejo, Carro, & Torres-Aleman, 2001; van Praag, Kempermann, & Gage, 1999).

In the clinical literature, exercise has demonstrated efficacy in ameliorating major depression (Babyak et al., 2000; Hoffman et al., 2011) with effect sizes comparable to pharmacological interventions (Greenwood & Fleshner, 2008). In a study in which 156 persons were randomized to exercise, to Zoloft, or to a combination of the two, there were no differences at 4 months among the conditions; however, at 6 months, only 15% of the exercise group remained depressed contrasted with 46% in the Zoloft group and 40% in the combination group. In terms of those who got better but then relapsed, relapse occurred in 8% in the exercise group, 38% in the medication group, and 31% in the combination group.

Beyond inflammation, learning new physical skills will integrate the new neurons produced in the hippocampus during neurogenesis into circuits and rescue them from early death (Curlik, Maeng, Agarwal, & Shors, 2013; Shors, Anderson, Curlik, & Nokia, 2012).

Meditation

The literature on compassion meditation and mindfulness meditation is expanding. Persons who practice meditation display less stress in response to the Trier Social Stress Test, faster cortisol recovery after the Trier Social Stress Test, and lower elevations in inflammatory markers (Kaliman et al., 2014; Pace et al., 2009). Their amygdalae activate to a lesser extent in response to emotional stimuli (Desbordes et al., 2012). Mindfulness meditation has also proven successful in reducing levels of depression and lowering levels of neural activity when sadness was provoked by the experimenters (Farb et al., 2010). As reviewed by Slavich and Irwin (2014), a number of studies find that meditation decreases the production of many inflammatory cytokines. Yoga integrates many components of meditation and may be more appealing for people who like to have specific foci as they learn to regulate their capacity for focusing attention. The results of yoga in reducing distress have been documented (Balasubramaniam, Telles, & Doraiswamy, 2013; Khalsa, 2013; Kiecolt-Glaser et al., 2010).

Social Engagement

Positive social interactions increase levels of oxytocin. Oxytocin is anti-inflammatory (Gouin et al., 2010). As discussed in Chapter 2, oxytocin lowers anxiety levels. Humans are social animals. The centrality of human interactions is paramount. Chapter 10 will offer additional findings on the relationship between positive social interactions and mental health.

SUMMARY

There are many alternatives available for treating depression. Cognitive behavioral therapy is as effective as antidepressants, although it may be slower to achieve results. CBT is associated with lower probability of relapse compared to antidepressants. New talk therapies targeting regulatory capacity are being developed. Lifestyle changes involving diet, exercise, and positive interaction with others are also effective in decreasing depression. The lifestyle changes reviewed in this chapter are the same interventions recommended to prevent heart disease and cancer. A drawback to making lifestyle changes is that they require developing new habits, similar to the lifestyle changes recovering alcoholics must implement in their lives to stay sober. Although this may seem daunting, it is also the case that small changes can yield big payoffs. In the last chapter of this book, we will look at ways to make and sustain lifestyle changes.

USEFUL WEBSITES AND INFORMATION ON FOOD

International Scientific Association for Probiotics and Prebiotics: A Consumer Guide: http://www.isapp.net
WGO Practice Guildelines: http://www.worldgastroenterology.org/probiotics-prebiotics.html

National Center for Complementary and Alternative Medicine: http://nccam
.nih.gov/health/probiotics/introduction.htm

ConsumerLab.com: www.consumerlab.com/reviews. Website that provides
information on probiotics.

Aggarwal, B. B., & Yost, D. (2011) *Healing spices: How to use 50 everyday and exotic
spices to boost health and beat disease*. New York, NY: Sterling Press. This is a
great cookbook. Aggarwal is an immunologist who is employed at Anderson
Cancer Center in Houston, TX.

REFERENCES

Adler, H. S., & Steinbrink, K. (2007). Tolerogenic dendritic cells in health and disease: Friend and foe! *European Journal of Dermatology: EJD, 17*(6), 476–491.

Adorini, L., & Penna, G. (2009). Dendritic cell tolerogenicity: A key mechanism
in immunomodulation by vitamin D receptor agonists. *Human Immunology,
70*(5), 345–352.

Aggarwal, B. B. (2010). Targeting inflammation-induced obesity and metabolic
diseases by curcumin and other nutraceuticals. *Annual Review of Nutrition,
30*, 173–199.

Aizawa, H., Cui, W., Tanaka, K., & Okamoto, H. (2013). Hyperactivation of the
habenula as a link between depression and sleep disturbance. *Frontiers in
Human Neuroscience, 7*, Article 826, 1–6.

Akasheh, G., Sirati, L., Noshad Kamran, A. R., & Sepehrmanesh, Z. (2014).
Comparison of the effect of sertraline with behavioral therapy on semen
parameters in men with primary premature ejaculation. *Urology, 83*(4),
800–804.

Alvarez-Maqueda, M., El Bekay, R., Monteseirín, J., Alba, G., Chacón, P., Vega,
A.,…Sobrino, F. (2004). Homocysteine enhances superoxide anion release
and NADPH oxidase assembly by human neutrophils. Effects on MAPK activation and neutrophil migration. *Atherosclerosis, 172*(2), 229–238.

American Psychiatric Association. (2013). *Diagnostic and statistical manual of mental disorders* (5th ed.). Washington, DC: Author.

Anand, P., Kunnumakkara, A. B., Newman, R. A., & Aggarwal, B. B. (2007).
Bioavailability of curcumin: Problems and promises. *Molecular Pharmaceutics,
4*(6), 807–818.

Andersohn, F., Schade, R., Suissa, S., & Garbe, E. (2009). Long-term use of antidepressants for depressive disorders and the risk of diabetes mellitus. *American
Journal of Psychiatry, 166*(5), 591–598.

Arita, M., Bianchini, F., Aliberti, J., Sher, A., Chiang, N., Hong, S.,…Serhan, C.
N. (2005). Stereochemical assignment, antiinflammatory properties, and

receptor for the omega-3 lipid mediator resolvin E1. *Journal of Experimental Medicine, 201*(5), 713–722.

Babyak, M., Blumenthal, J. A., Herman, S., Khatri, P., Doraiswamy, M., Moore, K.,...Krishnan, K. R. (2000). Exercise treatment for major depression: Maintenance of therapeutic benefit at 10 months. *Psychosomatic Medicine, 62*(5), 633–638.

Balasubramaniam, M., Telles, S., & Doraiswamy, P. M. (2013). Effectiveness of yoga therapy as a complementary treatment for major psychiatric disorders: A meta-analysis. *Frontiers in Psychiatry, 3*, 117.

Balcita-Pedicino, J. J., Omelchenko, N., Bell, R., & Sesack, S. R. (2011). The inhibitory influence of the lateral habenula on midbrain dopamine cells: Ultrastructural evidence for indirect mediation via the rostromedial mesopontine tegmental nucleus. *Journal of Comparative Neurology, 519*(6), 1143–1164.

Beck, A. T. (1967). *Depression: Causes and treatment.* Philadelphia, PA: University of Pennsylvania Press.

Bernardi, L., Sleight, P., Bandinelli, G., Cencetti, S., Fattorini, L., Wdowczyc-Szulc, J., & Lagi, A. (2001). Effect of rosary prayer and yoga mantras on autonomic cardiovascular rhythms: Comparative study. *British Medical Journal, 323*(7327), 1446–1449.

Beydoun, M. A., Shroff, M. R., Beydoun, H. A., & Zonderman, A. B. (2010). Serum folate, vitamin B-12, and homocysteine and their association with depressive symptoms among U.S. adults. *Psychosomatic Medicine, 72*(9), 862–873.

Blackburn, I. M., & Moore, R. G. (1997). Controlled acute and follow-up trial of cognitive therapy and pharmacotherapy in out-patients with recurrent depression. *British Journal of Psychiatry, 171*, 328–334.

Bliziotes, M. (2010). Update in serotonin and bone. *Journal of Clinical Endocrinology and Metabolism, 95*(9), 4124–4132.

Bockting, C. L., ten Doesschate, M. C., Spijker, J., Spinhoven, P., Koeter, M. W., Schene, A. H., & DELTA study group. (2008). Continuation and maintenance use of antidepressants in recurrent depression. *Psychotherapy and Psychosomatics, 77*(1), 17–26.

Borowski, T., Kokkinidis, L., Merali, Z., & Anisman, H. (1998). Lipopolysaccharide, central in vivo biogenic amine variations, and anhedonia. *Neuroreport, 9*(17), 3797–3802.

Boyer, E. W., & Shannon, M. (2005). The serotonin syndrome. *New England Journal of Medicine, 352*(11), 1112–1120.

Burgdorf, J., Zhang, X. L., Nicholson, K. L., Balster, R. L., Leander, J. D., Stanton, P. K.,...Moskal, J. R. (2013). GLYX-13, a NMDA receptor glycine-site functional partial agonist, induces antidepressant-like effects without ketamine-like side effects. *Neuropsychopharmacology, 38*(5), 729–742.

Byrne, S. E., & Rothschild, A. J. (1998). Loss of antidepressant efficacy during maintenance therapy: Possible mechanisms and treatments. *Journal of Clinical Psychiatry, 59*(6), 279–288.

Capuron, L., Pagnoni, G., Demetrashvili, M., Woolwine, B. J., Nemeroff, C. B., Berns, G. S., & Miller, A. H. (2005). Anterior cingulate activation and error processing during interferon-alpha treatment. *Biological Psychiatry, 58*(3), 190–196.

Capuron, L., Pagnoni, G., Drake, D. F., Woolwine, B. J., Spivey, J. R., Crowe, R. J., ... Miller, A. H. (2012). Dopaminergic mechanisms of reduced basal ganglia responses to hedonic reward during interferon alfa administration. *Archives of General Psychiatry, 69*(10), 1044–1053.

Ceccherini-Nelli, A., Bardellini, L., Cur, A., Guazzelli, M., Maggini, C., & Dilsaver, S. C. (1993). Antidepressant withdrawal: Prospective findings. *American Journal of Psychiatry, 150*(1), 165.

Chambers, C. D., Hernandez-Diaz, S., Van Marter, L. J., Werler, M. M., Louik, C., Jones, K. L., & Mitchell, A. A. (2006). Selective serotonin-reuptake inhibitors and risk of persistent pulmonary hypertension of the newborn. *New England Journal of Medicine, 354*(6), 579–587.

Champe, P. C., Harvey, R. A., & Ferrier, D. R. (2008). *Biochemistry* (4th ed.). Baltimore, MD: Lippincott Williams & Wilkins.

Chang, H. A., Chang, C. C., Tzeng, N. S., Kuo, T. B., Lu, R. B., & Huang, S. Y. (2013). Generalized anxiety disorder, comorbid major depression and heart rate variability: A case-control study in Taiwan. *Psychiatry Investigation, 10*(4), 326–335.

Chassaing, B. (2013, August 29). *Dietary emulsifying agents promote intestinal inflammation.* Address to the Digestive Disease Research Group at Georgia State University, Atlanta, GA.

Cintra, D. E., Ropelle, E. R., Moraes, J. C., Pauli, J. R., Morari, J., Souza, C. T., ... Velloso, L. A. (2012). Unsaturated fatty acids revert diet-induced hypothalamic inflammation in obesity. *PLoS ONE, 7*(1), e30571. doi:10.1371/journl .pone.0030571

Coats, A. J., Adamopoulos, S., Radaelli, A., McCance, A., Meyer, T. E., Bernardi, L., ... Forfar, C. (1992). Controlled trial of physical training in chronic heart failure. Exercise performance, hemodynamics, ventilation, and autonomic function. *Circulation, 85*(6), 2119–2131.

Cole, S. W., Hawkley, L. C., Arevalo, J. M., Sung, C. Y., Rose, R. M., & Cacioppo, J. T. (2007). Social regulation of gene expression in human leukocytes. *Genome Biology, 8*(9), R189.

Cooper, W. O., Willy, M. E., Pont, S. J., & Ray, W. A. (2007). Increasing use of antidepressants in pregnancy. *American Journal of Obstetrics and Gynecology, 196*(6), 544.e1–544.e5.

Cotman, C. W., Berchtold, N. C., & Christie, L. A. (2007). Exercise builds brain health: Key roles of growth factor cascades and inflammation. *Trends in Neurosciences, 30*(9), 464–472.

Crestani, F., Seguy, F., & Dantzer, R. (1991). Behavioural effects of peripherally injected interleukin-1: Role of prostaglandins. *Brain Research, 542*(2), 330–335.

Croen, L. A., Grether, J. K., Yoshida, C. K., Odouli, R., & Hendrick, V. (2011). Antidepressant use during pregnancy and childhood autism spectrum disorders. *Archives of General Psychiatry, 68*(11), 1104–1112.

Csoka, A. B., Csoka, A., Bahrick, A., & Mehtonen, C. P. (2008). Persistent sexual dysfunction after discontinuation of selective serotonin reuptake inhibitors. *Journal of Sexual Medicine, 5*(1), 227–233.

Curlik, D. M., Maeng, L. Y., Agarwal, P. R., & Shors, T. J. (2013). Physical skill training increases the number of surviving new cells in the adult hippocampus. *PLoS ONE, 8*(2), e55850.

Dai, J., Miller, A. H., Bremner, J. D., Goldberg, J., Jones, L., Shallenberger, L.,...Vaccarino, V. (2008). Adherence to the Mediterranean diet is inversely associated with circulating interleukin-6 among middle-aged men: A twin study. *Circulation, 117*(2), 169–175.

Damsa, C., Bumb, A., Bianchi-Demicheli, F., Vidailhet, P., Sterck, R., Andreoli, A., & Beyenburg, S. (2004). "Dopamine-dependent" side effects of selective serotonin reuptake inhibitors: A clinical review. *Journal of Clinical Psychiatry, 65*(8), 1064–1068.

Dannon, P. N., Iancu, I., Lowengrub, K., Gonopolsky, Y., Musin, E., Grunhaus, L., & Kotler, M. (2007). A naturalistic long-term comparison study of selective serotonin reuptake inhibitors in the treatment of panic disorder. *Clinical Neuropharmacology, 30*(6), 326–334.

Dantzer, R., O'Connor, J. C., Lawson, M. A., & Kelley, K. W. (2011). Inflammation-associated depression: From serotonin to kynurenine. *Psychoneuroendocrinology, 36*(3), 426–436.

Davidson, R. J., & Irwin, W. (1999). The functional neuroanatomy of emotion and affective style. *Trends in Cognitive Sciences, 3*(1), 11–21.

Davidson, R. J., Pizzagalli, D., Nitschke, J. B., & Putnam, K. (2002). Depression: Perspectives from affective neuroscience. *Annual Review of Psychology, 53*, 545–574.

Dawood, T., Lambert, E. A., Barton, D. A., Laude, D., Elghozi, J. L., Esler, M. D.,...Lambert, G. W. (2007). Specific serotonin reuptake inhibition in major depressive disorder adversely affects novel markers of cardiac risk. *Hypertension Research, 30*(4), 285–293.

De La Serre, C. B., Ellis, C. L., Lee, J., Hartman, A. L., Rutledge, J. C., & Raybould, H. E. (2010). Propensity to high-fat diet-induced obesity in rats is changed in the gut microbiota and gut inflammation. *American Journal of Physiology: Gastrointestinal and Liver Physiology, 299*(2), G440–G448.

Demirtas-Tatlidede, A., & Mechanic-Hamilton, D. (2006). An open-label, prospective study of the repetitive transcranial magnetic stimulation (rTMS) in the long-term treatment of refractory depression: Reproducibility and duration of the antidepressant effect in medication-free patients. *Journal of Clinical Psychiatry, 69*(6), 930–934.

De Raedt, R., Leyman, L., Baeken, C., Van Schuerbeek, P., Luypaert, R., Vanderhasselt, M. A., & Dannlowski, U. (2010). Neurocognitive effects of HF-rTMS over the dorsolateral prefrontal cortex on the attentional processing of emotional information in healthy women: An event-related fMRI study. *Biological Psychology, 85*(3), 487–495.

Der-Avakian, A., & Markou, A. (2012). The neurobiology of anhedonia and other reward-related deficits. *Trends in Neurosciences, 35*(1), 68–77.

DeRubeis, R. J., Fournier, J. C., & Fawcett, J. (2010). Depression severity and effects of antidepressant medications. *Journal of the American Medical Association, 303*(16), 1599.

DeRubeis, R. J., Gelfand, L. A., Tang, T. Z., & Simons, A. D. (1999). Medications versus cognitive behavior therapy for severely depressed outpatients: Mega-analysis of four randomized comparisons. *American Journal of Psychiatry, 156*(7), 1007–1013.

DeRubeis, R. J., Hollon, S. D., Amsterdam, J. D., Shelton, R. C., Young, P. R., Salomon, R. M.,...Gallop, R. (2005). Cognitive therapy vs. medications in the treatment of moderate to severe depression. *Archives of General Psychiatry, 62*(4), 409–416.

Desbordes, G., Negi, L. T., Pace, T. W., Wallace, B. A., Raison, C. L., & Schwartz, E. L. (2012). Effects of mindful-attention and compassion meditation training on amygdala response to emotional stimuli in an ordinary, non-meditative state. *Frontiers in Human Neuroscience, 6*, 292.

Dewall, C. N., Macdonald, G., Webster, G. D., Masten, C. L., Baumeister, R. F., Powell, C.,...Eisenberger, N. I. (2010). Acetaminophen reduces social pain: Behavioral and neural evidence. *Psychological Science, 21*(7), 931–937.

Dhir, A., Padi, S. S., Naidu, P. S., & Kulkarni, S. K. (2006). Protective effect of naproxen (non-selective COX-inhibitor) or rofecoxib (selective COX-2 inhibitor) on immobilization stress-induced behavioral and biochemical alterations in mice. *European Journal of Pharmacology, 535*(1–3), 192–198.

Dichter, G. S., Tomarken, A. J., Shelton, R. C., & Sutton, S. K. (2004). Early- and late-onset startle modulation in unipolar depression. *Psychophysiology, 41*(3), 433–440.

Dolberg, O. T., Schreiber, S., & Grunhaus, L. (2001). Transcranial magnetic stimulation-induced switch into mania: A report of two cases. *Biological Psychiatry, 49*(5), 468–470.

Domar, A. D., Moragianni, V. A., Ryley, D. A., & Urato, A. C. (2013). The risks of selective serotonin reuptake inhibitor use in infertile women: A review of the impact on fertility, pregnancy, neonatal health and beyond. *Human Reproduction, 28*(1), 160–171.

Dowlati, Y., Herrmann, N., Swardfager, W., Liu, H., Sham, L., Reim, E. K., & Lanctôt, K. L. (2010). A meta-analysis of cytokines in major depression. *Biological Psychiatry, 67*(5), 446–457.

Duman, R. S., & Voleti, B. (2012). Signaling pathways underlying the pathophysiology and treatment of depression: Novel mechanisms for rapid-acting agents. *Trends in Neurosciences, 35*(1), 47–56.

Dunlop, B. W., & Nemeroff, C. B. (2007). The role of dopamine in the pathophysiology of depression. *Archives of General Psychiatry, 64*(3), 327–337.

Eisenberger, N. I., Berkman, E. T., Inagaki, T. K., Rameson, L. T., Mashal, N. M., & Irwin, M. R. (2011). Inflammation-induced anhedonia: Endotoxin reduces ventral striatum responses to reward. *Biological Psychiatry, 68*(8), 748–754.

Eisenberger, N., Inagaki, T. K., Rameson, L. T., Marshal, N. M., & Irwin, M. R. (2009). An fMRI study of cytokine-induced depressed mood and social pain: The role of sex differences. *Neuroimage, 47*(3), 881–890.

Elkin, I., Shea, M. T., Watkins, J. T., Imber, S. D., Sotsky, S. M., Collins, J. F.,...Docherty, J. P. (1989). National Institute of Mental Health Treatment of Depression Collaborative Research Program. General effectiveness of treatments. *Archives of General Psychiatry, 46*(11), 971–982; discussion 983.

Engler, H., Doenlen, R., Engler, A., Riether, C., Prager, G., Niemi, M. B.,...Schedlowski, M. (2011). Acute amygdaloid response to systemic inflammation. *Brain, Behavior, and Immunity, 25*(7), 1384–1392.

Evans, M. D., Hollon, S. D., DeRubeis, R. J., Piasecki, J. M., Grove, W. M., Garvey, M. J., & Tuason, V. B. (1992). Differential relapse following cognitive therapy and pharmacotherapy for depression. *Archives of General Psychiatry, 49*(10), 802–808.

Farb, N. A., Anderson, A. K., Mayberg, H., Bean, J., McKeon, D., & Segal, Z. V. (2010). Minding one's emotions: Mindfulness training alters the neural expression of sadness. *Emotion, 10*(1), 25–33.

Farooqui, A. A., Ong, W. Y., Horrocks, L. A., Chen, P., & Farooqui, T. (2007). Comparison of biochemical effects of statins and fish oil in brain: The battle of the titans. *Brain Research Reviews, 56*(2), 443–471.

Fava, G. A., & Offidani, E. (2011). The mechanisms of tolerance in antidepressant action. *Progress in Neuropsychopharmacology and Biological Psychiatry, 35*(7), 1593–1602. doi: S0278–5846(10)00292–7

Fava, M. (2000). Weight gain and antidepressants. *Journal of Clinical Psychiatry, 61*(Suppl. 11), 37–41.

Fava, M., Graves, L. M., Benazzi, F., Scalia, M. J., Iosifescu, D. V., Alpert, J. E., & Papakostas, G. I. (2006). A cross-sectional study of the prevalence of cognitive and physical symptoms during long-term antidepressant treatment. *Journal of Clinical Psychiatry, 67*(11), 1754–1759.

Feder, A., Nestler, E. J., & Charney, D. S. (2009). Psychobiology and molecular genetics of resilience. *Nature Reviews. Neuroscience, 10*(6), 446–457.

Ferder, L., Ferder, M. D., & Inserra, F. (2010). The role of high-fructose corn syrup in metabolic syndrome and hypertension. *Current Hypertension Reports, 12*(2), 105–112.

Fitzgerald, P. B., Benitez, J., de Castella, A., Daskalakis, Z. J., Brown, T. L., & Kulkarni, J. (2006). A randomized, controlled trial of sequential bilateral repetitive transcranial magnetic stimulation for treatment-resistant depression. *American Journal of Psychiatry, 163*(1), 88–94.

Forgeard, M. J., Haigh, E. A., Beck, A. T., Davidson, R. J., Henn, F. A., Maier, S. F.,...Seligman, M. E. (2011). Beyond depression: Towards a process-based approach to research, diagnosis, and treatment. *Clinical Psychology, 18*(4), 275–299.

Forsythe, P., Sudo, N., Dinan, T., Taylor, V. H., & Bienenstock, J. (2010). Mood and gut feelings. *Brain, Behavior, and Immunity, 24*(1), 9–16.

Frank, E., Kupfer, D. J., & Perel, J. M. (1989). Early recurrence in unipolar depression. *Archives of General Psychiatry, 46*(5), 397–400.

Frenois, F., Moreau, M., O'Connor, J., Lawson, M., Micon, C., Lestage, J.,...Castanon, N. (2007). Lipopolysaccharide induces delayed FosB/DeltaFosB immunostaining within the mouse extended amygdala, hippocampus and hypothalamus, that parallel the expression of depressive-like behavior. *Psychoneuroendocrinology, 32*(5), 516–531.

Friedman, A., Lax, E., Dikshtein, Y., Abraham, L., Flaumenhaft, Y., Sudai, E.,...Yadid, G. (2011). Electrical stimulation of the lateral habenula produces an inhibitory effect on sucrose self-administration. *Neuropharmacology, 60*(2–3), 381–387.

Fromont, A., De Seze, J., Fleury, M. C., Maillefert, J. F., & Moreau, T. (2009). Inflammatory demyelinating events following treatment with anti-tumor necrosis factor. *Cytokine, 45*(2), 55–57.

George, M. S., Lisanby, S. H., Avery, D., McDonald, W. M., Durkalski, V., Pavlicova, M.,...Sackeim, H. A. (2010). Daily left prefrontal transcranial magnetic stimulation therapy for major depressive disorder: A sham-controlled randomized trial. *Archives of General Psychiatry, 67*(5), 507–516.

Glenmullen, J. (2005). *The antidepressant solution: A step-by-step guide to safely overcoming antidepressant withdrawal, dependence, and "addiction."* New York, NY: Free Press.

Goldstein, T. R., Frye, M. A., Denicoff, K. D., Smith-Jackson, E., Leverich, G. S., Bryan, A. L.,... & Post, R. M. (1999). Antidepressant discontinuation-related mania: Critical prospective observation and theoretical implications in bipolar disorder. *Journal of Clinical Psychiatry, 60*(8), 563–567; quiz 568.

Gotlib, I. H., & Joormann, J. (2010). Cognition and depression: Current status and future directions. *Annual Review of Clinical Psychology, 6*, 285–312.

Gotlib, I. H., Joormann, J., Minor, K. L., & Hallmayer, J. (2008). HPA axis reactivity: A mechanism underlying the associations among 5-HTTLPR, stress, and depression. *Biological Psychiatry, 63*(9), 847–851.

Gotzsche, P. C. (2013). *Deadly medicines and organized crime: How big phama has corrupted healthcare.* New York, NY: Radcliffe.

Gouin, J. P., Carter, C. S., Pournajafi-Nazarloo, H., Glaser, R., Malarkey, W. B., Loving, T. J.,... Kiecolt-Glaser, J. K. (2010). Marital behavior, oxytocin, vasopressin, and wound healing. *Psychoneuroendocrinology, 35*(7), 1082–1090.

Grant, B. F., Stinson, F. S., Hasin, D. S., Dawson, D. A., Chou, S. P., & Anderson, K. (2004). Immigration and lifetime prevalence of DSM-IV psychiatric disorders among Mexican Americans and non-Hispanic whites in the United States: Results from the National Epidemiologic Survey on Alcohol and Related Conditions. *Archives of General Psychiatry, 61*(12), 1226–1233.

Greenwood, B. N., & Fleshner, M. (2008). Exercise, learned helplessness, and the stress-resistant brain. *Neuromolecular Medicine, 10*(2), 81–98.

Greenwood, B. N., & Fleshner, M. (2011). Exercise, stress resistance, and central serotonergic systems. *Exercise and Sport Sciences Reviews, 39*(3), 140–149.

Grippo, A. J., Lamb, D. G., Carter, C. S., & Porges, S. W. (2007). Social isolation disrupts autonomic regulation of the heart and influences negative affective behaviors. *Biological Psychiatry, 62*(10), 1162–1170.

Grippo, A. J., Trahanas, D. M., Zimmerman, R. R., Porges, S. W., & Carter, C. S. (2009). Oxytocin protects against negative behavioral and autonomic consequences of long-term social isolation. *Psychoneuroendocrinology, 34*(10), 1542–1553.

Haddad, P. (1997). Newer antidepressants and the discontinuation syndrome. *Journal of Clinical Psychiatry, 58*(Suppl. 7), 17–21; discussion 22.

Haddad, P. M. (2001). Antidepressant discontinuation syndromes. *Drug Safety, 24*(3), 183–197.

Haddad, P. M., & Dursun, S. M. (2008). Neurological complications of psychiatric drugs: Clinical features and management. *Human Psychopharmacology, 23*(Suppl. 1), 15–26.

Hamer, M., Batty, G. D., Marmot, M. G., Singh-Manoux, A., & Kivimäki, M. (2011). Anti-depressant medication use and C-reactive protein: Results from two population-based studies. *Brain, Behavior, and Immunity, 25*(1), 168–173.

Hamer, M., & Steptoe, A. (2007). Association between physical fitness, parasympathetic control, and proinflammatory responses to mental stress. *Psychosomatic Medicine, 69*(7), 660–666.

Hansen, A. L., Johnsen, B. H., Sollers, J. J., 3rd, Stenvik, K., & Thayer, J. F. (2004). Heart rate variability and its relation to prefrontal cognitive function: The effects of training and detraining. *European Journal of Applied Physiology, 93*, 263–272.

Hariri, A. R., Mattay, V. S., Tessitore, A., Kolachana, B., Fera, F., Goldman, D., ... Weinberger, D. R. (2002). Serotonin transporter genetic variation and the response of the human amygdala. *Science, 297*(5580), 400–403.

Harrison, N. A., Brydon, L., Walker, C., Gray, M. A., Steptoe, A., & Critchley, H. D. (2009). Inflammation causes mood changes through alterations in subgenual cingulate activity and mesolimbic connectivity. *Biological Psychiatry, 66*(5), 407–414.

Hartley, C. A., & Phelps, E. A. (2010). Changing fear: The neurocircuitry of emotion regulation. *Neuropsychopharmacology, 35*(1), 136–146.

Heller, A. S., Johnstone, T., Shackman, A. J., Light, S. N., Peterson, M. J., Kolden, G. G., ... Davidson, R. J. (2009). Reduced capacity to sustain positive emotion in major depression reflects diminished maintenance of fronto-striatal brain activation. *Proceedings of the National Academy of Sciences of the United States of America, 106*(52), 22445–22450.

Hikosaka, O. (2010). The habenula: From stress evasion to value-based decision-making. *Nature Reviews. Neuroscience, 11*(7), 503–513.

Hikosaka, O. (2011). *Habenula*. Retrieved July 7, 2014, from http://www.scholarpedia.org/article/habenula

Hoffman, B. M., Babyak, M. A., Craighead, W. E., Sherwood, A., Doraiswamy, P. M., Coons, M. J., & Blumenthal, J. A. (2011). Exercise and pharmacotherapy in patients with major depression: One-year follow-up of the SMILE study. *Psychosomatic Medicine, 73*(2), 127–133.

Hong, S., Nelesen, R. A., Krohn, P. L., Mills, P. J., & Dimsdale, J. E. (2006). The association of social status and blood pressure with markers of vascular inflammation. *Psychosomatic Medicine, 68*(4), 517–523.

Howren, M. B., Lamkin, D. M., & Suls, J. (2009). Associations of depression with C-reactive protein, IL-1, and IL-6: A meta-analysis. *Psychosomatic Medicine, 71*(2), 171–186.

Inagaki, T. K., Muscatell, K. A., Irwin, M. R., Cole, S. W., & Eisenberger, N. I. (2012). Inflammation selectively enhances amygdala activity to socially threatening images. *NeuroImage, 59*(4), 3222–3226.

Irwin, M. R., Wang, M., Campomayor, C. O., Collado-Hidalgo, A., & Cole, S. (2006). Sleep deprivation and activation of morning levels of cellular and genomic markers of inflammation. *Archives of Internal Medicine, 166*(16), 1756–1762.

Iwami, D., Nonomura, K., Shirasugi, N., & Niimi, M. (2011). Immunomodulatory effects of eicosapentaenoic acid through induction of regulatory T cells. *International Immunopharmacology, 11*(3), 384–389.

Ji, R. R., Xu, Z. Z., Strichartz, G., & Serhan, C. N. (2011). Emerging roles of resolvins in the resolution of inflammation and pain. *Trends in Neurosciences, 34*(11), 599–609.

Johansen-Berg, H., Gutman, D. A., Behrens, T. E., Matthews, P. M., Rushworth, M. F., Katz, E.,…Mayberg, H. S. (2008). Anatomical connectivity of the subgenual cingulate region targeted with deep brain stimulation for treatment-resistant depression. *Cerebral Cortex, 18*(6), 1374–1383.

Johnstone, T., van Reekum, C. M., Urry, H. L., Kalin, N. H., & Davidson, R. J. (2007). Failure to regulate: Counterproductive recruitment of top-down prefrontal-subcortical circuitry in major depression. *Journal of Neuroscience, 27*(33), 8877–8884.

Kaliman, P., Alvarez-López, M. J., Cosín-Tomás, M., Rosenkranz, M. A., Lutz, A., & Davidson, R. J. (2014). Rapid changes in histone deacetylases and inflammatory gene expression in expert meditators. *Psychoneuroendocrinology, 40*, 96–107.

Karavidas, M. K., Lehrer, P. M., Vaschillo, E., Vaschillo, B., Marin, H., Buyske, S.,…Hassett, A. (2007). Preliminary results of an open label study of heart rate variability biofeedback for the treatment of major depression. *Applied Psychophysiology and Biofeedback, 32*(1), 19–30.

Kaufman, J., Yang, B. Z., Douglas-Palumberi, H., Houshyar, S., Lipschitz, D., Krystal, J. H., & Gelernter, J. (2004). Social supports and serotonin transporter gene moderate depression in maltreated children. *Proceedings of the National Academy of Sciences of the United States of America, 101*(49), 17316–17321.

Kawai, M., & Rosen, C. J. (2010). Minireview: A skeleton in serotonin's closet? *Endocrinology, 151*(9), 4103–4108.

Keller, M. B., Trivedi, M. H., Thase, M. E., Shelton, R. C., Kornstein, S. G., Nemeroff, C. B.,…Ninan, P. T. (2007). The Prevention of Recurrent Episodes of Depression with Venlafaxine for Two Years (PREVENT) study: Outcomes from the acute and continuation phases. *Biological Psychiatry, 62*(12), 1371–1379.

Keller, M. C., Neale, M. C., & Kendler, K. S. (2007). Association of different adverse life events with distinct patterns of depressive symptoms. *American Journal of Psychiatry, 164*(10), 1521–1529; quiz 1622.

Kemp, A. H., Quintana, D. S., Felmingham, K. L., Matthews, S., & Jelinek, H. F. (2012). Depression, comorbid anxiety disorders, heart rate variability in physically healthy, unmedicated patients: Implications for cardiovascular risk. *PLoS ONE, 7*(2), e30777. doi:10.1371/journal.pone.0030777

Kemp, A. H., Quintana, D. S., Gray, M. A., Felmingham, K. L., Brown, K., & Gatt, J. M. (2010). Impact of depression and antidepressant treatment on heart rate variability: A review and meta-analysis. *Biological Psychiatry, 67*(11), 1067–1074.

Kemp, A. H., Quintana, D. S., Kuhnert, R. L., Griffiths, K., Hickie, I. B., & Guastella, A. J. (2012). Oxytocin increases heart rate variability in humans at rest: Implications for social approach-related motivation and capacity for social engagement. *PLoS ONE, 7*(8), e44014.

Kendler, K. S., Hettema, J. M., Butera, F., Gardner, C. O., & Prescott, C. A. (2003). Life event dimensions of loss, humiliation, entrapment, and danger in the prediction of onsets of major depression and generalized anxiety. *Archives of General Psychiatry, 60*(8), 789–796.

Khalsa, S. B. S. (2013). Yoga for psychiatry and mental health: An ancient practice with modern relevance. *Indian Journal of Psychiatry, 55*(Suppl. 3), S334–S336.

Kiecolt-Glaser, J. K. (2010). Stress, food, and inflammation: Psychoneuro-immunology and nutrition at the cutting edge. *Psychosomatic Medicine, 72*(4), 365–369.

Kiecolt-Glaser, J. K., Belury, M. A., Andridge, R., Malarkey, W. B., & Glaser, R. (2011). Omega-3 supplementation lowers inflammation and anxiety in medical students: A randomized controlled trial. *Brain, Behavior, and Immunity, 25*(8), 1725–1734.

Kiecolt-Glaser, J. K., Christian, L., Preston, H., Houts, C. R., Malarkey, W. B., Emery, C. F., & Glaser, R. (2010). Stress, inflammation, and yoga practice. *Psychosomatic Medicine, 72*(2), 113–121.

Kiecolt-Glaser, J. K., Preacher, K. J., MacCallum, R. C., Atkinson, C., Malarkey, W. B., & Glaser, R. (2003). Chronic stress and age-related increases in the proin-flammatory cytokine IL-6. *Proceedings of the National Academy of Sciences of the United States of America, 100*(15), 9090–9095.

Kirsch, I. (2010). *The emperor's new drugs: Exploding the antidepressant myth.* New York, NY: Basic Books.

Kivimäki, M., Hamer, M., Batty, G. D., Geddes, J. R., Tabak, A. G., Pentti, J., ... Vahtera, J. (2010). Antidepressant medication use, weight gain, and risk of type 2 diabetes: A population-based study. *Diabetes Care, 33*(12), 2611–2616.

Klein, D. F., Gittelman, R., Quitkin, F., & Rifkin, A. (1980). *Diagnosis and drug treatment of psychiatric disorders: Adults and children* (2nd ed.) Baltimore, MD: Williams & Wilkins.

Klerman, G. L., & Weissman, M. M. (1989). Increasing rates of depression. *Journal of the American Medical Association, 261*(15), 2229–2235.

Laje, G., Paddock, S., Manji, H., Rush, A. J., Wilson, A. F., Charney, D., & McMahon, F. J. (2007). Genetic markers of suicidal ideation emerging during citalopram treatment of major depression. *American Journal of Psychiatry, 164*(10), 1530–1538.

Lakshminarasimhan, H., & Chattarji, S. (2012). *Stress leads to contrasting effects on the levels of brain derived neurotrophic factor in the hippocampus and amygdala.* Retrieved from http://journals.plos.org/plosone/article?id=10.1371/journal. pone.0030481

Lam, Y. Y., Ha, C. W., Campbell, C. R., Mitchell, A. J., Dinudom, A., Oscarsson, J.,...Storlien, L. H. (2012). Increased gut permeability and microbiota change associate with mesenteric fat inflammation and metabolic dysfunction in diet-induced obese mice. *PLoS ONE, 7*(3), e34233. doi:10.1371/journal.pone.0034233

Lambert, K. G. (2006). Rising rates of depression in today's society: Consideration of the roles of effort-based rewards and enhanced resilience in day-to-day functioning. *Neuroscience and Biobehavioral Reviews, 30*(4), 497–510.

Lehmann, H. E. (1983). Clinical evaluation and natural course of depression. *Journal of Clinical Psychiatry, 44*(5, Pt. 2), 5–10.

Lehmann, M. L., & Herkenham, M. (2011). Environmental enrichment confers stress resiliency to social defeat through an infralimbic cortex-dependent neuroanatomical pathway. *Journal of Neuroscience, 31*(16), 6159–6173.

Lehrer, P. M., Vaschillo, E., Lu, S. E., Eckberg, D., Vaschillo, B., Scardella, A., & Habib, R. (2006). Heart rate variability biofeedback: Effects of age on heart rate variability, baroreflex gain, and asthma. *Chest, 129*(2), 278–284.

Lehrer, P. M., Vaschillo, E., Vaschillo, B., Lu, S. E., Eckberg, D. L., Edelberg, R.,...Hamer, R. M. (2003). Heart rate variability biofeedback increases baroreflex gain and peak expiratory flow. *Psychosomatic Medicine, 65*(5), 796–805.

Lejoyeux, M., & Adès, J. (1997). Antidepressant discontinuation: A review of the literature. *Journal of Clinical Psychiatry, 58*(Suppl. 7), 11–15; discussion 16.

Lenzer, J. (2005). FDA warns that antidepressants may increase suicidality in adults. *BMJ, 331*(7508), 70-b. doi: 10.1136.331.7508.70-b

Leo, R. J. (1996). Movement disorders associated with the serotonin selective reuptake inhibitors. *Journal of Clinical Psychiatry, 57*(10), 449–454.

Leverich, G. S., Altshuler, L. L., Frye, M. A., Suppes, T., McElroy, S. L., Keck, P. E.,...Post, R. M. (2006). Risk of switch in mood polarity to hypomania or mania in patients with bipolar depression during acute and continuation trials of venlafaxine, sertraline, and bupropion as adjuncts to mood stabilizers. *American Journal of Psychiatry, 163*(2), 232–239.

Li, Y., Xiao, B., Qiu, W., Yang, L., Hu, B., Tian, X., & Yang, H. (2010). Altered expression of CD4(+)CD25(+) regulatory T cells and its 5-HT(1a) receptor in patients with major depression disorder. *Journal of Affective Disorders, 124*(1–2), 68–75.

Licht, C. M., de Geus, E. J., Zitman, F. G., Hoogendijk, W. J., van Dyck, R., & Penninx, B. W. (2008). Association between major depressive disorder and heart rate variability in the Netherlands Study of Depression and Anxiety (NESDA). *Archives of General Psychiatry, 65*(12), 1358–1367.

Littrell, J. (1994). Relationship between time since reuptake-blocker antidepressant discontinuation and relapse. *Experimental and Clinical Psychopharmacology, 2*(1), 82–94.

Loke, Y. K., Trivedi, A. N., & Singh, S. (2008). Meta-analysis: Gastrointestinal bleeding due to interaction between selective serotonin uptake inhibitors and non-steroidal anti-inflammatory drugs. *Alimentary Pharmacology & Therapeutics, 27*(1), 31–40.

Lopresti, A. L., Maes, M., Maker, G. L., Hood, S. D., & Drummond, P. D. (2014). Curcumin for the treatment of major depression: A randomised, double-blind, placebo controlled study. *Journal of Affective Disorders, 167,* 368–375.

Lucassen, P. J., Meerlo, P., Naylor, A. S., van Dam, A. M., Dayer, A. G., Fuchs, E., . . . Czéh, B. (2010). Regulation of adult neurogenesis by stress, sleep disruption, exercise and inflammation: Implications for depression and antidepressant action. *European Neuropsychopharmacology, 20*(1), 1–17.

Luciano, M., Mõttus, R., Starr, J. M., McNeill, G., Jia, X., Craig, L. C., & Deary, I. J. (2012). Depressive symptoms and diet: Their effects on prospective inflammation levels in the elderly. *Brain, Behavior, and Immunity, 26*(5), 717–720.

Luo, B., Xiang, D., Nieman, D. C., & Chen, P. (2014). The effects of moderate exercise on chronic stress-induced intestinal barrier dysfunction and antimicrobial defense. *Brain, Behavior, and Immunity, 39,* 99–106.

Maes, M., Christophe, A., Bosmans, E., Lin, A., & Neels, H. (2000). In humans, serum polyunsaturated fatty acid levels predict the response of proinflammatory cytokines to psychologic stress. *Biological Psychiatry, 47*(10), 910–920.

Maier, S. F., & Watkins, L. R. (1998). Cytokines for psychologists: Implications of bidirectional immune-to-brain communication for understanding behavior, mood, and cognition. *Psychological Review, 105*(1), 83–107.

Maric, T., Woodside, B., & Luheshi, G. N. (2014). The effects of dietary saturated fat on basal hypothalamic neuroinflammation in rats. *Brain, Behavior, and Immunity, 36,* 35–45.

Maris, R., Berman, A., & Silverman, M. (2000). *Comprehensive textbook of suicidality.* New York, NY: Guilford Press.

Mathur, N., & Pedersen, B. K. (2008). Exercise as a means to control low-grade systemic inflammation. *Mediators of Inflammation, 2008,* 109502. doi: 10.1155/2008/109502.

Mayberg, H. (2007, April 21). *The subgenual cingulate cortex.* Seminar delivered to Frontiers in Neuroscience, Emory University, Atlanta, GA.

McCabe, C., Mishor, Z., Cowen, P. J., & Harmer, C. J. (2010). Diminished neural processing of aversive and rewarding stimuli during selective serotonin reuptake inhibitor treatment. *Biological Psychiatry, 67*(5), 439–445.

McGrath, P. J., Stewart, J. W., Tricamo, E., Nunes, E. N., & Quitkin, F. M. (1993). Paradoxical mood shifts to euthymia or hypomania upon withdrawal of antidepressant agents. *Journal of Clinical Psychopharmacology, 13*(3), 224–225.

McQuaid, R. J., McInnis, O. A., Stead, J. D., Matheson, K., & Anisman, H. (2013). A paradoxical association of an oxytocin receptor gene polymorphism: Early-life adversity and vulnerability to depression. *Frontiers in Neuroscience, 7,* 128.

Milanski, M., Degasperi, G., Coope, A., Morari, J., Denis, R., Cintra, D. E.,...Velloso, L. A. (2009). Saturated fatty acids produce an inflammatory response predominantly through the activation of TLR4 signaling in hypothalamus: Implications for the pathogenesis of obesity. *Journal of Neuroscience, 29*(2), 359–370.

Miller, A. H., Haroon, E., Raison, C. L., & Felger, J. C. (2013). Cytokine targets in the brain: Impact on neurotransmitters and neurocircuits. *Depression and Anxiety, 30*(4), 297–306.

Mischoulon, D., Papakostas, G. I., Dording, C. M., Farabaugh, A. H., Sonawalla, S. B., Agoston, A. M.,... Fava, M. (2009). A double-blind, randomized controlled trial of ethyl-eicosapentaenoate for major depressive disorder. *Journal of Clinical Psychiatry, 70*(12), 1636–1644.

Mohan, N., Edwards, E. T., Cupps, T. R., Oliverio, P. J., Sandberg, G., Crayton, H.,...Siegel, J. N. (2001). Demyelination occurring during anti-tumor necrosis factor alpha therapy for inflammatory arthritides. *Arthritis and Rheumatism, 44*(12), 2862–2869.

Moore, T. J., Glenmullen, J., & Furberg, C. D. (2010). Prescription drugs associated with reports of violence towards others. *PLoS ONE, 5*(12), e15337.

Mozaffarian, D., Stein, P. K., Prineas, R. J., & Siscovick, D. S. (2008). Dietary fish and omega-3 fatty acid consumption and heart rate variability in US adults. *Circulation, 117*(9), 1130–1137.

Müller, M. B., & Holsboer, F. (2006). Mice with mutations in the HPA-system as models for symptoms of depression. *Biological Psychiatry, 59*(12), 1104–1115.

Müller, N., Schwarz, M. J., Dehning, S., Douhe, A., Cerovecki, A., Goldstein-Müller, B.,...Riedel, M. (2006). The cyclooxygenase-2 inhibitor celecoxib has therapeutic effects in major depression: Results of a double-blind, randomized, placebo controlled, add-on pilot study to reboxetine. *Molecular Psychiatry, 11*(7), 680–684.

Murrough, J. W., Iosifescu, D. V., Chang, L. C., Al Jurdi, R. K., Green, C. E., Perez, A. M.,...Mathew, S. J. (2013). Antidepressant efficacy of ketamine in treatment-resistant major depression: A two-site randomized controlled trial. *American Journal of Psychiatry, 170*(10), 1134–1142.

Musselman, D. L., Miller, A. H., Porter, M. R., Manatunga, A., Gao, F., Penna, S.,...Nemeroff, C. B. (2001). Higher than normal plasma interleukin-6 concentrations in cancer patients with depression: Preliminary findings. *American Journal of Psychiatry, 158*(8), 1252–1257.

Nadjar, A., Bluthé, R. M., May, M. J., Dantzer, R., & Parnet, P. (2005). Inactivation of the cerebral NFkappaB pathway inhibits interleukin-1beta-induced sickness behavior and c-Fos expression in various brain nuclei. *Neuropsychopharmacology, 30*(8), 1492–1499.

Narayan, V., & Haddad, P. M. (2011). Antidepressant discontinuation manic states: A critical review of the literature and suggested diagnostic criteria. *Journal of Psychopharmacology, 25*(3), 306–313.

National Institute for Clinical Excellence. (2009). *Depression: The treatment and management of depression in adults.* Retrieved from http://www.webcitation .org/66XJTiQ0v

Naudé, P. J., Mommersteeg, P. M., Zijlstra, W. P., Gouweleeuw, L., Kupper, N., Eisel, U. L.,...Schoemaker, R. G. (2014). Neutrophil gelatinase-associated Lipocalin and depression in patients with chronic heart failure. *Brain, Behavior, and Immunity, 38*, 59–65.

Nemeroff, C. B. (2001). Progress in the battle with the black dog: Advances in the treatment of depression. *American Journal of Psychiatry, 158*(10), 1555–1557.

Nierenberg, A. A., Ostacher, M. J., Huffman, J. C., Ametrano, R. M., Fava, M., & Perlis, R. H. (2008). A brief review of antidepressant efficacy, effectiveness, indications, and usage for major depressive disorder. *Journal of Occupational and Environmental Medicine/American College of Occupational and Environmental Medicine, 50*(4), 428–436.

O'Brien, S. M., Scully, P., Fitzgerald, P., Scott, L. V., & Dinan, T. G. (2007). Plasma cytokine profiles in depressed patients who fail to respond to selective serotonin reuptake inhibitor therapy. *Journal of Psychiatric Research, 41*(3–4), 326–331.

Oh, D. Y., & Olefsky, J. M. (2012). Omega 3 fatty acids and GPR120. *Cell Metabolism, 15*(5), 564–565.

Oh, D. Y., Talukdar, S., Bae, E. J., Imamura, T., Morinaga, H., Fan, W.,...Olefsky, J. M. (2010). GPR120 is an omega-3 fatty acid receptor mediating potent anti-inflammatory and insulin-sensitizing effects. *Cell, 142*(5), 687–698.

Oke, S. L., & Tracey, K. J. (2009). The inflammatory reflex and the role of complementary and alternative medical therapies. *Annals of the New York Academy of Sciences, 1172*, 172–180.

Omelchenko, N., Bell, R., & Sesack, S. R. (2009). Lateral habenula projections to dopamine and GABA neurons in the rat ventral tegmental area. *European Journal of Neuroscience, 30*(7), 1239–1250.

O'Reardon, J. P., Solvason, H. B., Janicak, P. G., Sampson, S., Isenberg, K. E., Nahas, Z.,...Sackeim, H. A. (2007). Efficacy and safety of transcranial magnetic stimulation in the acute treatment of major depression: A multisite randomized controlled trial. *Biological Psychiatry, 62*(11), 1208–1216.

Otto, M. W., Smits, J. A. J., & Reese, H. E. (2006). Combined psychotherapy and pharmacotherapy for mood and anxiety disorders in adults: Review and analysis. *Focus, 4*(2), 72–86.

Pace, T. W., & Miller, A. H. (2009). Cytokines and glucocorticoid receptor signaling. Relevance to major depression. *Annals of the New York Academy of Sciences, 1179*, 86–105.

Pace, T. W., Mletzko, T. C., Alagbe, O., Musselman, D. L., Nemeroff, C. B., Miller, A. H., & Heim, C. M. (2006). Increased stress-induced inflammatory responses in male patients with major depression and increased early life stress. *American Journal of Psychiatry, 163*(9), 1630–1633.

Pace, T. W., Negi, L. T., Adame, D. D., Cole, S. P., Sivilli, T. I., Brown, T. D., . . . Raison, C. L. (2009). Effect of compassion meditation on neuroendocrine, innate immune and behavioral responses to psychosocial stress. *Psychoneuroendocrinology, 34*(1), 87–98.

Panksepp, J., Wright, J. S., Döbrössy, Schlaepfer, T. E., & Coenen, V. A. (2014). Affective neurosience strategies for understanding and treating depression: From preclinical models to three novel therapeutics. *Clinical Psychological Science, 2*, 472–494.

Papakostas, G. I., Mischoulon, D., Shyu, I., Alpert, J. E., & Fava, M. (2010). S-adenosyl methionine (SAMe) augmentation of serotonin reuptake inhibitors for antidepressant nonresponders with major depressive disorder: A double-blind, randomized clinical trial. *American Journal of Psychiatry, 167*(8), 942–948.

Parker, G., Gladstone, G., & Chee, K. T. (2001). Depression in the planet's largest ethnic group: The Chinese. *American Journal of Psychiatry, 158*(6), 857–864.

Pato, M. T., Zohar-Kadouch, R., Zohar, J., & Murphy, D. L. (1988). Return of symptoms after discontinuation of clomipramine in patients with obsessive-compulsive disorder. *American Journal of Psychiatry, 145*(12), 1521–1525.

Pavlov, V. A., & Tracey, K. J. (2005). The cholinergic anti-inflammatory pathway. *Brain, Behavior, and Immunity, 19*(6), 493–499.

PDR Network, LLC. (2015). *Physicians' desk reference* (69th ed.) Montvale, NJ: Author.

Pedersen, L. H., Henriksen, T. B., Vestergaard, M., Olsen, J., & Bech, B. H. (2009). Selective serotonin reuptake inhibitors in pregnancy and congenital malformations: Population based cohort study. *BMJ, 339*, b3569. doi: 10.1136/bmj.b3569.

Pezawas, L., Meyer-Lindenberg, A., Drabant, E. M., Verchinski, B. A., Munoz, K. E., Kolachana, B. S., . . . Weinberger, D. R. (2005). 5-HTTLPR polymorphism impacts human cingulate-amygdala interactions: A genetic susceptibility mechanism for depression. *Nature Neuroscience, 8*(6), 828–834.

Pilc, A., Wieronska, J. M., & Skolnick, P. (2013). Glutamate-based antidepressants: Preclinical psychopharmacology. *Biological Psychiatry, 73*(12), 1125–1132.

Pizzagalli, D. A. (2011). Frontocingulate dysfunction in depression: Toward bio-markers of treatment response. *Neuropsychopharmacology, 36*(1), 183–206.

Pizzagalli, D. A., Holmes, A. J., Dillon, D. G., Goetz, E. L., Birk, J. L., Bogdan, R.,...Fava, M. (2009). Reduced caudate and nucleus accumbens response to rewards in unmedicated individuals with major depressive disorder. *American Journal of Psychiatry, 166*(6), 702–710.

Post, R. M., Denicoff, K. D., Leverich, G. S., & Frye, M. A. (1997). Drug-induced switching in bipolar disorder. *CNS Drugs, 8,* 352–365.

Posternak, M. A., & Miller, I. (2001). Untreated short-term course of major depres-sion: A meta-analysis of outcomes from studies using wait-list control groups. *Journal of Affective Disorders, 66*(2–3), 139–146.

Posternak, M. A., Solomon, D. A., Leon, A. C., Mueller, T. I., Shea, M. T., Endicott, J., & Keller, M. B. (2006). The naturalistic course of unipolar major depression in the absence of somatic therapy. *Journal of Nervous and Mental Disease, 194*(5), 324–329.

Pratt, L. A., Brody, D. J., & Gu, Q. (2011, October). Antidepressant use in persons aged 12 and over: United States, 2005–2008. *NCHS Data Brief, 76.* Retrieved from www.cdc.gov/nchs/data/datbriefs/

Pridmore, S. (1999). Rapid transcranial magnetic stimulation and normalization of the dexamethasone suppression test. *Psychiatry and Clinical Neurosciences, 53*(1), 33–37.

Raeder, M. B., Bjelland, I., Emil Vollset, S., & Steen, V. M. (2006). Obesity, dys-lipidemia, and diabetes with selective serotonin reuptake inhibitors: The Hordaland Health Study. *Journal of Clinical Psychiatry, 67*(12), 1974–1982.

Rai, D., Lee, B. K., Dalman, C., Golding, J., Lewis, G., & Magnusson, C. (2013). Parental depression, maternal antidepressant use during pregnancy, and risk of autism spectrum disorders: Population based case-control study. *BMJ 346,* f2059. doi: 101136/bmj.f2059

Raison, C. L., Capuron, L., & Miller, A. H. (2006). Cytokines sing the blues: Inflammation and the pathogenesis of depression. *Trends in Immunology, 27*(1), 24–31.

Raison, C. L., Rutherford, R. E., Woolwine, B. J., Shuo, C., Schettler, P., Drake, D. F.,...Miller, A. H. (2013). A randomized controlled trial of the tumor necrosis factor antagonist infliximab for treatment-resistant depression: The role of baseline inflammatory biomarkers. *Journal of the American Medical Association Psychiatry, 70*(1), 31–41.

Rajagopalan, S., Brook, R., Rubenfire, M., Pitt, E., Young, E., & Pitt, B. (2001). Abnormal brachial artery flow-mediated vasodilation in young adults with major depression. *American Journal of Cardiology, 88*(2), 196– 198, A7.

Ramachandruni, S., Handberg, E., & Sheps, D. S. (2004). Acute and chronic psycho-logical stress in coronary disease. *Current Opinion in Cardiology, 19*(5), 494–499.

Redwine, L., Hauger, R. L., Gillin, J. C., & Irwin, M. (2000). Effects of sleep and sleep deprivation on interleukin-6, growth hormone, cortisol, and melatonin levels in humans. *Journal of Clinical Endocrinology and Metabolism, 85*(10), 3597–3603.

Ressler, K. J., & Mayberg, H. S. (2007). Targeting abnormal neural circuits in mood and anxiety disorders: From the laboratory to the clinic. *Nature Neuroscience, 10*(9), 1116–1124.

Rook, G. A., & Lowry, C. A. (2008). The hygiene hypothesis and psychiatric disorders. *Trends in Immunology, 29*(4), 150–158.

Rook, G. A., & Lowry, C. A. (2009). The hygiene hypothesis and affective and anxiety disorders. In G. A. W. Rook (Ed.), *The hygiene hypothesis and Darwinian medicine* (pp. 189–220). Berlin, Germany: Birkhauser.

Rosas-Ballina, M., & Tracey, K. J. (2009). The neurology of the immune system: Neural reflexes regulate immunity. *Neuron, 64*(1), 28–32.

Rosen, R. C., Lane, R. M., & Menza, M. (1999). Effects of SSRIs on sexual function: A critical review. *Journal of Clinical Psychopharmacology, 19*(1), 67–85.

Ross, L. E., Grigoriadis, S., Mamisashvili, L., Vonderporten, E. H., Roerecke, M., Rehm, J.,…Cheung, A. (2013). Selected pregnancy and delivery outcomes after exposure to antidepressant medication: A systematic review and meta-analysis. *JAMA Psychiatry, 70*(4), 436–443.

Rubin, R. R., Ma, Y., Peyrot, M., Marrero, D. G., Price, D. W., Barrett-Connor, E., Knowler, W. C., & Diabetes Prevention Program Research Group. (2010). Antidepressant medicine use and risk of developing diabetes during the Diabetes Prevention Program and Diabetes Prevention Program Outcomes Study. *Diabetes Care, 33*(12), 2549–2551.

Sánchez-Villegas, A., Delgado-Rodríguez, M., Alonso, A., Schlatter, J., Lahortiga, F., Serra Majem, L., & Martínez-González, M. A. (2009). Association of the Mediterranean dietary pattern with the incidence of depression: The Seguimiento Universidad de Navarra/University of Navarra follow-up (SUN) cohort. *Archives of General Psychiatry, 66*(10), 1090–1098.

Sartorius, A., Kiening, K. L., Kirsch, P., von Gall, C. C., Haberkorn, U., Unterberg, A. W.,…Meyer-Lindenberg, A. (2010). Remission of major depression under deep brain stimulation of the lateral habenula in a therapy-refractory patient. *Biological Psychiatry, 67*(2), e9–e11.

Schatzberg, A. F. (2014). A word to the wise about ketamine. *American Journal of Psychiatry, 171*(3), 262–264.

Schiepers, O. J., Wichers, M. C., & Maes, M. (2005). Cytokines and major depression. *Progress in Neuro-Psychopharmacology & Biological Psychiatry, 29*(2), 201–217.

Schneeberger, M., Dietrich, M. O., Sebastián, D., Imbernón, M., Castaño, C., Garcia, A.,…Claret, M. (2013). Mitofusin 2 in POMC neurons connects ER stress with leptin resistance and energy imbalance. *Cell, 155*(1), 172–187.

Serebruany, V. L. (2006). Selective serotonin reuptake inhibitors and increased bleeding risk: Are we missing something? *American Journal of Medicine, 119*(2), 113–116.

Serretti, A., & Mandelli, L. (2010). Antidepressants and body weight: A comprehensive review and meta-analysis. *Journal of Clinical Psychiatry, 71*(10), 1259–1272.

Shaffer, J. A., Edmondson, D., Wasson, L. T., Falzon, L., Homma, K., Ezeokoli, N.,…Davidson, K. W. (2014). Vitamin D supplementation for depressive symptoms: A systematic review and meta-analysis of randomized controlled trials. *Psychosomatic Medicine, 76*(3), 190–196.

Shea, M. T., Elkin, I., Imber, S. D., Sotsky, S. M., Watkins, J. T., Collins, J. F.,…Dolan, R. T. (1992). Course of depressive symptoms over follow-up. Findings from the National Institute of Mental Health Treatment of Depression Collaborative Research Program. *Archives of General Psychiatry, 49*(10), 782–787.

Shehzad, A., Rehman, G., & Lee, Y. S. (2013). Curcumin in inflammatory diseases. *BioFactors, 39*(1), 69–77.

Sheldon, T. (2012). Reserve antidepressants for cases of severe depression, Dutch doctors are told. *British Medical Journal, 344*, e4211. doi:10.1136/bmj.e4211

Sheline, Y. I. (2000). 3D MRI studies of neuroanatomic changes in unipolar major depression: The role of stress and medical comorbidity. *Biological Psychiatry, 48*(8), 791–800.

Sheline, Y. I., Barch, D. M., Price, J. L., Rundle, M. M., Vaishnavi, S. N., Snyder, A. Z.,…Raichle, M. E. (2009). The default mode network and self-referential processes in depression. *Proceedings of the National Academy of Sciences of the United States of America, 106*(6), 1942–1947.

Shors, T. J., Anderson, M. L., Curlik, D. M., & Nokia, M. S. (2012). Use it or lose it: How neurogenesis keeps the brain fit for learning. *Behavioural Brain Research, 227*(2), 450–458.

Siegle, G. J., Shinassi, F., & Thase, M. E. (2007). Neurobehavioral therapies in the 21st century: Summary of an emerging field and an extended example of cognitive training for depression. *Cognitive Therapy and Research, 31*, 235–262.

Simons, A. D., Murphy, G. E., Levine, J. L., & Wetzel, R. D. (1986). Cognitive therapy and pharmacotherapy for depression. Sustained improvement over one year. *Archives of General Psychiatry, 43*(1), 43–48.

Siow, Y. L., Au-Yeung, K. K., Woo, C. W., & O, K. (2006). Homocysteine stimulates phosphorylation of NADPH oxidase p47phox and p67phox subunits in monocytes via protein kinase Cbeta activation. *Biochemical Journal, 398*(1), 73–82.

Slavich, G. M., & Irwin, M. R. (2014). From stress to inflammation and major depressive disorder: A social signal transduction theory of depression. *Psychological Bulletin, 140*(3), 774–815.

Slavich, G. M., Monroe, S. M., & Gotlib, I. H. (2011). Early parental loss and depression history: Associations with recent life stress in major depressive disorder. *Journal of Psychiatric Research, 45*(9), 1146–1152.

Slavich, G. M., O'Donovan, A., Epel, E. S., & Kemeny, M. E. (2010). Black sheep get the blues: A psychobiological model of social rejection and depression. *Neuroscience and Biobehavioral Reviews, 35*(1), 39–45.

Slavich, G. M., Thornton, T., Torres, L. D., Monroe, S. M., & Gotlib, I. H. (2009). Targeted rejection predicts hastened onset of major depression. *Journal of Social and Clinical Psychology, 28*(2), 223–243.

Slavich, G. M., Way, B. M., Eisenberger, N. I., & Taylor, S. E. (2010). Neural sensitivity to social rejection is associated with inflammatory responses to social stress. *Proceedings of the National Academy of Sciences of the United States of America, 107*(33), 14817–14822.

Sleek, S. (2014, February). Genetically ever after: Heritable factors in marital satisfaction. *APA Monitor, 2,* 14–17.

Sobesky, J. L., Barrientos, R. M., De May, H. S., Thompson, B. M., Weber, M. D., Watkins, L. R., & Maier, S. F. (2014). High-fat diet consumption disrupts memory and primes elevations in hippocampal IL-1ß, an effect that can be prevented with dietary reversal or IL-1 receptor antagonism. *Brain, Behavior, and Immunity, 42,* 22–32.

Sørensen, M. J., Grønborg, T. K., Christensen, J., Parner, E. T., Vestergaard, M., Schendel, D., & Pedersen, L. H. (2013). Antidepressant exposure in pregnancy and risk of autism spectrum disorders. *Clinical Epidemiology, 5,* 449–459.

Steptoe, A., Kunz-Ebrecht, S., Owen, N., Feldman, P. J., Rumley, A., Lowe, G. D., & Marmot, M. (2003). Influence of socioeconomic status and job control on plasma fibrinogen responses to acute mental stress. *Psychosomatic Medicine, 65*(1), 137–144.

Stoukides, J. A., & Stoukides, C. A. (1991). Extrapyramidal symptoms upon discontinuation of fluoxetine. *American Journal of Psychiatry, 148*(9), 1263.

Tappy, L., & Lê, K. A. (2010). Metabolic effects of fructose and the worldwide increase in obesity. *Physiological Reviews, 90*(1), 23–46.

Teeling, J. L., Cunningham, C., Newman, T. A., & Perry, V. H. (2010). The effect of non-steroidal anti-inflammatory agents on behavioural changes and cytokine production following systemic inflammation: Implications for a role of COX-1. *Brain, Behavior, and Immunity, 24*(3), 409–419.

Thase, M. E., Haight, B. R., Richard, N., Rockett, C. B., Mitton, M., Modell, J. G., ... Wang, Y. (2005). Remission rates following antidepressant therapy with bupropion or selective serotonin reuptake inhibitors: A meta-analysis of original data from 7 randomized controlled trials. *Journal of Clinical Psychiatry, 66*(8), 974–981.

Tint, A., Haddad, P. M., & Anderson, I. M. (2008). The effect of rate of antidepressant tapering on the incidence of discontinuation symptoms: A randomised study. *Journal of Psychopharmacology, 22*(3), 330–332.

Tomarken, A. J., & Keener, A. D. (1998). Frontal brain asymmetry and depression: A self-regulatory perspective. *Cognition & Emotion, 12*(3), 387–420.

Tranter, R., O'Donovan, C., Chandarana, P., & Kennedy, S. (2002). Prevalence and outcome of partial remission in depression. *Journal of Psychiatry & Neuroscience, 27*(4), 241–247.

Treadway, M. T., Bossaller, N. A., Shelton, R. C., & Zald, D. H. (2012). Effort-based decision-making in major depressive disorder: A translational model of motivational anhedonia. *Journal of Abnormal Psychology, 121*(3), 553–558.

Treadway, M. T., & Zald, D. H. (2011). Reconsidering anhedonia in depression: Lessons from translational neuroscience. *Neuroscience and Biobehavioral Reviews, 35*(3), 537–555.

Trejo, J. L., Carro, E., & Torres-Aleman, I. (2001). Circulating insulin-like growth factor I mediates exercise-induced increases in the number of new neurons in the adult hippocampus. *Journal of Neuroscience, 21*(5), 1628–1634.

Uher, R., Caspi, A., Houts, R., Sugden, K., Williams, B., Poulton, R., & Moffitt, T. E. (2011). Serotonin transporter gene moderates childhood maltreatment's effects on persistent but not single-episode depression: Replications and implications for resolving inconsistent results. *Journal of Affective Disorders, 135*(1–3), 56–65.

van Praag, H., Kempermann, G., & Gage, F. H. (1999). Running increases cell proliferation and neurogenesis in the adult mouse dentate gyrus. *Nature Neuroscience, 2*(3), 266–270.

Vgontzas, A. N., Zoumakis, E., Bixler, E. O., Lin, H. M., Follett, H., Kales, A., & Chrousos, G. P. (2004). Adverse effects of modest sleep restriction on sleepiness, performance, and inflammatory cytokines. *Journal of Clinical Endocrinology and Metabolism, 89*(5), 2119–2126.

von Känel, R., Dimsdale, J. E., Mills, P. J., Ancoli-Israel, S., Patterson, T. L., Mausbach, B. T., & Grant, I. (2006). Effect of Alzheimer caregiving stress and age on frailty markers interleukin-6, C-reactive protein, and D-dimer. *Journals of Gerontology, 61*(9), 963–969.

von Känel, R., Mills, P. J., Fainman, C., & Dimsdale, J. E. (2001). Effects of psychological stress and psychiatric disorders on blood coagulation and fibrinolysis: A biobehavioral pathway to coronary artery disease? *Psychosomatic Medicine, 63*(4), 531–544.

Wallis, C. (2014). Gut reactions. *Scientific American, 310*(6), 30, 33.

Wang, G., Siow, Y. L., & O. K. (2000). Homocysteine stimulates nuclear factor kappaB activity and monocyte chemoattractant protein-1 expression in vascular smooth-muscle cells: A possible role for protein kinase C. *Biochemical Journal, 352*(Pt. 3), 817–826.

Wang, R., Xu, Y., Wu, H. L., Li, Y. B., Li, Y. H., Guo, J. B., & Li, X. J. (2008). The antidepressant effects of curcumin in the forced swimming test involve 5-HT1 and 5-HT2 receptors. *European Journal of Pharmacology, 578*(1), 43–50.

Wang, Y., & Kasper, L. H. (2014). The role of microbiome in central nervous system disorders. *Brain, Behavior, and Immunity, 38,* 1–12.

Warner-Schmidt, J. L., Vanover, K. E., Chen, E. Y., Marshall, J. J., & Greengard, P. (2011). Antidepressant effects of selective serotonin reuptake inhibitors (SSRIs) are attenuated by antiinflammatory drugs in mice and humans. *Proceedings of the National Academy of Sciences of the United States of America, 108*(22), 9262–9267.

Watkins, E. R., & Nolen-Hoeksema, S. (2014). A habit-goal framework of depressive rumination. *Journal of Abnormal Psychology, 123*(1), 24–34.

Watkins, J. T., Leber, W. R., Imber, S. D., Collins, J. F., Elkin, I., Pilkonis, P. A.,...Glass, D. R. (1993). Temporal course of change of depression. *Journal of Consulting and Clinical Psychology, 61*(5), 858–864.

Way, B. M., & Taylor, S. E. (2010). Social influences on health: Is serotonin a critical mediator? *Psychosomatic Medicine, 72*(2), 107–112.

Weymann, K. B., Wood, L. J., Zhu, X., & Marks, D. L. (2014). A role for orexin in cytotoxic chemotherapy-induced fatigue. *Brain, Behavior, and Immunity, 37,* 84–94.

Whitaker, R. (2010). *Anatomy of an epidemic.* New York, NY: Crown.

Wickramaratne, P. J., Weissman, M. M., Leaf, P. J., & Holford, T. R. (1989). Age, period and cohort effects on the risk of major depression: Results from five United States communities. *Journal of Clinical Epidemiology, 42*(4), 333–343.

Williams, N., Simpson, A. N., Simpson, K., & Nahas, Z. (2009). Relapse rates with long-term antidepressant drug therapy: A meta-analysis. *Human Psychopharmacology, 24*(5), 401–408.

Woo, T. U. (2013). Neurobiology of schizophrenia onset. *Current Topics in Behavioral Neuroscience, 16,* 267–295. doi:10.1007.7854_2103_243

Wu, C. S., Wang, S. C., Cheng, Y. C., & Gau, S. S. (2011). Association of cerebrovascular events with antidepressant use: A case-crossover study. *American Journal of Psychiatry, 168*(5), 511–521.

Yadid, G., & Friedman, A. (2008). Dynamics of the dopaminergic system as a key component to the understanding of depression. *Progress in Brain Research, 172,* 265–286.

Ye, X., Lai, C. Q., Crott, J. W., Troen, A. M., Ordovas, J. M., & Tucker, K. L. (2011). The folate hydrolase 1561C>T polymorphism is associated with depressive symptoms in Puerto Rican adults. *Psychosomatic Medicine, 73*(5), 385–392.

Yoshimura, R., Hori, H., Ikenouchi-Sugita, A., Umene-Nakano, W., Ueda, N., & Nakamura, J. (2009). Higher plasma interleukin-6 (IL-6) level is associated with SSRI- or SNRI-refractory depression. *Progress in Neuro-Psychopharmacology & Biological Psychiatry, 33*(4), 722–726.

Yuen, K. W., Garner, J. P., Carson, D. S., Keller, J., Lembke, A., Hyde, S. A.,...Parker, K. J. (2014). Plasma oxytocin concentrations are lower in depressed vs. healthy control women and are independent of cortisol. *Journal of Psychiatric Research, 51*, 30–36.

Zak, P. J., Kurzban, R., & Matzner, W. T. (2005). Oxytocin is associated with human trustworthiness. *Hormones and Behavior, 48*(5), 522–527.

Zhou, F. M., Liang, Y., Salas, R., Zhang, L., De Biasi, M., & Dani, J. A. (2005). Corelease of dopamine and serotonin from striatal dopamine terminals. *Neuron, 46*(1), 65–74.

Zis, A. P., & Goodwin, F. K. (1979). Major affective disorder as a recurrent illness: A critical review. *Archives of General Psychiatry, 36*(8 Spec. No.), 835–839.

Zorrilla, E. P., Luborsky, L., McKay, J. R., Rosenthal, R., Houldin, A., Tax, A.,...Schmidt, K. (2001). The relationship of depression and stressors to immunological assays: A meta-analytic review. *Brain, Behavior, and Immunity, 15*(3), 199–226.

5

Anxiety

This chapter focuses on anxiety disorders. It begins with a discussion of the physiology of anxiety, including the major structures involved in the creation of a fear memory. The mechanisms for extinction of conditioned anxiety will be considered. As will be explained, extinction does not eliminate the memory. Rather, with extinction, the prefrontal cortex (PFC) overrides the memory. Recent research suggests that there may be a way to eliminate the fear memory. This new possibility is called reconsolidation. When an unsettling memory is brought into awareness, there may be a window of time for altering the memory so that when the old memory is placed back into storage (the reconsolidation process), the old memory gets replaced with a new version or is even eliminated.

Following discussion of the basic physiology of fear conditioning, specific anxiety disorders (generalized anxiety, obsessive-compulsive disorder [OCD], and posttraumatic stress disorder [PTSD]) are discussed. Finally, treatments are considered. The chapter ends with a review of the literature about how clients can talk about their fears to minimize them and how relabeling or reappraising of past events can be helpful.

THE PHYSIOLOGY OF ANXIETY

Basic Physiology of Fear

The emotion for which the neuronal connections have been best articulated is fear. Identification of the amygdala as a prime player in anxiety emerged when Kluver and Bucy in 1937 made lesions in the amygdala of monkeys. These monkeys exhibited fearlessness in approaching objects that previously had frightened them. In fact, they were prone to orally explore previously feared stimuli (Phelps, 2006). About 40 years later, Joseph LeDoux became a pioneer in mapping out the parts and the connections of the amygdala. The amygdala plays a prominent role in both fear in response to natural fear inducers (fox urine if one is a rodent) and in fear conditioning. In fear conditioning, a natural fear stimulus, for example, fox urine, is presented with a tone. Later, presentation of the tone alone (called a conditioned stimulus) will elicit the fear response (conditioned response) similar to the way in which the fox urine (unconditioned stimulus) had elicited the unconditioned fear response.

Different parts of the amygdala are activated in response to natural stimuli versus a conditioned stimulus. The medial amygdala activates in response to the unconditioned stimulus. The lateral amygdala is involved in learning the association of the conditioned stimulus with the unconditioned stimulus. In terms of the output from the amygdala, the amygdala projects to the hypothalamus so that the proper autonomic responses (activation of the sympathetic nervous system) and hormonal responses (activation of the hypothalamic–pituitary–adrenal axis) occur. The medial amygdala, which processes innate fear, also projects outward. Eventually, for innate fears, the medial amygdala sends output to the nucleus accumbens and the dorsal periaqueductal gray (for fight or flight). The lateral amygdala, the association area for learning the connection between conditioned and unconditioned stimuli, projects to the central amygdala, which in turn then signals to the ventral periaqueductal gray for freezing. Thus, depending on the signaling in the amgydala, the fear response can be fight or flight or freezing (Chen, Shemyakin, & Wiedenmayer, 2006; Fogaca et al., 2012; LeDoux, 1998, 2003; Walker, Toufexis, & Davis, 2003). In terms of higher order structures, the dorsal anterior cingulate cortex, which also projects to the basolateral amygdala, is activated in response to viewing a fearful expression (Milad, Wright, et al., 2007) and there are connections from the amygdala to the anterior cingulate cortex (Paus, 2001).

Human work exploring fear or anxiety has also used the paradigm of fear conditioning. A shock is paired with a light. The light will soon elicit activation of the amygdala and sweaty palms. Consistent with animal data, imaging work in persons with damage to the amygdala finds that they fail to learn conditioned fear responses. Although persons with damaged amygdala can report that the light means the shock is coming, their hands do not perspire in response to the light (Phelps, 2006).

The amygdala will respond to minimal cues signaling danger. For example, Whalen et al. demonstrated that the stimulus of "eyes which were opened wide" was enough to evoke a response in the amygdala (Whalen et al., 2004). Even when fear-inducing stimuli are presented at subthreshold for awareness levels, the amygdala can be activated (Phelps, 2006; Shin & Liberzon, 2010). Fear conditioning can occur through observation of another person receiving shock paired with a conditioned stimulus. Even when the observer has never been shocked, but has observed another person shocked in the presence of the conditioned stimulus, the observer will display amygdala activation and increased palm perspiration in response to the conditioned stimulus (Phelps, 2006).

Differentiating Anxiety From Fear

Michael Davis has focused on the distinction between fear and anxiety. Although fear describes a response to a specific stimulus, anxiety refers to an unsettling apprehension, a fear of something anticipated, with the object of dread not necessarily specified or only vaguely understood. Anxiety is more future focused, rather than the here and now of fear. Anxiety can be measured by presenting an annoying stimulus (an airpuff to the eyes, a loud noise) and measuring the startle response (the degree of muscle tension around the eyes). A number of manipulations will increase a startle response. Thinking about bad things or looking at gruesome pictures, being threatened verbally, awaiting unpredictable shock, or being in the dark will all enhance the startle response. The area of the brain involved in anxiety has been identified. Anxiety-potentiated startle involves activation of the bed nucleus of the stria terminalis (BNST), considered to be part of the extended amygdala. In terms of the molecules involved in activating the BNST, corticotropin-releasing factor (CRF) and calcitonin gene-related peptides are involved (Davis, Walker, Miles, & Grillon, 2010). In contrast, progesterone and testosterone (hormones) seem to ameliorate fear-potentiated startle (Toufexis, Myers, & Davis, 2006).

It should be noted that the amygdala and the BNST are also involved in responding to positive stimuli. Some nuclei in the BNST also project to the ventral tegmental area (VTA) and may play a role in stress-elicited drug-seeking behavior (Kim et al., 2013; Silberman & Winder, 2013). The responses of the amygdala and BNST nuclei to positive stimuli have received less attention in the literature.

Fear Memories

In the 1990s, much controversy was generated over whether memories of traumatic events could be repressed and forgotten. A general consensus has now emerged. Fear memories are more vivid and more strongly formed than other memories. Strong activation of the amygdala involves more epinephrine–adrenaline and norepinephrine–noradrenaline release from the adrenal glands (glands above the kidney). These hormones operate on the hippocampus, where episodic memories (where-and-when memories) are formed (Arnsten, 1998; Phelps, 2006). (The process of creating a long-lasting memory of the event is called consolidation of the memory.) Greater activation of the amygdala at the time of an event results in a stronger memory of the event (Shin & Liberzon, 2010). However, amygdala activation at the time of the frightening event narrows attention. Additionally, cortisol, the stress hormone, will impair memory for nonessential contextual features around the event. The central features of the situation will be better remembered, although details may not be retained (LeDoux, 2003; Phelps, 2006).

Memory researcher James McGaugh's work informs us that when a fear-inducing event has been experienced, it does take some time for the memory to be consolidated in the hippocampus. James McGaugh was well aware that norepinephrine release at the time of memory formation can strengthen this memory. Norepinephrine acts on norepinephrine receptors (beta-adrenergic receptors), which enhance the encoding of fear memories. If this process can be interrupted, for example, by administering a blood pressure medication (propranolol, a beta-adrenergic antagonist), the formation of the strong emotional memory can be interrupted. Blocking memory consolidation has made it to the clinic. Earlier, McGaugh suggested that if people who had suffered a trauma (such as a car accident) were given propranolol (an antagonist to the norepinephrine receptor), then the memory consolidation would be blocked (Phelps, 2006). In clinical trials of accident victims, those given propranolol at the time of the accident were less likely to develop posttraumatic stress disorder (PTSD; Ressler & Mayberg, 2007).

How Does Extinction Happen?

Behaviorists have long known that it is possible to extinguish a conditioned fear response by presenting the conditioned stimulus (tone) without the unconditioned stimulus (fox urine). Rather than unlearning, the extinction process involves new learning. The neurocircuitry for this process is now known. Basically, neurons in the ventromedial PFC area (more specifically the infralimbic region) project to GABAergic (gamma-aminobutyric acid–ergic) intercalating neurons in the amygdala, which block other neurons in the amygdala. The fear response is nullified. Rather than being erased, the conditioned fear circuitry is still intact. If the animal has its cortex removed or inactivated, the old fear returns (Maroun, 2013; Milad, Quirk, et al., 2007; Shin & Liberzon, 2010). Furthermore, creating frightening conditions for the animal will also reinstate the previously extinguished fear response (Maroun, 2013). Considering this process in people, for example, if an aging veteran, who has lived successfully without PTSD symptoms for 40 years, loses his spouse, old war fears may return. It is to be expected.

Under stressful conditions, it is difficult to extinguish a previously learned conditioned fear response. Under stressful conditions, impairment in the plasticity of new connections in the medial prefrontal cortex may occur (Maroun, 2013).

In contrast to the conditions that make extinction harder, others have found ways to enhance the extinction process. Because extinction involves making new synapses from neurons in the medial PFC to inhibitory neurons in the amygdala, Mike Davis et al. sought to determine whether d-cycloserine, an N-methyl-d-aspartate (NMDA) agonist and a potentiator of new synapse formation, would facilitate extinction during the extinction process. Davis et al. were successful in strengthening the speed of extinction with d-cycloserine (Ressler et al., 2004). It should be noted that the d-cycloserine is only administered during the extinction; it is not given for an extended period of time.

Possibility of Reconsolidation

Memory researchers have reasons to believe that when a memory is brought into awareness, it can be altered in some way or even prevented from being placed back in storage. The term *reconsolidation* refers to the process of placing a previously consolidated memory trace back into storage after it is recalled. In an original demonstration, Nader, Schafe, and Le Doux (2000) re-exposed a rat to a conditioned fear stimulus, but then injected a protein expression inhibitor in the amygdala. (The initial consolidation of a memory and reconsolidation of a memory trace requires synthesis of new proteins.) After the interference with reconsolidation, the rat was no longer fearful of the conditioned stimulus and there was no fear reinstatement later, as is observed sometimes with an extinction process. This demonstration generated a great deal of excitement in the clinical community. It showed that following recall of a memory, there is an opportunity to recast or "reconsolidate" the memory with the window of opportunity being between 1 and 6 hours. Unlike extinction, which entails a formation of a new connection of the ventromedial PFC to downregulate the amygdala, a reconsolidated memory would not be subject to reinstatement given a stressful period.

Disrupting reconsolidation has been employed in the treatment of PTSD. Because propranolol (the norepinephrine receptor blocker, i.e., a beta-adrenergic antagonist) blocks the formation of the first memory trace, it seemed reasonable to block reconsolidation of the memory trace with propranolol. (Propranolol is a relatively innocuous blood pressure medication that inhibits receptors for adrenaline/noradrenaline.) Providing propranolol systemically and with intra-amygdala application, Debiec and LeDoux (2004) were able to block reconsolidation in rodents. Kindt, Soeter, and Vervliet (2009) used propranolol in the laboratory to block reconsolidation in humans. Roger Pitman, a PTSD researcher, used propranolol during exposure sessions in an attempt to alter reconsolidation (Ressler & Mayberg, 2007). Following propranolol treatment during and after exposure to a fearful memory script, those with PTSD displayed lower levels of sympathetic nervous system (SNS) activation when thinking about their fear in a subsequent exposure session (Brunet et al., 2008).

There is a complication. The animal work indicates, at most, a 6-hour window for changing the reconsolidation process. Furthermore, it is known that old memories are more stable than more recently formed memories. In people with PTSD, many of the memories are old memories. Graff et al. (2014) speculated that old memories were more stable than recently formed memories because of epigenetic modifications to a gene for a protein involved in neuronal cell activation (c-Fos).

The details here are dicey and probably not vital for appreciating the bottom line, but a brief explanation is provided for those who want detail. C-Fos is a marker of brain activity in an area and signals the availability of a window for changing a memory in the reconsolidation process. More c-Fos is a marker for greater plasticity, that is, greater capacity to alter neuronal connections. An enzyme, histone deacetylase 2, will prevent the increase of c-Fos by changing the c-Fos gene's DNA's accessibility. (Recall from Chapter 2 that altering the accessibility of DNA is called an epigenetic change.) Graff et al. speculated that if they employed a chemical to knock out the enzyme (histone deacetylase 2) that was precluding the increase in c-Fos, they could increase the malleability of the memory and alter the reconsolidation process. Graff et al. were able to inject their chemical into the body cavity in mice, which inhibited histone deacetylase, allowing more c-Fos to be expressed. Following administration of the histone deacetylase inhibitor, Graff et al. showed that the "trauma" memory was erased. This was a clever demonstration in animals, in which you can deliver a chemical to the site in the brain where you want it. In people, drug delivery may or will constitute a problem with this type of intervention. However, the experiment did constitute a "proof of concept."

Teaching Active Coping

Animal work has also shown that fear responses can be eclipsed by creating active responses. In a particular demonstration, after learning conditioned fear, some animals were allowed to make the active response of moving into safe territory. In the active animals, rather than the lateral amygdala signaling to the central amygdala to generate the downstream syndrome of fear, signaling was diverted through another structure in the amygdala (lateral amygdala to basal amygdala) and then to the ventral striatum (location of the nucleus accumbens). The animals making the active coping response failed to display freezing, the conditioned fear behavior (Amorapanth, LeDoux, & Nader, 2000). In reviewing this study, LeDoux and Gorman (2001) suggested that development of PTSD can be precluded by producing active coping responses following exposure to fear-inducing events.

TYPES OF ANXIETY DISORDERS

Anxiety disorders are the most common form of disorder. At any point in time, 12% of the population meets criteria for an anxiety disorder. Over the course of a lifetime, 28.8% of the population will experience an anxiety disorder (Kessler et al., 2005). For some anxiety disorders, the stimulus bringing on the anxiety is clear. The anxiety-evoking stimuli are clear for PTSD and for phobias. Similarly, with OCD, the fear-eliciting stimuli that precipitate the anxiety-reducing ritualistic behaviors are clear. The precipitant for those with panic attacks is also clear. (Those with panic attacks seem to respond to small, nonharmful changes in their blood chemistry.) In contrast, in generalized anxiety disorder (GAD), fear-eliciting stimuli are less easily identified.

There is a great deal of overlap between anxiety and depression. One third to one half of those with depression also meet criteria for anxiety disorder; 40% to 50% of those with anxiety will meet depression criteria at some point (Murphy et al., 2004). Panic disorder is a particular problem in primary care. The medical utilization rates are higher for those with panic disorder than those with other anxiety disorders (Deacon, Lickel, & Abramowitz, 2008).

Generalized Anxiety Disorder

GAD is characterized by worry and apprehension. Feeling "keyed up" or "on edge," being readily fatigued, having difficulty sleeping, muscle tension, irritability, and difficulty concentrating contribute to the diagnosis.

Persons who are high on trait anxiety do exhibit more amygdala activation when shown frightening images, even when the presentation of these images is too brief to allow cognitive processing (Etkin et al., 2004; Ewbank et al., 2009). There is also support for the view that anxious people do selectively attend to and dwell on dangers. Persons who are selected for extreme scores on measures of anxiety are quicker in finding angry faces and fearful faces in a crowd (Doty, Japee, Ingvar, & Ungerleider, 2013; Phelps, 2006). When working on another task, those selected for high trait anxiety are more distracted by fearful faces or words that can evoke emotion. The results of a meta-analysis confirmed the hypothesis that the attention of anxious individuals is drawn to threat stimuli (Bar-Haim, Lamy, Pergamin, Bakermans-Kranenburg, & van Ijzendoon, 2007).

The dorsolateral PFC (DLPFC), an area implicated in emotional regulation, is hypothesized to exercise some control over the brain's fear structure, the amygdala. Experimental results confirm that the DLPFC can downregulate the brain's fear response. Although research participants exhibit activation of the amygdala in response to fearful faces, when asked to categorize the emotion in the faces, the DLPFC is active and there is less activity in the amygdala (Hariri, Bookheimer, & Mazziotta, 2000). Thus, the DLPFC offers a mechanism for restraining the amygdala's capacity for generating anxiety.

Those with anxiety disorders may be less effective in inhibiting the amygdala. Research with young adults with high anxiety levels suggests a low level of connectivity between the DLPFC and the amygdala, as evidenced by a weaker negative correlation between these two areas compared to healthy controls (Hardee et al., 2013; Monk et al., 2008). Inhibited (shy) children often exhibit high anxiety levels as adults. An imaging study of young adults who had earlier been identified as inhibited children confirmed lower levels of connectivity between the DLPFC and the amygdala (Hardee et al., 2013). In addition to using the DLPFC to downregulate the amygdala, the parasympathetic nervous system, as measured by greater heart rate variability, is also involved in downregulating anxiety. Those with high vagal tone (greater heart rate variability) are better at regulating fear (see Chapter 2, Polyvagal Theory section). However, those with anxiety disorders exhibit lower levels of heart rate variability (Thayer, Friedman, & Borkovec, 1996). Thus, both emotional regulation through the DLPFC regulation and regulation through the parasympathetic nervous system (specifically the vagus nerve) appear to be deficient in those with anxiety disorders.

Many of the same genetic risk factors predispose to GAD, panic disorder, and PTSD. Phobias, however, seem to be genetically independent (Chantarujikapong et al., 2001; Craske & Waters, 2005). The short serotonin transporter has received much attention as a risk factor for depression and anxiety. The adjective *short* refers to the promoter region of the serotonin transporter. Because the promoter region is smaller, less of the serotonin transporter is made. (Recall that the transporter's job is to remove serotonin from the synapse.) Thus, in those who are anxious, serotonin remains in the synapse for a longer period of time.

The short serotonin transporter allele is a risk factor for anxiety. However, genetic studies suggest that symptoms developing in a person with the short transporter risk allele are highly dependent on environmental factors. In a representative study, Petersen et al. (2012) genotyped children on their serotonin transporter allele as well as assessing the stressfulness of their environments. Petersen et al. found that when coupled with a stressful childhood environment, those with both the stress and the short transporter were more likely to exhibit symptoms of both depression and anxiety in adolescence. (Those with the long transporter were resilient in the stressful environment.) Although some researchers have focused on the interaction of alleles for the serotonin transporter and stressful environments, Way and Taylor (2010) examined how those with the short serotonin transporter fare in supportive environments. They found that those with the short serotonin transporter exhibited better mental health outcomes than others when raised in supportive environments. Thus, the short allele for the serotonin transporter should probably be characterized as conferring greater responsiveness to the environment rather than being a depression–anxiety risk factor.

The impact of the serotonin transporter alleles on momentary responses has also been evaluated. Hariri et al. genotyped people on the serotonin transporter and then scanned their brains as they observed frightening or gruesome photos (Munafo, Brown, & Hariri, 2008). Those with the short transporter exhibited more activation in their amygdalae. Lonsdorf et al. (2009) found that those with the short transporter exhibited stronger fear-potentiated startle (where the presentation of a loud noise increased subsequent startle to an air puff), another marker of anxiety.

Summary

Those with GAD differ from others in particular ways. They do seem to focus and be drawn in by negative stimuli. In terms of the physiology for regulating distressing emotions, they show deficits. There are genetic variations that predispose to anxiety; however, genetic risk factors require particular environments before anxiety symptoms are manifested. All of these findings are consistent with the possibility that anxiety symptoms can be modified through environmental interventions. In the section on treatment, we consider ways to increase emotional regulation and change the manner in which people deploy their attention.

Obsessive-Compulsive Disorder

Persons with OCD become anxious at particular times and develop rituals that serve to decrease their anxiety. The concept of "negative reinforcement" explains how this works. When behaviors turn off a negative experience, the behaviors become "negatively reinforced" and increase in frequency. OCD rituals decrease subjective, internal anxiety and, thus, the behavioral ritual becomes negatively reinforced (Christianson et al., 2012). In fact, in an experiment in which persons with OCD were induced to perform their escape or anxiety behaviors at a higher level, each time escaping their initial anxiety, their fears of contamination were even more enhanced (Deacon & Maack, 2008). A negative reinforcement effect was noted. The study suggests that giving into the urges to perform OCD rituals will increase their tenacity.

Although the OCD of most individuals is another form of an anxiety disorder, earlier it was noted that some of those with OCD exhibited problems in other brain circuits not generally associated with anxiety (Rapoport, 1989). There is evidence suggesting that the basal ganglia, structures associated with the control of movement, are involved in the expression of OCD behaviors in subsets of those with OCD. A variety of observations led to the emergence of this evidence.

Some persons who are infected with group A beta-hemolytic streptococcus pharyngeal (throat) infection subsequently develop rheumatic fever. Rheumatic fever affects the heart. Later, Sydenham's chorea follows (Swedo et al., 1989). Sydenham's chorea involves tics, that is, involuntary, repetitive movements of the upper body and the face. Along with the tics, some (17% in the Hounie et al. [2007] sample) develop compulsions to avoid germs and rituals to avoid contamination, for example, wiping doors, washing hands, and avoiding contact with presumably contaminated areas. Thus, there seemed to be a connection among infection with a particular bacterium, an autoimmune response to the heart, movement problems, and characteristic OCD behaviors.

With advances in immunology and understanding of antibodies, it became possible to assess antibody titers in the blood of persons with

Sydenham's chorea. In fact, it was confirmed that those with documented Sydenham's chorea did have antibodies to proteins expressed in the basal ganglia (an area of the brain involved in controlling movements). The explanation for the antibody elevation is that proteins expressed by streptococcus bacteria are similar in structure to proteins expressed in the basal ganglia. Thus, the antibodies to the bacteria cross-react with proteins (lysoganglioside receptors) in the basal ganglia (Hounie et al., 2007). These findings implied that the basal ganglia may be a key structure in the expression of OCD-associated behaviors. Consistent with this, some individuals displaying OCD behaviors have a documented history of scarlet fever followed by Sydenham's chorea (Hounie et al., 2007; Mercadante et al., 2005).

Some individuals with OCD also meet criteria for Tourette's syndrome. Tourette's syndrome is characterized by tics, which may include eye blinking; grimacing; jaw, neck shoulder, or limb movements; sniffing; grunting; chirping; throat clearing; corprolalic utterances (compulsion to make offensive statements); biting; and/or hitting. In children with Tourette's, 60% to 70% also exhibit hyperactivity and 50% exhibit obsessive-compulsive behaviors (Swain, Scahill, Lombroso, King, & Leckman, 2007). The joint occurrence of tics and ritualistic compulsions suggests that the OCD behaviors of some can be considered to be a type of movement disorder.

Recent studies have confirmed that basal ganglia structures are critical to the expression of OCD behaviors. Recordings from neurons in the basal ganglia confirm that this area of the brain is active during the expression of OCD behaviors, such as excessive checking (Burbaud et al., 2013).

Super Recollectors

Other data are consistent with the basal ganglia, structures involved in motor regulation, being relevant in OCD. James McGaugh and Larry Cahill have recruited persons with exceptional long-term memories. (For example, these individuals remember everything they did on each Tuesday of their lives.) McGaugh and Cahill were fascinated by these individuals and wanted to explore the ways in which they differed from other people. Brain imaging work on these individuals noted that they have larger than average right anterior putamens and caudates, structures of the basal ganglia (LePort et al., 2012). The basal ganglia are thought to mediate memory for habits, particularly motor habits. Thus, it is understandable why increased basal ganglia size might be found in those with superior memories (Graybiel, 2008; Leckman & Riddle, 2000). In addition to their superior memories, McGaugh and Cahill's research subjects with superior memories also exhibited features of OCD. Several of them hoarded or collected items, required detailed organization of their physical environments, and displayed heightened fear of germs. (For example, one individual insisted on organizing her closet in sections based on clothing color.) With regard to social function, McGaugh and Cahill's super-memory individuals displayed normal social interactions. None of McGaugh and Cahill's subjects with superior memory regretted his or her superior memories or reported that his or her memories interfered with his or her daily life activities (LePort et al., 2012). Although there is no evidence to suggest that those with superior memories have antibodies to proteins in the basal ganglia, the finding of larger basal ganglia does suggest that basal ganglia are implicated in both superior memories and OCD.

Possibility of More Targeted Treatment

The recognition that some persons with OCD may actually suffer from an autoimmune disorder does suggest that targeting the immune system may offer a better way to ameliorate distress. Swain, Scahill, Lombroso, King, and Leckman (2007) report mixed results for intravenous infusion of antibodies to other antibodies. The recognition that the basal ganglia are involved in symptom production has led to the development of deep brain stimulation in this brain area as another treatment strategy (Burbaud et al., 2013). The selective serotonin reuptake inhibitors (SSRIs) are also employed (Rapoport, 1989).

Even when OCD emanates from dysfunction in movement structures of the brain, developing regulatory capacity offers a productive treatment strategy. Observations of children with Tourette's syndrome confirm that brain regulatory areas can suppress symptoms. Interestingly, persons with tics can suppress the tic for a given time interval, but the tension associated with suppression builds. At some point, they succumb and move their bodies. Recall that the ventrolateral PFC is involved in regulating attention and in suppressing motoric behavior. When persons with tics are engaged in activities requiring focused attention, possibly engaging the ventrolateral PFC (the regulation center introduced in Chapter 2), symptoms subside (Swain et al., 2007). For those with compulsions and obsessions, whether the OCD behaviors arise from the basal ganglia or other brain areas, developing the brain's regulatory capacity constitutes a treatment strategy. Presently, response prevention (i.e., restraining the urge to perform a compelled behavior) following exposure to ritual-eliciting stimuli is recommended for the treatment of OCD (Foa, 2005; Swain et al., 2007).

Posttraumatic Stress Disorder

PTSD is the fourth most common psychiatric disorder, occurring in 10% of men and 18% of women (Breslau et al., 1998). The diagnosis of PTSD requires exposure to some fear or horror-evoking situation that others would evaluate as horrific. Witnessing harm to another person can also qualify as trauma. Following trauma, the individual is plagued by intrusive thoughts, strong physiological responses given reminders of the previous trauma, a generalization of the fear reaction to other stimuli, active avoidance of reminders, emotional numbing, enhanced startle response, and hypervigilance. Although symptoms most often develop shortly after the traumatic event, in some people, there is a delay in the development of PTSD symptoms. There is an interesting difference in those with PTSD as contrasted with other anxiety disorders. Most anxiety disorders are associated with higher levels of cortisol. Those with PTSD exhibit lower baseline levels of cortisol compared to controls, although higher levels of CRF, a hormone that is involved in initiating the release of cortisol, have been found in their cerebrospinal fluid (Jovanovic et al., 2010b).

Factors Associated With Enhanced Risk for PTSD

Why do some develop PTSD while others do not? Even when given exposure to trauma, 80% to 90% of individuals are resilient and do not develop PTSD (Gillespie et al., 2009; Hoge et al., 2004; Jovanovic & Ressler, 2010). In a study in Sweden, the type of trauma predicted 16.7% of the variance in determining whether PTSD would develop after the trauma. In terms of the types of life-threatening events that result in PTSD, traumatic events caused by people are more likely to result in PTSD than other types of events. Traumas, such as an accident or a fire, result in PTSD less than 10% of the time, in contrast to events, such as rape or combat exposure, which have occurrence rates between 20% and 60%. Traumas associated with a loss of trust in other human beings result in more frequent development of PTSD. Charuvastra and Cloitre (2008), who reviewed this literature, raise the issue of whether the loss of trust in others is a mediator for when an event will result in PTSD.

Consistent with the idea that loss of trust in others is a key factor in PTSD development, social support during the time immediately following the stressor does decrease the emergence of PTSD (Boscarino, 1995; Charuvastra & Cloitre, 2008). Early abuse, such as child abuse, increases risk (Charuvastra & Cloitre, 2008; Duncan, Saunders, Kilpatrick, Hanson, & Resnick, 1996). Repeated exposure to stressors also increases the probability of developing PTSD (Ozbay et al., 2007).

Personal characteristics also influence whether a person will develop PTSD following exposure to trauma. Having a greater propensity to experience anxiety increases the risk of developing PTSD after trauma. Those displaying greater skin conductance to threat and slower habituation to frightening stimuli are more likely to develop PTSD following trauma (Guthrie & Bryant, 2006; Pole et al., 2009). Among firefighters, those exhibiting a strong startle response, as assessed prior to exposure to a fire, were more likely to develop PTSD after a fire (Gilbertson et al., 2002). Those who experience dissociation at the time of the event are more likely to develop PTSD (Charuvastra & Cloitre, 2008).

In Chapter 2, the role of the ventrolateral PFC in regulating responses was reviewed. The possibility that those with PTSD will have less emotional regulatory capacity has been tested. New et al. (2009) compared three groups: persons with PTSD, persons who had not been exposed to trauma, and persons without PTSD but who had been exposed to trauma. Research participants were asked to either suppress or magnify their response to negative pictures while their brains were scanned. Those with PTSD exhibited less ability to alter (suppress or magnify) their responses than others. During the suppression instructions, those with PTSD showed less activity in the ventrolateral PFC than those who were never exposed to trauma, although the difference between those with and without PTSD who had been trauma exposed was not statistically significant. In terms of the capacity to magnify distress, the two groups without PTSD activated similar regions and differed from those with PTSD. These findings suggest that self-regulatory capacity may be impaired in those with PTSD. Consistent with this, structural differences in the ventromedial PFC of those with PTSD (Christianson et al., 2012), an area that can inhibit fear experience and expression, have also been identified.

Persons with PTSD do, as a group, have smaller hippocampi. The finding of smaller hippocampal volume has been attributed to greater exposure to cortisol, the stress hormone. However, Pitman et al. questioned whether a reduction in hippocampus volume occurs after trauma, or whether the small hippocampus precedes the trauma and renders an individual susceptible to the development of PTSD. To address their question, Roger Pittman and colleagues (Gilbertson et al., 2002) examined the hippocampi of the never–trauma-exposed identical twins of Vietnam veterans with PTSD. The hippocampi of identical twins who had never been exposed to trauma were also smaller. This finding suggested that a small hippocampus might be a risk factor for PTSD rather than a consequence.

Several allelic variations in genes have been identified as associated with PTSD: a variation in the gene for catechol-O-methyltransferase, which is an enzyme for degrading dopamine, norepinephrine, and epinephrine (Norrholm et al., 2013); a variation in the FKBP5 gene, which is involved in regulating sensitivity to cortisol (Mehta et al., 2011); a variation in the gene for the receptor for CRF, which is involved in responding to stress hormones (Feder, Nestler, & Charney, 2009). The pituitary adenylate cyclase-activating peptide (PACAP) protein receptor is one of the latest genes to be identified as risk factors for PTSD. In women, a single nucleotide change in the receptor for pituitary adenylate cyclase-activating polypeptide (PACAPR, which means the receptor for PACAP) has been linked with PTSD, as has high circulating levels of the PACAP protein itself. It is known that the PACAP system is involved in regulating CRF levels (Lehmann, Mustafa, Eiden, Herkenham, & Eiden, 2013). Persons without PTSD have been evaluated to determine how the PACAPR genetic risk factor influences response to threat. Researchers found that women carrying the risk factor for genetic variation for PACAPR display heightened amygdala activation to threat stimuli as assessed by functionalMRI (Ressler et al., 2011; Stevens et al., 2014). In summary, variations in proteins involved in responding to the cortisol and to the stimulus for cortisol production (CRF) increase the risk for PTSD.

PTSD Recovery

Two distinct processes may occur when an individual recovers from PTSD: extinction and learning safety cues. As discussed earlier, extinction occurs through a process during which conditioned stimuli are encountered without being followed by the unconditioned stimulus. Extinction does not erase the original memory trace through the amygdala. Rather, the ventromedial PFC inhibits the amygdala. The previously discussed research suggests that those with PTSD may have deficit capacity for regulation of emotional responding, a capacity relevant for the process of extinction.

Recovery from PTSD can also involve another type of conditioning: learning safety cues. This type of learning entails associating a relaxation response to safety signals. In their daily lives, persons with PTSD more often fail to distinguish threatening from nonthreatening environments. They are hypervigilant even in safe environments (Christianson et al., 2012; Jovanovic, Kazama, Bachevalier, & Davis, 2012; Jovanovic & Norrholm, 2011). Laboratory demonstrations are consistent with the hypothesis that those with PTSD fail to learn safety signals. Javanovic and colleagues developed a procedure to show that those with PTSD have difficulty learning to acquire proper responses to safety signals. In the laboratory, fear-potentiated startle can be measured. For most people, if a soothing stimulus precedes a loud noise, the eye contractions (startle response) are decreased relative to when an aversive stimulus (gruesome pictures) precedes the loud noise. In a laboratory test, researchers conditioned particular symbols to be associated with presentation of an aversive stimulus and some stimuli to signal safety. Those with PTSD startled to the same extent when soothing stimuli (safety signal) preceded the loud noise as when the disturbing stimuli preceded the loud noise. This occurred despite the fact that those with PTSD were cognitively aware that the soothing stimuli were signals for relaxation (Jovanovic et al., 2010a; Jovanovic et al., 2012). Thus, in those with PTSD, there are obstacles to both the extinction process and the learning safety-cue route to recovery.

Another potential system that might facilitate or impair the capacity for recovery from PTSD is the immune system. The involvement of inflammation in creating symptoms of major depression was reviewed in the chapter on depression (Chapter 4). Changes in immune system function are also associated with PTSD. Epigenetic changes in genes coding for proteins in the immune system have been noted. Those with PTSD exhibit higher levels of tumor necrosis factor alpha (TNF-alpha) in plasma. They are also lower on interleukin 4 (IL-4), a cytokine that exerts an anti-inflammatory effect in the brain (Smith et al., 2011). Those with PTSD exhibit lower heart rate variability (Minassian et al., 2014), a factor that suggests less control over inflammation. Recall that Naomi Eisenberger et al. found that with systemic inflammation, there is less activation of the nucleus accumbens in response to reward (see Chapter 4, section on inflammation). Consistent with the impact of inflammation on reward structures, those with PTSD also display less activation in the nucleus accumbens in response to social and monetary reward (Elman et al., 2009).

In terms of avenues for recovery from PTSD, strengthening the regulatory capacity of the PFC should facilitate both extinction and conditioning a relaxation response to safety cues. Activating strategies for decreasing systemic inflammation offers another route for enhancing recovery. We will look at further avenues in the next section on treatments.

TREATMENTS

Talk Therapies

Behavioral treatments are a major approach to treating anxiety disorders. For phobias and PTSD, persons are exposed to stimuli associated with their fear without the occurrence of actual harm. For OCD, individuals are exposed to stimuli that elicit compulsive behavior and not allowed to perform their rituals. For those with panic attack, inducing bodily changes with lactic acid infusion brings on the fear, which is then allowed to extinguish. These treatments yield effect sizes in the range of 0.79 to 1.38 (Deacon & Abramowitz, 2004). After treatment, there is evidence of brain changes. For example, Straube, Glauer, Dilger, Mentzel, and Miltner (2006) found that following exposure treatment, persons with specific phobias displayed less activity in the insula (an area that detects distress in internal organs) and anterior cingulate cortex when viewing the feared object. Those with OCD, after treatment, showed reductions in the activity of basal ganglia (Schwartz, Stoessel, Baxter, Martin, & Phelps, 1996).

Because GAD is not associated with specific fear-eliciting stimuli, exposure and response prevention are not appropriate. Specific versions of cognitive behavioral therapy have been developed for treating GAD. Treatment entails cognitive restructuring, relaxation, and self-monitoring to ease anxiety symptoms. Progressive muscle relaxation and training in self-monitoring are employed so that relaxation can be applied at particular times. Learning to counter catastrophic thinking is also addressed (Deacon & Abramowitz, 2004). For panic attacks, learning methods of control of breathing offers an additional tool.

Cognitive behavioral therapy is effective in the treatment of generalized anxiety. A study of youth with GAD compared the effects of cognitive behavioral therapy to SSRIs at 2 weeks after the end of treatment. Both groups had improved on measures of daily anxiety. Both treated groups showed enhanced levels of right ventrolateral PFC activation when viewing pictures of angry faces compared to a nontreated group. As the ventrolateral PFC is believed to be an area of emotional regulation, the imaging results affirmed the efficacy of both procedures (Maslowsky et al., 2010).

Medications for Anxiety

Benzodiazepines are often used to treat acute anxiety. Benzodiazepines are also frequently prescribed for sleep. Selection among benzodiazepines is based on their half-lives. Those with shorter half-lives include Halcion (triazolam) and Restoril (temazepam). Although Halcion is less likely to result in morning sedation, it can induce agitation and psychosis. All of the benzodiazepines can result in blackouts, such that individuals fail to remember what occurred while they were under the drug's influence. Benzodiazepines do impair driving ability. Tolerance to these drugs develops after 2 to 3 weeks' use (Trevor & Way, 2013). After use for extended periods of time, benzodiazepine discontinuation is associated with withdrawal symptoms, including anxiety, agitation, and possible seizures. Withdrawal symptoms can be lethal. Benzodiazepines are associated with increased risk for Alzheimer's disease (Billioti de Gage et al., 2014; Roy, Scola, Boustani, & Fairbanks, 2014).

There is concern that medicating persons with anxiety will decrease the efficacy of exposure therapy. Extinction during exposure therapy involves making new connections such that a patient learns that in a given context, the unconditioned stimulus will not occur. In order to learn new associations during exposure therapy, the anxiety response needs to be evoked. Part of the anxiety response involves sensations from the body. However, if a patient is medicated during the exposure training, internal anxiety will not be generated. Theoretically, there will be insufficient anxiety for the extinction process to take place. When the drugs are discontinued, then any apparent gains of exposure training will disappear. Clinical outcomes are consistent with this thinking (Otto, Smits, & Reese, 2006; Rothbaum et al., 2014).

Selective serotonin reuptake inhibitors are also used in the treatment of anxiety disorders. Between 20% and 33% of individuals fail to respond to the SSRIs. Response, when it occurs, is usually delayed for about 2 to 6 weeks (Farach et al., 2012). A meta-analysis, including all of the studies provided to the Food and Drug Administration (FDA) on paroxetine for anxiety, found that paroxetine decreased scores on the Hamilton Rating Scale for Anxiety (HRSA) by only 2.31 more points compared to placebo. (There are 56 possible points on the HRSA.) The difference in change between placebo and drug was significant, but effect sizes were small. There was some variation in efficacy across types of anxiety disorders. Treatment effects were a little higher for panic disorder than for GAD. Unlike the efficacy of SSRIs, which differ as a function of severity of depression, treatment efficacy did not differ for those with mild, moderate, and extreme anxiety levels. As in the studies on depression, much of the change in baseline scores could be attributed to placebo effects (Sugarman, Loree, Baltes, Grekin, & Kirsch, 2014). In terms of making a cost/benefit analysis, all of the side effects of antidepressants discussed in Chapter 4 can be expected to occur when taken for the treatment of anxiety disorders.

Other Nondrug Treatments

In Chapter 4, the role of inflammation in depression was reviewed. In those with anxiety, elevations in inflammatory factors also have been noted (Hou & Baldwin, 2012; Salim, Chugh, & Asghar, 2012). Consistent with the idea that anxiety also involves inflammation, Thayer, Friedman, and Borkovec (1996) have found lower heart rate variability in those with generalized anxiety. (Recall that lower heart rate variability is associated with greater systemic inflammation.) In Chapter 2, approaches to decreasing inflammation were reviewed. Some of these approaches have been applied to anxiety. Increasing consumption of omega-3s was shown to lower anxiety in medical students during examination periods (Kiecolt-Glaser, Belury, Andridge, Malarkey, & Glaser, 2011) and in substance abusers (Buydens-Branchey, Branchey, & Hibbeln, 2008). Exercise is an effective anxiety reducer and lowers systemic inflammation (Otto & Jasper, 2011).

There are additional strategies for lowering anxiety levels. Tai Chi practice has been found to lower anxiety levels (Song et al., 2014). Oxytocin is the hormone released during social bonding. There are oxytocin receptors in the central amygdala that, when activated by oxytocin, will decrease freezing in response to conditioned stimuli in animals (Viviani et al., 2011). Researchers have increased oxytocin by using nasal spray. Oxytocin nasal spray, administered as individuals see fearful stimuli, diminishes cortisol levels, amygdala activation, and subjective distress (Kirsch et al., 2005). Thus, there are theoretical reasons for increasing time with trusted friends, an activity that might raise oxytocin levels (Zak, Kurban, & Matzner, 2004). It can be effective in lowering anxiety levels.

Ways in Which to Talk About and Deal With Past Traumatic Events

In their review of the literature on PTSD, Charuvastra and Cloitre (2008, p. 18) express the widely held view that "One of the essential components of treatment is the 'emotional processing' of memories of trauma, with the goal of diminishing and resolving feelings of fear associated with memories." Charuvastra and Cloitre acknowledge that this requirement is consistent with Freud's view of the necessity of catharsis.

One of the assumptions made by followers of Freud is that expression of emotion will dissipate the emotion. Freud was a contemporary of those who developed the first law of thermodynamics, which states that energy can be transformed from one form to another but it can never be created or destroyed. Drawing an analogy from physics, the thinking was that if trauma created energy in a person's body, it needed to be released through catharsis, or it would be trapped in the body leading to psychosomatic illness (Breuer & Freud (1895/2013); Consedine, Magai, & Bonnano, 2002; Gross, 1998). Unfortunately, viewing emotions as trapped energy may not capture how human emotions function. Many formal studies of catharsis in which research participants are angered and then either distracted or allowed to vent find that venting seems to solidify the intensity of the subject's feelings. On a subsequent encounter, those who have vented are more bothered rather than less bothered by the irritant (Bushman, Baumeister, & Strack, 1999; Bushman, Bonacci, Pedersen, Vasquez, & Miller, 2005; Ebbesen, Ducan, & Konecni, 1975; Green & Murray, 1975). Thus, allowing emotional expression will not necessarily drain the emotion, as suggested by Freud's catharsis model.

There may be ways to revisit memories of past traumatic events that will prove beneficial. Exposure therapy involves revisiting memories of traumatic events and, because nothing terrible follows, the distress extinguishes. There is support for the efficacy of this approach. Consistent with beneficial effects of revisiting painful experiences, there is a large literature evaluating the impact of writing about distressing events. Jamie Pennebaker has repeatedly shown that writing about trauma can have beneficial effects. Persons who write about their own past trauma or the past trauma of others exhibit better coping skills, lower levels of distress, and make fewer health care visits. However, the beneficial effects are found in those who reach some type of cognitive resolution. Those who achieve benefit from writing about trauma use more words such as *because of* and *understanding* (Littrell, 1998, 2009). If revisiting emotion fails to lead to a change in perspective, then a beneficial effect will not occur. Consistent with this view, Dickerson, Kemeny, Aziz, Kim, and Fahey (2004) had research participants write about a time when they felt ashamed. After writing, research participants were not only more distressed, but they also exhibited elevations in inflammatory markers. In another study, evaluating the impact of catharsis, mothers whose pregnancies resulted in stillbirths were assigned to hold their deceased infants and were compared to matched controls who had not held their infants. Those presented with their stillborn children were more depressed or anxious and less able to bond with their subsequently born children (Hughes, Turton, Hopper, & Evans, 2002). Consistent with the observations from the Pennebaker studies, revisiting emotionally painful events only works to dissipate pain when some new positive cognitive message is achieved. Merely reexperiencing pain does not appear to be helpful.

The experimental literature on reappraising distressing stimuli provides some suggestions about ways to talk about painful events in ways that are helpful. When stimuli are described in neutral terms, then people exhibit less arousal and less activation in the brain's distress centers (dorsal anterior cingulate). Making nonemotional judgments rather than emotional judgments is associated with reduced amygdala activity and more prefrontal cortex activity (Tracy, Klonsky, & Proudfit, 2014). This approach is quite consistent with the process of meditation. When meditating, thoughts are not judged, they are just acknowledged. Jacobs et al. (2010, p. 3) characterize mindfulness as occurs during meditation as, "the abilities to carefully observe and label internal or external experience in a non-reactive, non-judgmental manner." Consistent with this, Creswell, Way, Eisenberger, and Lieberman (2007) measured people on their tendencies to adopt mindfulness, a nonjudgmental approach to their feelings. Those who rated higher on mindfulness, or the tendency to allow thoughts to pass without judgment, exhibited more activation in the PFC and less amygdala activation as they labeled the emotional faces of others.

The studies on labeling emotion raise the question of whether distress might be enhanced if people label their emotions in such a way that they magnify their distress. Ayduk, Mischel, and Downey (2002) make a distinction between talking about a painful experience in a manner that makes it more abstract (cool focus) versus ways that enhance immersion in the experience (hot focus). In a study in which subjects were instructed to talk about an event with either a hot or cool focus, the hot focus magnified distress. Kross, Ayduk, and Mischel (2005) replicated this finding in a study in which a painful experience involving anger was discussed from a distance stance or intense emotional stance. Only the distance stance reduced anger about the situation.

Reestablishing Connections to Others

Charuvastra and Cloitre (2008) make the case that the creation of PTSD symptoms in those experiencing trauma may be mediated by the threat to social bonds and trust in others that the trauma creates. As a treatment for PTSD, enhancing social bonds may be a very important component. When anticipating shock, holding the hand of a loved one decreases the fear registering in the dorsal anterior cingulate cortex (Eisenberger et al., 2011). It is also the case that those Vietnam veterans who became involved in their communities were more likely to exhibit resolution of PTSD than those who did not establish bonds in the community (Koenen, Stellman, Stellman, & Sommer, 2003). Thus, the evidence suggests that social bonding can ameliorate anxiety and is consistent with the idea that it can relieve PTSD symptoms.

Lisa Najavits has developed a therapy of "seeking safety treatment" for those substance abusers with PTSD. For those with both PTSD and substance abuse, Najavits argues that exposure therapy in early sobriety can jeopardize sobriety and lead to relapse. Najavits avoids stirring up painful remembrances by detailing prior trauma. She acknowledges the trauma that her clients have experienced, but does not focus on it. Rather, she helps clients identify safe places and safe people to be with. When flashbacks occur, clients are taught the coping mechanism of focusing elsewhere. Her results have been encouraging (Najavits, Weiss, Shaw, & Muenz, 1998).

Various talk therapy interventions have been shown to successfully resolve the distress of prior trauma. Bleiberg and Markowitz (2005) used interpersonal therapy to ameliorate PTSD symptoms. David Spiegel randomly assigned survivors of childhood sexual abuse to "talk about it in group therapy" or "talk about daily life in a supportive environment." At the end of treatment, there was no difference in outcome (Classen, Koopman, Neville-Manning, & Spiegel, 2001). Perhaps social support is sufficient to decrease anxiety levels for the long term (Littrell, 2008). The question remains: If PTSD symptoms dissipate through establishing bonds and learning where it is safe, is anything to be gained through once again revisiting painful memories?

The Importance of Self-Concept

As discussed earlier, research shows that physical expression of an emotion intensifies rather than dissipates the feeling. During a display of strong emotions, an individual will be observing himself or herself feeling that emotion. Consistent with the theorizing of William James (discussed in Chapter 2), subjective experience is influenced by self-observation of overt behavior. Persons who have their facial muscles positioned into an expression consistent with the evoked emotion report a more intense subjective experience. For example, James Laird had subjects either frown or assume a neutral expression while observing pictures of the Klu Klux Klan. Those who scowled reported more anger (Laird, 1984). The principle here is that if I see myself expressing a particular emotion, a certain amount of self-definition is conveyed in this observation. It follows that if emotional arousal during an exposure session fails to decline, this failure offers evidence reinforcing the self-concept of not being in control. The emotion may be evoked with stronger intensity on a subsequent occasion.

Studies of PTSD in combat experience have suggested the importance of self-concept in contributing to PTSD symptoms. Various countries have different ways of responding to their soldiers when they have experienced distress from battle. Evacuating them from the front lines and treating people in hospitals where they wear pajamas can be contrasted with keeping soldiers on the front lines, staying in uniform, and providing "aid in place." The latter is associated with less subsequent PTSD (Solomon & Benbenishty, 1986). During World War II, faster recovery was also noted when soldiers were treated on the front lines rather than being evacuated to hospital units (Grob, 1991; Littrell, 1998). Consistent with this thinking, the U.S. military has changed its approach to PTSD. There is much more emphasis on fitness and resilience rather than on labeling symptoms as disability (Cornum, Matthews, & Seligman, 2011; Vergun, 2012). Military hospitals in Afghanistan are referred to as fitness centers. Rituals for honoring fallen comrades are held. Each day the company commander visits the disabled soldier and conveys the message that he is very much missed and that other soldiers are counting on the disabled soldier's return. There is much acknowledgement of the trauma associated with witnessing comrades die, but the person with PTSD is portrayed as capable of resilience and not assigned a "patient" role.

Other therapists who work with PTSD have focused on the narratives that individuals tell themselves about their experiences. Frank Neuner (Bichescu, Neuner, Schauer, & Elbert, 2007) works with African children who have been captured by warlords and then forced to become soldiers who brutally attack others while under the influence of stimulants. Neuner has developed narrative therapy. The idea is for the children to redefine themselves, viewing the trauma as a smaller interlude in their lives, which entails a much bigger story of involvement in their families and communities. Children are encouraged to create a physical, visual time line for telling who they are by placing rocks for the hard times and flowers for the good times. Don Meichenbaum (2007), a widely recognized psychologist who has contributed treatment videos for the American Psychological Association, also views treatment of PTSD as helping clients to tell a broader narrative. Although the horror of particular events can be dramatic and attention grabbing, each individual is encouraged to tell "the rest of the story," which entails strength and survival and the beauty of friendship with and love for lost loved ones. Hassija and Cloitre (2014) emphasize to clients that "you own the memory" and "the memory does not own you." Haissija and Cloitre have developed the Skills Training in Affective and Interpersonal Regulation (STAIR) narrative model for treating PTSD. The STAIR model incorporates training in emotional regulation and changing assumptions of the availability of social support. In the STAIR model, clients learn to identify opportunities for social support and skills for accessing this support. The frequent experience of anxiety and/or depressive feelings can shake self-confidence. Again, frequent distress can become self-defining.

Journalist Scott Stossel (2014), in his story about his own anxiety disorder, discusses how he resolved his problem. He found solace in the realization that anxiety has a great deal of survival value, at least for the species. He uses this perspective to quit labeling his propensity to become anxious as a problem. In general, redefining a difficult problem offers an opportunity for new ways of looking at it. In fact, there is a literature on finding benefit in trauma. Those who can identify benefit from hard times exhibit fewer symptoms of distress (McMillen, 1999).

Making Decisions About How to Proceed

Many tools to treat anxiety are available: exposure therapy; more indirect routes to recovery from anxiety such as meditation, diet, exercise, involvement in support groups; or medication. Perhaps the determining factor in deciding what to do should be the client's preference. The best predictor of outcome for a wide range of problems is the therapeutic alliance (Martin, Garske, & Davis, 2000). As we would expect, when therapist and client agree on the problem and the strategy for relieving distress, better results ensue.

REFERENCES

Amorapanth, P., LeDoux, J. E., & Nader, K. (2000). Different lateral amygdala outputs mediate reactions and actions elicited by a fear-arousing stimulus. *Nature Neuroscience, 3,* 74–79.

Arnsten, A. F. (1998). The biology of being frazzled. *Science, 280*(5370), 1711–1712.

Ayduk, O., Mischel, W., & Downey, G. (2002). Attentional mechanisms linking rejection to hostile reactivity: The role of "hot" and "cool" focus. *Psychological Science, 13*, 443–448.

Bar-Haim, Y., Lamy, D., Pergamin, L., Bakermans-Kranenburg, M. J., & van Ijzendoon, M. H. (2007). Threat-related attentional bias in anxious and nonanxious individuals: A meta-analytic study. *Psychological Bulletin, 133*(1), 1–24.

Bichescu, D., Neuner, F., Schauer, M., & Elbert, T. (2007). Narrative exposure therapy for political imprisonment-related chronic posttraumatic stress disorder and depression. *Behaviour Research and Therapy, 45*(9), 2212–2220.

Billioti de Gage, S., Moride, Y., Ducruet, T., Kurth, T., Verdoux, H., Tournier, M.,...Bégaud, B. (2014). Benzodiazepine use and risk of Alzheimer's disease: Case-control study. *British Medical Journal, 349*, g5205. doi:10.1136bmj.g5205

Bleiberg, K. L., & Markowitz, J. C. (2005). A pilot study of interpersonal psychotherapy for posttraumatic stress disorder. *American Journal of Psychiatry, 162*(1), 181–183.

Boscarino, J. A. (1995). Post-traumatic stress and associated disorders among Vietnam veterans: The significance of combat exposure and social support. *Journal of Trauma and Stress, 8*(2), 317–336.

Breslau, N., Kessler, R. C., Chilcoat, H. D., Schultz, L. R., Davis, G. C., & Andreski, P. (1998). Trauma and posttraumatic stress disorder in the community: The 1996 Detroit Area Survey of Trauma. *Archives of General Psychiatry, 55*(7), 626–632.

Breuer, J., & Freud, S. (2013). *Studies in hysteria* (A. A. Brill, Trans.). New York, NY: Penguin Classics. (Original work published 1895)

Brunet, A., Orr, S. P., Tremblay, J., Robertson, K., Nader, K., & Pitman, R. K. (2008). Effect of post-retrieval propranolol on psychophysiologic responding during subsequent script-driven traumatic imagery in post-traumatic stress disorder. *Journal of Psychiatric Research, 42*(6), 503–506.

Burbaud, P., Clair, A.-H., Langbour, N., Fernandez-Vidal, S., Coillandeau, M., Michelet, T.,...Mallet, L. (2013). Neuronal activity correlated with checking behavior in the subthalamic nucleus of patients with obsessive-compulsive disorder. *Brain, 136*(1), 304–317.

Bushman, B. J., Baumeister, R. F., & Stack, A. D. (1999). Catharsis, aggression, and persuasive influence: Self-fulfilling or self-defeating prophecies? *Journal of Personality and Social Psychology, 76*, 367–376.

Bushman, B. J., Bonacci, A. M., Pedersen, W. C., Vasquez, E. A., & Miller, N. (2005). Chewing on it can chew you up: Effects of reumination on triggered displaced aggression. *Journal of Peronality and Social Psychology, 88*, 969–983.

Buydens-Branchey, L., Branchey, M., & Hibbeln, J. R. (2008). Associations between increases in plasma n-3 polyunsaturated fatty acids following supplementation and decreases in anger and anxiety in substance abusers. *Progress in Neuropsychopharmacology and Biological Psychiatry, 32*(2), 568–575.

Chantarujikapong, S. I., Scherrer, J. F., Xian, H., Eisen, S. A., Lyons, M. J., Goldberg, J.,… True, W. R. (2001). A twin study of generalized anxiety disorder symptoms, panic disorder symptoms and post-traumatic stress disorder in men. *Psychiatry Research, 103*(2–3), 133–145.

Charuvastra, A., & Cloitre, M. (2008). Social bonds and posttraumatic stress disorder. *Annual Review of Psychology, 59,* 301–328.

Chen, S. W. C., Shemyakin, A., & Wiedenmayer, C. P. (2006). The role of the amygdala and olfaction in unconditioned fear in developing rats. *Journal of Neuroscience, 26*(1), 233–240.

Christianson, J. P., Fernando, A. B., Kazama, A. M., Jovanovic, T., Ostroff, L. E., & Sangha, S. (2012). Inhibition of fear by learned safety signals: A mini-symposium review. *Journal of Neuroscience, 32*(41), 14118–14124.

Classen, C., Koopman, C., Neville-Manning, K., & Spiegel, D. (2001). A preliminary report comparing trauma-focused and person-focused group therapy against a wait-list control condition among childhood sexual abuse survivors with PTSD. *Journal of Aggression, Maltreatment, & Trauma, 4,* 265–288.

Consedine, N. S., Magai, C., & Bonnano, G. A. (2002). Moderators of emotion inhibition-health relationship: A review and research agenda. *Review of General Psychology, 6,* 204–228.

Cornum, R., Matthews, M. D., & Seligman, M. E. P. (2011). Comprehensive soldier fitness: Building resilence in a challenging institutional context. *American Psychologist, 66*(1), 4–9.

Craske, M. G., & Waters, A. M. (2005). Panic disorder, phobias, and generalized anxiety disorder. *Annual Review of Clinical Psychology, 1,* 197–225.

Creswell, J. D., Way, B. M., Eisenverger, N. I., & Lieberman, M. D. (2007). Neural correlates of dispositional mindfulness during affect labeling. *Psychosomatic Medicine, 69,* 560–565.

Davis, M., Walker, D. L., Miles, L., & Grillon, C. (2010). Phasic vs sustained fear in rats and humans: Role of the extended amygdala in fear vs anxiety. *Neuropsychopharmacology, 35*(1), 105–135.

Deacon, B., & Maack, D. J. (2008). The effects of safety behaviors on the fear of contamination: An experimental investigation. *Behavior Research and Therapy, 46,* 537–547.

Deacon, B. J., & Abramowitz, J. S. (2004). Cognitive and behavioral treatments for anxiety disorders: A review of meta-analytic findings. *Journal of Clinical Psychology, 60*(4), 429–441.

Deacon, B. J., Lickel, J., & Abramowitz, J. S. (2008). Medical utilization across the anxiety disorders. *Anxiety Disorders, 22,* 344–350.

Debiec, J., & Ledoux, J. E. (2004). Disruption of reconsolidation but not consolidation of auditory fear conditioning by noradrenergic blockade in the amygdala. *Neuroscience, 129*(2), 267–272.

Dickerson, S. S., Kemeny, M. E., Aziz, N., Kim, K. H., & Fahey, J. L. (2004). Immunological effects of induced shame and guilt. *Psychosomatic Medicine*, 66(1), 124–131.

Doty, T. J., Japee, S., Ingvar, M., & Ungerleider, L. G. (2013). Fearful face detection sensitivity in healthy adults correlates with anxiety-related traits. *Emotion*, 13(2), 182–188.

Duncan, R. D., Saunders, B. E., Kilpatrick, D. G., Hanson, R. F., & Resnick, H. S. (1996). Childhood physical assault as a risk factor for PTSD, depression, and substance abuse: Findings from a national survey. *American Journal of Orthopsychiatry*, 66(3), 437–448.

Ebbesen, E. B., Duncan, B., & Konecni, V. J. (1975). Effects of content of verbal aggression on future verbal aggression: A field experiment. *Journal of Experimental Social Psychology*, 11, 192–204.

Eisenberger, N. I., Master, S. L., Inagaki, T. K., Taylor, S. E., Shirinyan, D., Lieberman, M. D., & Naliboff, B. D. (2011). Attachment figures activate a safety signal-related neural region and reduce pain experience. *Proceedings of the National Academy of Sciences of the United States of America*, 108(28), 11721–11726.

Elman, I., Lowen, S., Frederick, B. B., Chi, W., Becerra, L., & Pitman, R. K. (2009). Functional neuroimaging of reward circuitry responsivity to monetary gains and losses in posttraumatic stress disorder. *Biological Psychiatry*, 66(12), 1083–1090.

Etkin, A., Klemenhagen, K. C., Dudman, J. T., Rogan, M. T., Hen, R., Kandel, E. R., & Hirsch, J. (2004). Individual differences in trait anxiety predict the response of the basolateral amygdala to unconsciously processed fearful faces. *Neuron*, 44(6), 1043–1055.

Ewbank, M. P., Lawrence, A. D., Passamonti, L., Keane, J., Peers, P. V., & Calder, A. J. (2009). Anxiety predicts a differential neural response to attended and unattended facial signals of anger and fear. *NeuroImage*, 44(3), 1144–1151.

Farach, F. J., Pruitt, L. D., Jun, J. J., Jerud, A. B., Zoellner, L. A., & Roy-Byrne, P. P. (2012). Pharmacological treatment of anxiety disorders: Current treatments and future directions. *Journal of Anxiety Disorders*, 26(8), 833–843.

Feder, A., Nestler, E. J., & Charney, D. S. (2009). Psychobiology and molecular genetics of resilience. *Nature Reviews Neuroscience*, 10(6), 446–457.

Foa, E. B. (2005). Cognitive behavioral therapy of obsessive-compulsive disorder. *Dialogues in Clinical Neuroscience*, 12(2), 199–207.

Fogaca, M. V., Lisboa, S. F., Aguiar, D. C., Moreira, F. A., Gomes, F. V., Casarotto, P. C., & Guimarães, F. A. (2012). Fine-tuning of defensive behaviors in the dorsal periaqueductal gray by atypical neurotransmitters. *Brazilian Journal of Medical and Biological Research*, 45, 357–365.

Gilbertson, M. W., Shenton, M. E., Ciszewski, A., Kasai, K., Lasko, N. B., Orr, S. P., & Pitman, R. K. (2002). Smaller hippocampal volume predicts pathologic vulnerability to psychological trauma. *Nature Neuroscience*, 5(11), 1242–1247.

Gillespie, C. F., Bradley, B., Mercer, K., Smith, A. K., Conneely, K., Gapen, M.,...Ressler, K. J. (2009). Trauma exposure and stress-related disorders in inner city primary care patients. *General Hospital Psychiatry, 31*(6), 505–514.

Graff, J., Joseph, N. F., Horn, M. E., Samiei, A., Meng, J., Seo, J.,...Tsai, L. H. (2014). Epigenetic priming of memory updating during reconsolidation to attenuate remote fear memories. *Cell, 156*(1–2), 261–276.

Graybiel, A. M. (2008). Habits, rituals, and the evaluative brain. *Annual Review of Neuroscience, 31*, 359–387.

Green, R. A., & Murray, E. J. (1975). Expression of feeling and cognitive reinterpretation in the reduction of hostile aggression. *Journal of Consulting and Clinical Psychology, 43*, 375–387.

Grob, G. N. (1991). Origins of the DSM-1: A study in appearance and reality. *American Journal of Psychiatry, 148*(4), 421–431.

Gross, J. J. (1998). Antecedent- and response-focused emotion regulation: Divergent consequences for experience, expression, and physiology. *Journal of Personality and Social Psychology, 74*, 224–237.

Guthrie, R. M., & Bryant, R. A. (2006). Extinction learning before trauma and subsequent posttraumatic stress. *Psychosomatic Medicine, 68*(2), 307–311.

Hardee, J. E., Benson, B. E., Bar-Haim, Y., Mogg, K., Bradley, B. P., Chen, G.,...Perez-Edgar, K. (2013). Patterns of neural connectivity during an attentional bias task moderate associations between early childhood temperament and internalizing symptoms in young adulthood. *Biological Pyschiatry, 74*(4), 273–279.

Hariri, A. R., Bookheimer, S. Y., & Mazziotta, J. C. (2000). Modulating emotional responses: Effects of a neocortical network on the limbic system. *Neuroreport, 11*(1), 43–48.

Hassija, C. M., & Cloitre, M. (2014). The skills training in affective and interpersonal regulation (STAIR) narrative model: A treatment approach to promote resilience. In M. Kent, M. C. Davis, & J. W. Reich (Eds.), *The resilience handbook: Approaches to stress and trauma* (pp. 285–294). New York, NY: Routledge.

Hoge, C. W., Castro, C. A., Messer, S. C., McGurk, D., Cotting, D. I., & Koffman, R. L. (2004). Combat duty in Iraq and Afghanistan, mental health problems, and barriers to care. *New England Journal of Medicine, 351*(1), 13–22.

Hou, R., & Baldwin, D. S. (2012). A neuroimmunological perspective on anxiety disorders. *Human Psychopharmacology, 27*(1), 6–14.

Hounie, A. G., Pauls, D. L., do Rosario-Campos, M. C., Mercadante, M. T., Diniz, J. B., De Mathis, M. A.,...Miguel, E. C. (2007). Obsessive-compulsive spectrum disorders and rheumatic fever: A family study. *Biological Psychiatry, 61*(3), 266–272.

Hughes, P., Turton, P., Hopper, E., & Evans, C. D. H. (2002). Assessment of guidelines for good practice in psychosocial care of mothers after stillbirth: A cohort study. *Lancet, 360*, 114–118.

Jacobs, T. L., Epel, E. S., Lin, J., Blackburn, E. H., Wolkowitz, O. M., Bridwell, D. A.,...Saron, C. D. (2010). Intensive meditation training, immunee cell telomerase activity, and psychological mediators. *Psychoneuroimmunology, 36*(5), 664–681.

Jovanovic, T., Kazama, A., Bachevalier, J., & Davis, M. (2012). Impaired safety signal learning may be a biomarker of PTSD. *Neuropharmacology, 62*(2), 695–704.

Jovanovic, T., & Norrholm, S. D. (2011). Neural mechanisms of impaired fear inhibition in posttraumatic stress disorder. *Frontiers in Behavioral Neuroscience, 5*, 44. doi:10.3389/fnbeh.2011.00044

Jovanovic, T., Norrholm, S. D., Blanding, N. Q., Davis, M., Duncan, E., Bradley, B., & Ressler, K. J. (2010a). Impaired fear inhibition is a biomarker of PTSD but not depression. *Depression & Anxiety, 27*(3), 244–251.

Jovanovic, T., Norrholm, S. D., Blanding, N. Q., Phifer, J. E., Weiss, T., Davis, M.,...Ressler, K. (2010b). Fear potentiation is associated with hypothalamic-pituitary-adrenal axis function in PTSD. *Psychoneuroendocrinology, 35*(6), 846–857.

Jovanovic, T., & Ressler, K. J. (2010). How the neurocircuitry and genetics of fear inhibition may inform our understanding of PTSD. *American Journal of Psychiatry, 167*(6), 648–662.

Kessler, R. C., Berglund, P., Demler, O., Jin, R., Merikangas, K. R., & Walters, E. E. (2005). Lifetime prevalence and age-of-onset distributions of DSM-IV disorders in the National Comorbidity Survey Replication. *Archives of General Psychiatry, 62*(6), 593–602.

Kiecolt-Glaser, J. K., Belury, M. A., Andridge, R., Malarkey, W. B., & Glaser, R. (2011). Omega-3 supplementation lowers inflammation and anxiety in medical students: A randomized controlled trial. *Brain, Behavior & Immunity, 25*(8), 1725–1734.

Kim, S. Y., Adhikari, A., Lee, S. Y., Marshel, J. H., Kim, C. K., Mallory, C. S.,...Deisseroth, K. (2013). Diverging neural pathways assemble a behavioural state from separable features in anxiety. *Nature, 496*(7444), 219–223.

Kindt, M., Soeter, M., & Vervliet, B. (2009). Beyond extinction: Erasing human fear responses and preventing the return of fear. *Nature Neuroscience, 12*(3), 256–258.

Kirsch, P., Esslinger, C., Chen, Q., Mier, D., Lis, S., Siddhanti, S.,...Meyer-Lindenberg, A. (2005). Oxytocin modulates neural circuitry for social cognition and fear in humans. *Journal of Neuroscience, 25*(49), 11489–11493.

Koenen, K. C., Stellman, J. M., Stellman, S. D., & Sommer, J. F., Jr. (2003). Risk factors for course of posttraumatic stress disorder among Vietnam veterans: A 14-year follow-up of American Legionnaires. *Journal of Consulting and Clinical Psychology, 71*(6), 980–986.

Kross, E., Ayduk, O., & Mischel, W. (2005). When asking "why" does not hurt: Distinguishing rumination from reflective processing of negative emotions. *Psychological Science, 16*, 709–715.

Laird, J. D. (1984). The real role of facial response in experience of emotion: A reply to Tourangeau and Ellsworth, and others. *Journal of Personality and Social Psychology, 47,* 909–917.

Leckman, J. F., & Riddle, M. A. (2000). Tourette's syndrome: When habit-forming systems form habits of their own? *Neuron, 28*(2), 349–354.

LeDoux, J. (1998). *The emotional brain: The mysterious underpinnings of emotinal life.* New York, NY: Touchstone.

LeDoux, J. (2003). *Synaptic self: How our brains become who we are.* New York, NY: Viking Press.

LeDoux, J., & Gorman, J. M. (2001). A call to action: Overcoming anxiety through active coping. *American Journal of Psychiatry, 158*(12), 1953–1955.

Lehmann, M. L., Mustafa, T., Eiden, A. M., Herkenham, M., & Eiden, L. E. (2013). PACAP-deficient mice show attenuated corticosterone secretion and fail to develop depressive behavior during chronic social defeat stress. *Psychoneuroendocrinology, 38*(5), 702–715.

LePort, A. K., Mattfeld, A. T., Dickinson-Anson, H., Fallon, J. H., Stark, C. E., Kruggel, F.,…McGaugh, J. L. (2012). Behavioral and neuroanatomical investigation of highly superior autobiographical memory (HSAM). *Neurobiology of Learning and Memory, 98*(1), 78–92.

Littrell, J. (1998). Is the reexperience of painful emotion therapeutic? *Clinical Psychology Review, 18,* 71–102.

Littrell, J. (2008). The status of Freud's legacy on emotional processing: Contemporary revisions. *Journal of Human Behavior in the Social Environment, 46*(2), 477–499.

Littrell, J. (2009). Expression of emotion: When it causes trauma and when it helps. *Journal of Evidence-Based Social Work, 6*(3), 300–320.

Lonsdorf, T. B., Weike, A. I., Nikamo, P., Schalling, M., Hamm, A. O., & Ohman, A. (2009). Genetic gating of human fear learning and extinction: Possible implications for gene-environment interaction in anxiety disorder. *Psychological Science, 20*(2), 198–206.

Maroun, M. (2013). Medial prefrontal cortex: Multiple roles in fear and extinction. *Neuroscientist, 19*(4), 370–383.

Martin, D. J, Garske, J. P., & Davis, M. K. (2000). Relation of the therapeutic alliance with outcome and other variables: A meta-analytic review. *Journal of Consulting and Clinical Psychology, 68*(3), 438–450.

Maslowsky, J., Mogg, K., Bradley, B. P., McClure-Tone, E., Ernst, M., Pine, D.S., & Monk, C. S. (2010). A preliminary investigation of neural correlates of treatment in adolescents with generalized anxiety disorder. *Journal of Child and Adolescent Psychopharmacology, 20*(2), 105–111.

McMillen, J. C. (1999). Better for it: How people benefit from adversity. *Social Work, 44,* 455–468.

Mehta, D., Gonik, M., Klengel, T., Rex-Haffner, M., Menke, A., Rubel, J., ... Binder, E. B. (2011). Using polymorphisms in FKBP5 to define biologically distinct subtypes of posttraumatic stress disorder: Evidence from endocrine and gene expression studies. *Archives of Genernal Psychiatry, 68*(9), 901–910.

Meichenbaum, D. (2007). *Cognitive-behavioral therapy with Donald Meichenbaum.* American Psychological Association Videos. Series 1—Systems of Psychotherapy hosted by Jon Carlson. Washington, DC: American Psychological Association.

Mercadante, M. T., Diniz, J. B., Hounie, A. G., Ferrao, Y., Alvarenga, P., Brotto, S., & Miguel, E. C. (2005). Obsessive-compulsive spectrum disorders in rheumatic fever patients. *Journal of Neuropsychiatry and Clinical Neuroscience, 17*(4), 544–547.

Milad, M. R., Quirk, G. J., Pitman, R. K., Orr, S. P., Fischl, B., & Rauch, S. L. (2007). A role for the human dorsal anterior cingulate cortex in fear expression. *Biological Psychiatry, 62*(10), 1191–1194.

Milad, M. R., Wright, C. I., Orr, S. P., Pitman, R. K., Quirk, G. J., & Rauch, S. L. (2007). Recall of fear extinction in humans activates the ventromedial prefrontal cortex and hippocampus in concert. *Biological Psychiatry, 62*(5), 446–454.

Minassian, A., Geyer, M. A., Baker, D. G., Nievergelt, C. M., O'Connor, D. T., & Risbrough, V. B. (2014). Heart rate variability characteristics in a large group of active-duty marines and relationship to posttraumatic stress. *Psychosomatic Medicine, 76,* 292–301.

Monk, C. S., Telzer, E. H., Mogg, K., Bradley, B. P., Mai, X., Louro, H. M., ... Pine, D. S. (2008). Amygdala and ventrolateral prefrontal cortex activation to masked angry faces in children and adolescents with generalized anxiety disorder. *Archives of General Psychiatry, 65*(5), 568–576.

Munafo, M. R., Brown, S. M., & Hariri, A. R. (2008). Serotonin transporter (5-HTTLPR) genotype and amygdala activation: A meta-analysis. *Biological Psychiatry, 63*(9), 852–857.

Murphy, J. M., Horton, N. J., Laird, N. M., Monson, R. R., Sobol, A. M., & Leighton, A. H. (2004). Anxiety and depression: A 40-year perspective on relationships regarding prevalence, distribution, and comorbidity. *Acta Psychiatrica Scandinavica, 109*(5), 355–375.

Nader, K., Schafe, G. E., & Le Doux, J. E. (2000). Fear memories require protein synthesis in the amygdala for reconsolidation after retrieval. *Nature, 406*(6797), 722–726.

Najavits, L. M., Weiss, R. D., Shaw, S. R., & Muenz, L. R. (1998). "Seeking Safety": Outcome of a new cognitive-behavioral psychotherapy for women with posttraumatic stress disorder and substance abuse. *Journal of Traumatic Stress, 11*(3), 437–456.

New, A. S., Fan, J., Murrough, J. W., Liu, X., Liebman, R. E., Guise, K. G., ... Charney, D. S. (2009). A functional magnetic resonance imaging study of deliberate emotion regulation in resilience and posttraumatic stress disorder. *Biological Psychiatry, 66*(7), 656–664.

Norrholm, S. D., Jovanovic, T., Smith, A. K., Binder, E., Klengel, T., Conneely, K.,...Ressler, K. J. (2013). Differential genetic and epigenetic regulation of catechol-O-methyltransferase is associated with impaired fear inhibition in posttraumatic stress disorder. *Frontiers in Behavioral Neuroscience, 7*, 30. doi:10.3389/fnbeh.2013.00030

Otto, M. W., & Jasper, A. J. (2011). *Proven strategies for overcoming depression and enhancing well being.* New York, NY: Oxford Press.

Otto, M. W., Smits, J. A. J., & Reese, H. E. (2006). Combined psychotherapy and pharmacotherpay for mood and anxiety disorders in adults: Review and analysis. *Focus: The Journal of Lifelong Learning in Psychiatry, 4*(2), 72–86.

Ozbay, F., Johnson, D. C., Dimoulas, E., Morgan, C. A., Charney, D., & Southwick, S. (2007). Social support and resilience to stress: From neurobiology to clinical practice. *Psychiatry (Edgmont), 4*(5), 35–40.

Paus, T. (2001). Primate anterior cingulate cortex: Where motor control, drive and cognition interface. *Nature Reviews Neuroscience, 2*, 417–424.

Petersen, I. T., Bates, J. E., Goodnight, J. A., Dodge, K. A., Lansford, J. E., Pettit, G. S.,...Dick, D. M. (2012). Interaction between serotonin transporter polymorphism (5-HTTLPR) and stressful life events in adolescents' trajectories of anixous/depressed symptoms. *Developmental Psychology, 48*(5), 1463–1475.

Phelps, E. A. (2006). Emotion and cognition: Insights from studies of the human amygdala. [Review]. *Annual Review of Psychology, 57*, 27–53. doi:10.1146/annurev.psych.56.091103.070234

Pole, N., Neylan, T. C., Otte, C., Henn-Hasse, C., Metzler, T. J., & Marmar, C. R. (2009). Prospective prediction of posttraumatic stress disorder symptoms using fear potentiated auditory startle responses. *Biological Psychiatry, 65*(3), 235–240.

Rapoport, J. L. (1989). *The boy who couldn't stop washing: The experience and treatment of obsessive-compulsive disorder.* New York, NY: Dutton Press.

Ressler, K. J., & Mayberg, H. S. (2007). Targeting abnormal neural circuits in mood and anxiety disorders: From the laboratory to the clinic. *Nature Neuroscience, 10*(9), 1116–1124.

Ressler, K. J., Mercer, K. B., Bradley, B., Jovanovic, T., Mahan, A., Kerley, K.,...May, V. (2011). Post-traumatic stress disorder is associated with PACAP and the PAC1 receptor. *Nature, 470*(7335), 492–497.

Ressler, K. J., Rothbaum, B. O., Tannenbaum, L., Anderson, P., Graap, K., Zimand, E.,...Davis, M. (2004). Cognitive enhancers as adjuncts to psychotherapy: Use of D-cycloserine in phobic individuals to facilitate extinction of fear. *Archives of General Psychiatry, 61*(11), 1136–1144.

Rothbaum, B. O., Price, M., Jovanovic, T., Norrholm, S. D., Gerardi, M., Dunlop, B.,...Ressler, K. J. (2014). A randomized, double-blind evaluation of D-cycloserine or alprazolam combined with virtual reality exposure therapy for posttraumatic stress disorder in Iraq and Afghanistan war veterans. *American Journal of Psychiatry, 171*(6), 640–648.

Roy, K. Y., Scola, M., Boustani, M., & Fairbanks, R. M. (2014). Benzodiazepines and risk of Alzheimer's disease. *British Medical Journal, 349*, g5312. doi:10.1136/bmj.g5312

Salim, S., Chugh, G., & Asghar, M. (2012). Inflammation in anxiety. *Advances in Protein Chemical and Structural Biology, 88*, 1–25.

Schwartz, J. M., Stoessel, P. W., Baxter, L. R., Martin, K. M., & Phelps, M. E. (1996). Systemic changes in cerebral glucose metabolic rate after successful behavior modification treatment of obsessive-compulsive disorder. *Archives of General Psychiatry, 53*(2), 109–113.

Shin, L. M., & Liberzon, I. (2010). The neurocircuitry of fear, stress, and anxiety disorders. *Neuropsychopharmacology, 35*(1), 169–191.

Silberman, Y., & Winder, D. G. (2013). Emerging role for corticotropin releasing factor signaling in the bed nucleus of the stria terminalis at the intersection of stress and reward. *Frontiers in Psychiatry, 4*, 42. doi:10.3389/fpsyt.2013.00042

Smith, A. K., Conneely, K. N., Kilaru, V., Mercer, K. B., Weiss, T. E., Bradley, B.,...Ressler, K. J. (2011). Differential immune system DNA methylation and cytokine regulation in post-traumatic stress disorder. *American Journal of Medical Genetics B Neuropsychiatric Genetics, 156B*(6), 700–708.

Solomon, Z., & Benbenishty, R. (1986). The role of proximity, immediacy, and expectancy in frontline treatment of combat stress reaction among Israeli in the Lebanon war. *American Journal of Psychiatry, 143*(5), 613–617.

Song, Q. H., Shen, G. Q., Xu, R. M., Zhang, Q. H., Ma, M., Guo, Y. H.,...Han, Y. B. (2014). Effect of Tai Chi exercise on the physical and mental health of the elder patients suffered from anxiety disorder. *International Journal of Physiology, Pathophysiology and Pharmacology, 6*(1), 55–60.

Stevens, J. S., Almli, L. M., Fani, N., Gutman, D. A., Bradley, B., Norrholm, S. D.,...Ressler, K. J. (2014). PACAP receptor gene polymorphism impacts fear responses in the amygdala and hippocampus. *Proceedings of the National Academy of Science of the United States of America, 111*(8), 3158–3163.

Stossel, S. (2014). Surviving anxiety. *The Atlantic* (January/February). Retrieved from http:www.theatlantic.com/magazine/archive/2014/01/surviving_anxiety/355741

Straube, T., Glauer, M., Dilger, S., Mentzel, H. J., & Miltner, W. H. (2006). Effects of cognitive-behavioral therapy on brain activation in specific phobia. *NeuroImage, 29*(1), 125–135.

Sugarman, M. A., Loree, A. M., Baltes, B. B., Grekin, E. R., & Kirsch, I. (2014). The efficacy of paroxetine and placebo in treating anxiety and depression: A meta-analysis of change on the Hamilton Rating Scales. *PLoS ONE, 9*(8), e106337.

Swain, J. E., Scahill, L., Lombroso, P. J., King, R. A., & Leckman, J. F. (2007). Tourette syndrome and tic disorders: A decade of progress. *Journal of the American Academy of Child and Adolescent Psychiatry, 46*(8), 947–968.

Swedo, S. E., Rapoport, J. L., Cheslow, D. L., Leonard, H. L., Ayoub, E. M., Hosier, D. M., & Wald, E. R. (1989). High prevalence of obsessive-compulsive symptoms in patients with Sydenham's chorea. *American Journal of Psychiatry, 146*(2), 246–249.

Thayer, J. F., Friedman, B. H., & Borkovec, T. D. (1996). Autonomic characteristics of generalized anxiety disorder and worry. *Biological Psychiatry, 39*(4), 255–266.

Toufexis, D. J., Myers, K. M., & Davis, M. (2006). The effect of gonadal hormones and gender on anxiety and emotional learning. *Hormones and Behavior, 50*(4), 539–549.

Tracy, J. L., Klonsky, D., & Proudfit, G. H. (2014). How affective science can inform clinical science: An introduction to the special series on emotions and psychopathology. *Clinical Psychological Science, 2*, 317–386.

Trevor, A. J., & Way, W. L. (2013). Sedative-hypnotic drugs. In B. G. Katzyng (Ed.), *Basic and clinical pharmacology* (12th ed., pp. 373–388). New York: McGraw Hill.

Vergun, D. (2012, August 3). *Army standardizes PTSD diagnosis, treatment.* Retrieved from www.army.mil/article/84928

Viviani, D., Charlet, A., van den Burg, E., Robinet, C., Hurni, N., Abatis, M.,...Stroop, R. (2011). Oxytocin selectively gates fear responses through distinct outputs from the central amygdala. *Science, 333*, 104–107.

Walker, D. L., Toufexis, D. J., & Davis, M. (2003). Role of the bed nucleus of the stria terminalis versus the amygdala in fear, stress, and anxiety. *European Journal of Pharmacology, 463*(1–3), 199–216.

Way, B. M., & Taylor, S. E. (2010). Social influences on health: Is serotonin a critical mediator? *Psychosomatic Medicine, 72*(2), 107–112.

Whalen, P. J., Kagan, J., Cook, R. G., Davis, F. C., Kim, H., Polis, S.,...Johnstone, T. (2004). Human amygdala responsivity to masked fearful eye whites. *Science, 306*(5704), 2061. doi:10.1126/science.1103617

Zak, P. J., Kurban, R., & Matzner, W. T. (2004). The neurobiology of trust. *Annals of the New York Academy of Sciences, 1032*, 224–227.

6

Psychotic Disorders

This chapter focuses on psychotic disorders. The largest category of psychotic disorders is schizophrenia. Approximately 1% of individuals meet the criteria for this disorder. There are no blood tests available for the diagnosis of schizophrenia (Woo, 2013). Rather, schizophrenia is diagnosed on the basis of exhibition of particular symptoms for a period of several weeks (Steiner et al., 2013). More detailed descriptions of classical symptoms were offered by German psychiatrist Kurt Schneider in 1920. Now referred to as "first-rank symptoms," they include auditory hallucinations, somatic hallucinations, delusions of being controlled, thought withdrawal (someone is stealing one's thoughts), thought insertion (thoughts are being inserted), thought broadcasting (others know what you are thinking), and delusions of reference (the stop sign is sending a personal message to me). In categorizing the classic signs of schizophrenia, symptoms are organized into the categories of positive and negative signs. Positive signs are things that are normally not present, but are present with illness, for example, hallucinations and ideas of reference (the stop sign is sending a personal message to me). Negative signs are normally present, but are lacking in illness, for example, motivation is absent. This generalized apathy is also called "flat affect" (Woo, 2013).

PHYSIOLOGY OF PSYCHOSIS

The dopamine hypothesis for explaining symptoms of schizophrenia was promulgated several decades ago. It was based on the fact that drugs that are dopamine agonists, such as cocaine and amphetamine, can result in hallucinations and paranoia at high doses. Moreover, drugs that block dopamine 2 receptors do decrease the more dramatic symptoms of schizophrenia. In fact, there is good evidence that hallucinations may in fact be attributable to excessive dopamine release in the nucleus accumbens. When people with schizophrenia are given radiolabeled L-dopa (the precursor for making dopamine), the data are consistent with excessive amounts of dopamine in axons and excessive release. However, attempts to identify differences between patients and controls in genes controlling dopamine function or in proteins controlling dopamine function have not been successful (Grace, 2012; Howes & Kapur, 2009). Questions regarding those neurotransmitter systems that control dopamine release in the nucleus accumbens have yielded more insights into the physiology underpinning schizophrenia.

Fast-Spiking, GABA-Producing Interneurons

Parvalbumin-positive (PV+), gamma-aminobutyric acid (GABA)-producing, fast-spiking interneurons control the release of dopamine in the nucleus accumbens (Curley et al., 2011). They do this as follows: GABA interneurons project to neurons in the hippocampus that indirectly control the dopamine-releasing neurons in the nucleus accumbens (Grace, 2012; Howes & Kapur, 2009; Labrie & Roder, 2010; T. L. Schwartz, Sachdeva, & Stahl, 2012). A wide range of data implicates the fast-spiking GABA neurons and the receptors (N-methyl-d-aspartate [NMDA] receptors for glutamate) that control the activity of these neurons as being the core feature of the syndrome of behavior associated with schizophrenia.

Examination of the brains of those who had schizophrenia reveals aberrations in the GABA interneurons. Autopsies of the brains of those with schizophrenia find a deficiency in the enzyme GAD67, which produces the GABA neurotransmitter as well as PV protein (a marker protein for these neurons). There are fewer synaptic contacts of these GABA interneurons in those with schizophrenia (Curley et al., 2011; Lewis, Curely, Glausier, & Volk, 2012; Volman, Behrens, & Sejnowski, 2011; Woo, 2013).

The fast-spiking GABA interneurons produce gamma oscillations. Gamma oscillations are needed to form a coherent perception of sensory information, for encoding information, and for recall and storage of information (Bartos, Vida, & Jonas, 2007; Behrens & Sejnowski, 2009; Doischer et al., 2008). "Alterations in brain oscillatory activity is the hallmark of schizophrenia pathophysiology" according to Powell, Sejnowski, and Behrens (2012, p. 3) and, according to Steullet et al. (2010), again when referring to schizophrenia, "abnormality in synchronized neuronal activity driven by fast-spiking interneurons is a core feature of this disorder" (p. 2547). Deficits in gamma oscillations along with associated cognitive deficits have been noted in those with schizophrenia (Woo, 2013). Those with schizophrenia display performance deficits on short-term memory tasks and have difficulty detecting motion (Kantrowitz & Javitt, 2010b), distinguishing pure tones (Deo et al., 2013), distinguishing prosodic changes required for recognizing sarcasm, and understanding the meanings of words when used in a metaphorical sense (Kantrowitz, Hoptman, Leitman, Silipo, & Javitt, 2013; Kantrowitz & Javitt, 2010a). Many of those with schizophrenia (but not all) exhibit profound deficits in cognitive function, with one quarter scoring in the retarded range of intellectual function and, as a group, they score 1 standard deviation below the mean (van Os & Kapur, 2009).

Unusual behaviors are noted in those children for whom hallucinations emerge later in life. Walker, Lewine, and Neumann (1996) asked observers of home movies to identify those young children who would later develop schizophrenia. Observers were able to do so at better-than-chance levels. Unusual postures of these children were a clue. Additionally, the delay in meeting developmental milestones predicts the emergence of later psychosis (Sorensen et al., 2010).

The risk factors for schizophrenia do influence the development of the fast-spiking GABA interneurons. Rubella or influenza virus of the mother during the last two trimesters of pregnancy increases the risk of schizophrenia in the offspring by a factor of 5, and infection is estimated to explain 30% of those with schizophrenia (Brown & Derkits, 2010; Sullivan, 2005). Indeed factors associated with infection (the cytokines interleukin 8 [IL -8] and tumor necrosis factor alpha [TNF-alpha]) in the mother predict later schizophrenia in the offspring (Miller et al., 2013). In animals, exposing pregnant dams to infection during pregnancy results in a reduction of PV+ interneurons (i.e., the fast-spiking GABA interneurons) and changes in patterns of oscillation (Powell, Sejnowski, & Behrens, 2012; Volk & Lewis, 2013).

Cannabinoid 1 receptors are present on the GABA interneurons in the dorsolateral prefrontal cortex (PFC), where they inhibit GABA release. Adolescent marijuana smoking is a risk factor for schizophrenia (Eggan,

Stoyak, Verrico, & Lewis, 2010). The marijuana is believed to further impair the function of the GABA interneurons.

Problems With the NMDA Receptor

Although some investigators were exploring the role of fast-spiking GABA interneurons and gamma oscillations, others focused on NMDA receptors. NMDA receptors are receptors for glutamate. The NMDA receptor for glutamate on the membrane of the fast-spiking GABA interneurons contributes to the function and integrity of the fast-spiking GABA interneurons (Volman et al., 2011). In order to maintain levels of GAD67 (the enzyme-producing GABA) and PV in these neurons, the integrity of the NMDA receptors must be maintained (Kinney et al., 2006). Thus, the NMDA receptors are part of the story on the GABA interneurons, which produce the gamma oscillations. In this section, we consider the NMDA receptors.

Recognition that ketamine, an antagonist of the NMDA receptor, produces both the positive and negative symptoms of schizophrenia suggested that NMDA receptors might be relevant to schizophrenia. One way to measure the number of NMDA receptors is by using a detectable chemical that will bind at the receptor and then evaluating how much of the chemical can be seen. Occupancy of the NMDA receptors in the hippocampus has been measured in vivo in drug-free persons with schizophrenia, showing less receptor occupancy than controls (Pilowsky et al., 2006).

In fact, a multitude of factors can perturb the function of NMDA receptors. Some of these pathways are genetic. Others are not. According to Steullet, Neijt, Cuénod, and Do (2006, p. 816), referring to schizophrenia, "Because of the heterogeneity of illness, it is likely that several different defects cause hypofunction of NMDA receptors in different subgroups of schizophrenic patients." We now consider some of the ways in which NMDA receptor function can be disturbed.

The NMDA receptor is comprised of several subunits. One subunit will bind glutamate but only if another subunit has glycine or d-serine bound to it. Alleles for the proteins involved in d-serine metabolism are associated with the risk for schizophrenia (Labrie & Roder, 2010; Snyder & Gao, 2013). Those with schizophrenia exhibit lower levels of endogenous d-serine in plasma. Plasma levels of d-serine are inversely correlated with positive and negative symptoms of schizophrenia (Hashimoto et al., 2003).

Many of the genetic risk factors for schizophrenia code for proteins involved in the function of the NMDA receptor. These include neuroreglin 1, DISC, dysbindin, and G72 (Geddes, Huang, & Newell, 2011; Labrie & Roder, 2010; Powell et al., 2012; T. L. Schwartz et al., 2012; Snyder & Gao, 2013). In fact, lower levels of proteins involved in the expression of the NMDA receptor were noted in PV+ neurons in the autopsied brains of those with schizophrenia (Bitanihirwe, Lim, Kelley, Kaneko, & Woo, 2009). A very large N study confirmed genetic variations related to glutamate function as risk factors for schizophrenia (Schizophrenia Working Group, 2014). Consistent with the idea that there are multiple routes to the dysfunction of NMDA receptors and fast-spiking GABA interneurons, Arnedo et al. (2014) have identified multiple genetic pathways, each pathway involving more than one interacting protein variant, as predicting particular types of schizophrenia. The identified pathways differed in terms of the degree of risk that the alleles in the pathway conferred for the emergence of schizophrenia.

Environmental factors can also influence the function of NMDA receptors. Deficiency of vitamin D during pregnancy is a risk factor for schizophrenia in the offspring. In animal models, restricting vitamin D in the pregnant dam will decrease NMDA receptors in the offspring (McGrath, Burne, Feron, Mackay-Sim, & Eyles, 2010; Mittal, Ellman, & Cannon, 2008). Obstetric complications, particularly hypoxia, raise the risk of schizophrenia from 1% (general population) to 6% (Buka, Tsuang, & Lipsitt, 1993). Obstetric complications are associated with lower expression of NMDA receptors (Mittal et al., 2008). In addition to environmental factors being associated with NMDA receptor deficiencies, antibodies to NMDA receptors have been found in 10% of those with acute psychosis (Steiner et al., 2013).

Inflammatory Factors and Free Radicals

Free radicals are molecules with an unpaired electron. Free radicals can disrupt the enzyme for producing GABA and destroy GABAergic interneurons (Cabungcal, Steullet, Kraftsik, Cuenod, & Do, 2013; Carter,

2006; Powell et al., 2012). Inflammation would increase free radicals and impair the function of NMDA receptors (Behrens, Ali, & Dugan, 2008; Behrens & Sejnowski, 2009; Woo, 2013). Levels of free radicals are elevated in the plasma of those with schizophrenia, and these levels correlate with psychotic symptoms (Berk, Ng, Dean, Dodd, & Bush, 2008; Li et al., 2011).

Several factors influence the levels of free radicals. Mitochondria are the energy factories of all human cells; they are the location at which the products of glucose are handed off to oxygen to yield adenosine triphosphate (ATP), the energy currency of the cell. Because of the handoff of electrons, mitochondrial dysfunction can result in the production of free radicals, that is, molecules with an unpaired electron. Alterations in the mitochondria of those with schizophrenia have been observed (Karry, Klein, & Ben Shachar, 2004; Marchbanks et al., 2003).

Glutathione is the body's major molecule for "mopping up" free radicals. A number of investigators have reported lower levels of glutathione in the plasma and cerebrospinal fluid of drug-naive persons with schizophrenia (Browne et al., 2000; Do, Cabungcal, Frank, Steullet, & Cuenod, 2009; Gysin et al., 2007, 2011; Lipska & Weinberger, 2000; Rao, Williams, & Goldman-Rakic, 2000). Allelic variation in proteins involved in synthesizing glutathione is a risk factor for schizophrenia (Do et al., 2009; Gysin et al., 2011, 2007; Tosic et al., 2006; Wood et al., 2009a; Wood, Yucel, Pantelis, & Berk, 2009b). Levels of glutathione are particularly relevant for fast-spiking GABA interneurons. Decrements in glutathione are associated with decrements in the level of PV (Hashimoto et al., 2003) and with decrements in gamma oscillations and cognitive performance (Ballesteros et al., 2013). Glutathione is important not only for "mopping up" free radicals, but also for increasing the signaling at NMDA receptors (Lakhan, Caro, & Hadzimichalis, 2013).

Free radicals can trigger inflammation; they also increase with inflammation (Bitanihirwe & Woo, 2011). S100B is a marker of inflammation and those with schizophrenia exhibit elevations in S100B in the cerebrospinal fluid (Meyer, Schwartz, & Muller, 2011) as well as other inflammatory markers (Potvin et al., 2008). During inflammation, the enzyme indolamine 2,3 dioxygenase (IDO) is activated. The product of IDO (after another step) is kynurenic acid, which can also block the function of the NMDA receptor (Erhardt, Olsson, & Engberg, 2009). In the postmortem brains and cerebrospinal fluid of those with schizophrenia, elevated levels of kynurenic acid have been found (Erhardt et al., 2009; Linderholm et al., 2012).

There is a suggestive finding that inflammation anywhere in the body precipitates psychosis in those who are susceptible (Graham, Carson, Ezeoke, Buckley, & Miller, 2014). Miller et al. (2013) found that 35% of those who were experiencing relapse to psychosis had urinary tract infections, which were significantly higher in those with schizophrenia who were stable in the community. In fact, there are case reports of the resolution of psychosis after clearing of the peripheral infection (Kirkpatrick & Miller, 2013; Miller, 2014).

Limitations in Current Diagnostic Practices

As mentioned earlier, it has long been recognized that schizophrenia places individuals with diverse patterns of behavior into the same category. For most observers, those with paranoia appear very different from those with extreme disorganization (called hebephrenics, which is a term used in the *International Classification of Diseases-10* [ICD-10]). In fact, Bleuler, an early diagnostician, used the term "schizophrenias" suggesting diversity in underlying etiologies (Steiner et al., 2013). Clinically, the diversity of behaviors exhibited by people sharing the phenomena of hallucinations is striking. It is appreciated that there are many different ways in which the function of the GABA interneurons can be perturbed, ranging from those who fail to develop GABA interneurons in utero due to a viral infection in the mother to inflammation in later life. Unfortunately, in clinical practice, pinpointing the possible causes of dysfunction of the GABA interneurons is not done. However, with the recognition that inflammation and infection may be the culprit, checking for evidence of an acute infection may become part of routine examinations in the future.

Some individuals develop psychosis and catatonia (where the body is frozen in a particular position) without any childhood precursors. This was the case for author Susannah Cahalan, who, in 2013 wrote, "Brain on Fire: My Month of Madness." Development of antibodies to self sometimes occurs with cancer. (Susannah had a melanoma tumor.) Tumor cells express aberrant proteins, and the body develops antibodies to these never-before-seen proteins just as if they were proteins in a virus. If the leukocyte cell producing the antibody detects its target, then the cell divides and many antibodies of a particular type are produced. Antibodies to cancer proteins can sometimes react to self-proteins, including an NMDA receptor protein. This is what happened to Susannah, who produced antibodies to her NMDA receptors. She exhibited many features of schizophrenia, bipolar disorder, and epilepsy. Fortunately, the doctors (eventually) treated Susannah for an autoimmune disorder. The delusions went away when the disorder was treated as an immune system problem. Susannah's case does further establish the NMDA receptors as relevant for producing the symptoms of schizophrenia and bipolar disorder.

Some consider gamma oscillations to be the defining feature of schizophrenia, but *ICD-10* (WHO, 2015) diagnoses and *Diagnostic and Statistical Manual of Mental Disorders*, Fifth Edition (*DSM-5*; American Psychiatric Association, 2013) diagnoses are based on the presence of symptoms, namely, hallucinations of a particular duration. Gamma oscillations, reflecting GABA interneuron function, can be measured. As discussed, the gamma oscillations relate to both positive and negative symptoms of schizophrenia. However, such measurement is not part of clinical diagnosis.

It is possible that some persons may be misclassified with the schizophrenia label. About 8% of the general population report hearing voices, with about half of these individuals reporting distress over these voices (Howes & Kapur, 2009; Johns, Nazroo, Bebbington, & Kuipers, 2002). Heins et al.'s (2011) data suggest that early trauma may increase the probability of hearing voices later in life, although early trauma is not associated with the negative symptoms of schizophrenia (cognitive features and lack of motivation). Thus, whether Heins et al.'s research participants should be regarded as having schizophrenia is unclear. The "hearing voices" movement was begun by persons who experienced auditory hallucinations, declined medications, and went on to become high-functioning people. They now resent having been labeled and medicated. Eleanor Longden (2013), whose TED (technology, education, and design) Talk can be watched online, is representative of this movement. One hopes the future will yield improved ways to classify persons that better relate to the etiologies giving rise to symptoms.

CURRENT TREATMENTS

Antipsychotic drugs are the current mainstay treatment for psychosis. Both the older neuroleptics and the newer atypicals block dopamine

2-type receptors. In clinical studies, evaluation of these drugs usually occurs at 8 weeks. About 30% fail to respond adequately to these drugs (Nitta et al., 2013). Only 17% to 22% experience a benefit beyond placebo or natural recovery (Morrision, Hutton, Shiers, & Turkington, 2012). Studies following patients 1 to 2 years later find less relapse and less hospital readmission in those maintained on the drug (Leucht et al., 2012); however, relapse rates across studies are between 18% and 55% on the maintained drug (Samaha, Seema, Stewart, Rajabi, & Kapur, 2007). Many patients discontinue their medications (Robinson et al., 1999).

Side Effects With Current Treatments

As with many other pharmacological interventions, withdrawal effects shortly after drug discontinuation are likely. Antipsychotic drugs occupy the D2 receptors. The brain adjusts. More of these receptors are expressed in the nucleus accumbens to compensate for the blockade, and these new receptors are more likely to be of the high-affinity type (Grace, 2012; Seeman et al., 2005). As expected, if the drug is withdrawn, the brain will have too many receptors, and rebound effects are observed. When the patients discontinue medication, the relapse rates during the 6 to 10 months after discontinuation are much higher than those during later periods (Harrow & Jobe, 2013).

Drugs that block dopamine, both the older neuroleptics and the newer atypicals, are associated with shrinkage of regions of the cortex when taken at recommended dosages (Fusar-Poli et al., 2013; Ho, Andreasen, Ziebell, Pierson, & Magnotta, 2011). Although it is difficult to determine whether these changes are caused by the drugs because the studies did not exhibit random assignment, there are studies on macaques in which monkeys were randomly assigned to drugs. These studies also found brain volume decrement of about 11% in those monkeys maintained on antidopaminergic drugs (Dorph-Petersen et al., 2005; Konopaske et al., 2007, 2008). Glial cells (supportive fat cells), which release growth factors that maintain brain health (M. Schwartz & Schechter, 2011; Ziv & Schwartz, 2008), are reduced along with the cortex-volume reduction (Konopaske et al., 2008).

The old neuroleptics were notorious for causing extrapyramidal Parkinson's-type symptoms (muscle rigidity, hand tremor, shuffling gait, reduced movement of facial muscles), as well as tardive dyskinesia, a severe movement disorder that emerges over time. Over a 5-year period, about 25% of patients on traditional antipsychotics will develop tardive dyskinesia (Stahl, 2013, p. 134). Although the newer atypicals were initially believed to be free of movement disorder problems, the Clinical Antipsychotic Trials for Intervention Effectiveness (CATIE) trials found that the new atypicals also produce movement dysfunction (Casey, 2006). Additionally, the atypical antipsychotics are notorious for inducing severe obesity, dyslipidemia, and type 2 diabetes (Gianfrancesco, White, Wang, & Nasrallah, 2003; Pramyothin & Khaodhiar, 2010; van Os & Kapur, 2009). (In fact, the disparity in longevity with shorter life spans for those with schizophrenia has increased since the advent of the atypicals, van Os & Kapur, 2009.) Dopamine inhibits the release of prolactin from the pituitary gland. Drugs that block dopamine signaling increase prolactin levels. High prolactin levels can induce osteoporosis (Calarge, Zimmerman, Xia, Kuperman, & Schiechte, 2010) and breast development in 15% of men when taken over a 60-day period (Etminan, Heran, Carleton, & Brophy, 2014). Acutely, the atypicals can provoke potentially fatal cardiac arrhythmias (Haddad & Anderson, 2002; Meltzer, 2013). Antipsychotics are also associated with a rare, but potentially fatal phenomenon of neuroleptic malignant syndrome. Muscle tension, high temperature, and high blood pressure ensue (Katzung, 2013).

Most people do not like the subjective effect of the antipsychotics. If antipsychotics are taken by normal people, they become depressed (Morrision et al., 2012). As discussed in Chapter 2, dopamine is the neurotransmitter associated with motivation and drive. Blocking this neurotransmitter induces dysphoria and motivational impairment (van Os & Kapur, 2009).

Questions Raised by Long-Term Follow-Up Studies

Studies are now available that followed those with schizophrenia over an extended period of time. Wunderink, Nieboer, Wiersma, Sytema, and Nienhuis (2013) followed the patients for 7 years. Initially, Wunderink et al. recruited 128 research participants who had been stable for 6 months for a 2-year study. These research participants were either randomly assigned to be tapered off the drug over an 18-month period or maintained on drug. After the 18 months, further treatment was determined by clinicians in the community. Five years later, at 7 years after initial sample recruitment, Wunderink et al. were able to find 80.5% of the original sample: 52 from the discontinuation arm and 51 from the drug-maintenance arm. Over the course of the ensuing 5 years, those in the discontinuation arm were medicated less of the time and at lower doses. However, only eight of the patients from the discontinuation arm remained unmedicated throughout the entire 6.5 years of the follow-up.

Comparing outcomes of the two groups at 7 years, there was no statistical difference in the percentage that experienced relapses (61.5% in the discontinuation arm vs. 68.8% in the drug-continuation arm). There was no difference in the number of relapses during the 7-year period (1.13 vs. 1.35). However, in the discontinuation group, the relapses were more likely to have occurred during the first 2 years when the drugs were discontinued, whereas the relapses in the drug-maintenance group were distributed throughout the follow-up period. (It should be recalled that relapses occurring immediately after drug discontinuation may represent a withdrawal phenomenon rather than the natural cycling of the disorder.) The dramatic difference between the drug-discontinuation research participants and the drug-continued research participants was in functional recovery. In the drug-discontinuation arm, 46.2% achieved functional recovery versus 19.6% in the drug-continuation arm. Those for whom the drug was discontinued were more likely to be employed and to have established meaningful relationships with others.

Other findings are consistent with the Wunderink findings. Johnstone, Macmillian, Frith, Benn, and Crow (1990) found that those who remained unmedicated after a first episode were doing better than the medicated group at year 2. In fact, 40% of those in the unmedicated group remained well throughout the follow-up period. In a study by Gleeson et al. (2013) designed to evaluate enhanced treatment, the enhanced-treatment group was found to exhibit worse cognitive and social outcome at 2.5-year follow-up, which was statistically mediated by better medication compliance. That is, the worse outcomes were explained by better compliance with taking medications. Bola, Leihtinen, Culberg, and Ciompi (2009) examined the outcomes from five studies in which those with schizophrenia received minimal or no medications (27% to 43% of the samples received low levels of medications). In all studies, outcomes favored the minimally medicated group. Finally, according to the WHO, in developing countries, where only 16% are medicated, 66% of those with first-episode schizophrenia exhibit good outcome compared to 37% in developed countries, where 61% are medicated (Jablensky, 1992).

For the most part, the studies finding that those who are unmedicated do better in the long term have not been random-assignment studies. Harrow, Jobe, and Faull (2012) followed their patients over 20 years. Fifteen percent were always medicated, whereas 24% were never medicated. Those refusing medication were functioning higher on IQ tests and tests of abstract reasoning at study initiation. All outcomes, including relapse rates, were better for the unmedicated group. Available studies cannot answer the question of why those who are unmedicated do better. It may be that the drugs impair function. It may be that better functioning people are more likely to decline medication.

The findings of better outcome for the unmedicated have not gone unnoticed. McGorry, Alvarez-Jimenez, and Killackey (2013, p. 899), reflecting on the Wunderink et al. study, suggested that tolerating an initial relapse on drug discontinuation "may be a price worth paying for better longer-term functional recovery." Tom Insel, in response to the Wunderink et al. publication in his National Institute of Mental Health (NIMH) director's blog of August 28, 2013, acknowledged the failings with the current pharmacological approaches to schizophrenia.

Better Targets for Treatment

Antipsychotic drugs target D2 receptors. They do not target GABA interneurons. Several researchers have recognized that current treatments have the wrong targets. According to Howes and Kaput (2009, p. 556), "current antipsychotic drugs are not treating the primary abnormality and are acting downstream." According to Wunderink et al. (2013), "the dopamine system might play a more peripheral role in psychosis than previously thought, while hypothesized primary derangements, such as the N-methyl-D-aspartate receptor and/or interneuron dysfunction, remain untouched by dopamine blockade" (p. 919). In fact, a number of interventions targeting mechanisms more closely associated with NMDA receptors and/or GABA interneuron function have been successful.

Omega-3s

There are theoretical reasons why omega-3s (a fat in fish oil) will tar-get GABA interneuron function. Omega-3s are anti-inflammatory (Arita et al., 2005). They decrease free radical production as evidenced by less lipid peroxidation and less kynurenic acid. Because they reduce free radi-cals and kynurenic acid, they should be protective of GABA interneurons. Omega-3s also increase brain levels of glutathione (Berger et al., 2008). Tests of omega-3s as both a monotherapy and as adjunctive treatment have been positive.

Researchers have been able to identify particular children who are at higher risk for the emergence of psychosis (Thompson, Nelson, & Yung, 2011). In these children, many treatments, including psychotherapy, antip-sychotics, and omega-3s, have been tested for their efficacy in decreasing the emergence of frank psychosis. The Cochrane Collaboration (Marshall & Rathbone, 2011) found no benefit of psychotherapy, family interventions, and antipsychotic drugs. The only successful intervention was omega-3s. Over the 52-week period, psychosis emerged in 27.5% of the control group, but in only 4.9% of the omega-3 group (Amminger et al., 2010).

In a small *N* study, Peet, Brind, Ramchand, Shah, and Vankar (2001) used omega-3s as the sole treatment for early-episode psychosis. If psy-chosis failed to remit, then researchers treated with antipsychotics. All 12 of those on placebo required antidopaminergic medication to control symptoms, whereas 6 of 14 did not require medication in the omega-3 group. Even after medication, Peet et al. observed lower positive symp-toms in the omega-3 (eicosapentaenoic acid [EPA]-2 g/day) group. Puri and Richardson (1998), in a letter to the editor of *American Journal of Psychiatry*, reported on the reduction of both positive and negative symp-toms in a man who refused antipsychotic medications. Although very little can be concluded from one patient, it is reported here because it also suggests that using omega-3 as a sole intervention might be sufficient. In fact, this hypothesis has received very little study.

The late David Horrobin (2003) was an advocate of the use of omega-3s for those with schizophrenia, but he cautioned that for those who have been treated with antipsychotics for decades, the omega-3s may not be of much use. Several tests of omega-3s as an adjunct to antidopamine agents for those with recent onset psychosis were positive. Decreases in posi-tive symptoms and negative symptoms and less cognitive decline were noted in various studies. Additionally, a 20% reduction in the dosage of medication for adequately controlled symptoms in those taking omega-3s was found (Berger et al., 2007, 2008). Berger et al. (2007) further found that those taking omega-3s exhibited lower levels of Parkinson's disease symptoms. Moreover, omega-3 as an add-on in first-episode psychosis increased glutathione levels, which correlated with the improvement in negative symptoms (Berger et al., 2008).

Studies of omega-3s in persons who have been psychotic and medicated for decades have not been successful (Fenton, Dickerson, Boronow, Hibbeln, & Knable, 2001), although even in these studies (Arvindakshan, Ghate, Ranjekar, Evans, & Mahadik, 2003; Emsley, Myburgh, Oosthuizen, & van Rensburg, 2002; Laugharne, Mellor, & Peet, 1996; Reddy, Fleet-Michaliszyn, Condray, Yao, & Keshavan, 2011), higher functioning on global measures for those treated with omega-3s was noted. For example, Peet and Horrbin (2002) found that plasma values of unsaturated fatty acids, including omega-3s, correlated with a reduction in symptoms. However, meta-analyses have recognized that the data on efficacy have been inconsistent (Fusar-Poli & Berger, 2012; Joy, Mumby-Croft, & Joy, 2000; Maidment, 2000).

Peet (2004) emphasizes that for omega-3s to achieve efficacy, the entire diet requires change. The efficacy of omega-3s is probably attributable to a reduction in inflammatory factors. It is known that high levels of dietary saturated fats are inflammatory as is high-fructose corn syrup (Cani et al., 2008; Ferder, Ferder, & Inserra, 2010). Indeed, high intake of dietary saturated fats is associated with poorer outcomes in schizophrenia (Christensen & Christensen, 1988). Thus, to achieve maximum benefits, dietary strategies for treating schizophrenia will require a change in the total diet.

N-acetylcysteine

N-acetylcysteine is the precursor for the production of glutathione. As mentioned previously, glutathione is a scavenger for free radicals, and free radicals will damage the function of the fast-spiking GABA interneurons. Additionally, glutathione is anti-inflammatory and will also enhance the activity at an NMDA receptor (Labrie & Roder, 2010). Animal work has shown that N-acetylcysteine can prevent oxidative stress in fast-spiking interneurons in animals that are genetically altered to limit glutathione production (Cabungcal et al., 2013).

N-acetylcysteine has not been tested as a monotherapy for schizophrenia. However, Berk, Copolov, et al. (2008) used N-acetylcysteine as an adjunct to antipsychotic medications in schizophrenia. After 24 weeks, the group supplemented with N-acetyl-cysteine produced lower scores on negative symptoms, and exhibited fewer movement problems. There have also been tests of N-acetylcysteine as a mechanism for improving performance on tasks requiring gamma oscillations. Those who were on N-acetylcysteine achieved better electrophysiological performance on an auditory processing task, which is sensitive to NMDA receptor function (Lavoie et al., 2008). Furthermore, Carmeli, Knyazeva, Cuenod, and Do (2012) showed that N-acetylcysteine as an adjunct treatment for 60 days enabled better gamma oscillations and improvements in cognitive function.

Sarcosine

As mentioned previously, glycine and d-serine (both amino acids) bind at particular places in the NMDA receptor and enhance signaling. Sarcosine is related to the availability of glycine. Sarcosine will block the uptake of glycine into cells so that glycine is more available to bind to the NMDA receptor. Sarcosine has been tested as a monotherapy and an add-on. Lane et al. (2008) tested two dosages of sarcosine to treat drug-free acutely psychotic persons with schizophrenia. Twenty individuals were randomly assigned for sarcosine at a dose of 2 g or 1 g for 6 weeks. Both positive and negative symptoms were decreased by an average of 20% for the antipsychotic drug-naive research participants. Others have evaluated sarcosine as an adjunct to antipsychotic medication (Lane, Chang, Liu, Chiu, & Tsai, 2005; Lane et al., 2008; Tsai, Lane, Yang, Chong, & Lange, 2004). Sarcosine achieved significant reductions in positive and negative symptoms in those with schizophrenia.

Tsai and Lin (2010) conducted a meta-analysis on the efficacy of sarcosine as well as other strategies for increasing glycine and d-serine. They concluded that sarcosine improved both positive and negative symptoms, with effect sizes in the range of those of the newer antipsychotics. However, when sarcosine is employed as an adjunct, the type of antipsychotic drug made a difference. Positive effects were noted for those receiving risperidone or olanzapine. Tsai and Lin (2010) also concluded that sarcosine was well tolerated, although Tsai and Lin (2010) noted that most studies did not extensively report on side effects.

Anti-Inflammatory Drugs

Nitta et al. (2013) conducted a meta-analysis of the studies examining the use of nonsteroidal anti-inflammatories as an adjunct in the treatment of schizophrenia. Their analysis suggested a small effect size for aspirin on positive symptoms in those with first-episode schizophrenia.

Vitamins and Minerals

There are several pathways through which vitamins and minerals might alter function at the NMDA receptor and alter function of the GABA interneurons. High levels of the inflammatory factor homocysteine have been noted in the plasma of schizophrenics (Dietrich-Muszalska et al., 2012; Lipton et al., 1997). Adequate levels of folate and vitamin B are required for converting homocysteine (an inflammatory factor) back to methionine, an amino acid. Low folate levels have also been noted in first-episode, medication-naive persons with schizophrenia (Kale et al., 2010). In those with schizophrenia, serum folate correlates inversely with negative symptoms and homocysteine correlates positively with motor problems (Goff et al., 2004). Thus, adequate folate levels and B vitamins are needed to ensure low levels of the inflammatory factor, homocysteine.

The importance of serine for NMDA function has been explained. Regulation of the conversion of dietary serine (l-serine) to the form of serine (d-serine) that facilitates NMDA function requires several vitamins and minerals (Mg++ and B6; Labrie & Roder, 2010). Thus, it is important to ensure an adequate supply of vitamins and minerals in the diet.

Although little can be concluded from case studies and small N studies, they can indicate where interventions deserve to be evaluated. In a case study, the psychosis of a child remitted with ingestion of multivitamins

(Rodway et al., 2012). Positive results of treating schizophrenics with methylfolate have been reported (Godfrey et al., 1990).

Nonchemical Interventions

Demonstration projects treating those who hear voices with psychological treatments have been completed. In these demonstration projects, clients are not medicated immediately. If severe deterioration persists, then medications at low doses are added. Bola et al. (2009) identified the shared factors in the various projects as "respect for individual patients, a low-stress environment with clear expectations and dependable interpersonal relations, and an effort to involve the patients as active participants in their recovery process" (p. 12).

Soteria projects have been tested in the United States and in Switzerland. According to the Soteria project protocol, patients reside in the community in a small home-like atmosphere. The expectation of improvement is conveyed. Participation in daily tasks is expected. Psychotic symptoms are described in nonalarming terms. In the United States, one of the projects assigned patients based on bed availability and in the second cohort observed random assignment to Soteria or treatment as usual (Bola & Mosher, 2003).

Other demonstration projects have involved family members. The Swedish Parachute Project entails mental health professionals meeting with families several times per week and assisting family members in communicating with the distressed individual (Seikkula, Alakare, & Aaltonen, 2011). Mary Olson, a faculty member at Smith School of Social Work, was trained in this methodology and is now leading an evaluation of a similar project called "Open-Dialog" (Seikkula & Olson, 2003). Will Hall, an individual who reports hearing voices, is a clinician involved in this project. Will Hall regularly blogs about his experiences on his own website and at the Mad in America website (www.willhall .netopendialogue/).

Bola et al. (2009) evaluated five studies of demonstration treatments in which medications were kept to a minimum. They found that the outcome from these projects was moderately superior in functional outcome to the outcomes of treatment as usual with medications. Two to 3 years after beginning these treatments, across the studies by Bola et al., it was evaluated that 27% to 43% of individuals were doing well and had remained unmedicated.

DILEMMA FOR SOCIETY AND CLINICIANS

As the developments in the understanding of the neurological and biochemical mechanisms of schizophrenia have accelerated, philosophic change has also impacted the world of clinical treatment. "Psych Rehab" has emerged as a model for working with the seriously mentally ill. Rather than being trained to work in community mental health centers or state hospitals, Psych Rehab professionals focus on providing services to the community. Case management services are a primary vehicle for service rather than traditional psychotherapy. The emphasis is on hiring consumers (the new term for patients) as patient advocates and as case managers. The mantras are *empowerment, consumer choice, lived experience,* and *recovery* (Corrigan, Mueser, Bond, Drake, & Solomon, 2008; Pratt, Gill, Barrett, & Roberts, 2007; Rapp & Gosha, 2005). Psych Rehab has emerged as a new profession, with its own professional association. Advanced degree programs are now being offered at several universities (see www.uspra.org).

Since the closing of the state hospital systems in the 1960 to 1970s, many have documented the lack of services in the community for the chronically mentally ill (Torrey & Gorman, 2005). However, it is now possible in some states to bill Medicaid for case management services. Depending on the state, there may be a funding mechanism to provide services to those who were previously neglected. Thus, mechanisms for paying for the services provided by the newly minted Psych Rehab professional may now be available.

Social workers and other mental health professionals have served in the role of a psychoeducator for those with chronic mental illness and their families (Bentley, Walsh, & Farmer, 2005). The Ho, Andreasen, Ziebell, Pierson, and Magnotta (2011) study on brain-volume reduction as a result of antidopamine drugs has been widely publicized, as has the Wunderink et al. study, which found better outcomes in those who were unmedicated. It remains an ethical question of whether social workers and other mental health clinicians should be encouraging medication compliance with antidopaminergic drugs. If mental health clinicians impart information, questions remain about how the negative aspects of medications should be imparted.

Places such as the Copeland Center (www.copelandcenter.com) in Philadelphia provide training to the case managers in the state of Pennsylvania. The philosophy of the Copeland Center is to involve consumers in their treatment. Wellness Recovery Action Plan (WRAP) training, a treatment strategy of the Copeland Center, teaches case managers to work with consumers to develop action plans called WRAPs. WRAPs, similar to living wills, are directions for others to follow if the person relapses into psychosis. The WRAP philosophy is to assist consumers to be in charge of their recovery and to control their destinies. (Evaluation of the WRAP program has been positive, although the evaluators did not ask about compliance with medications [Cook et al., 2010].) Although not being openly against medications, at their training events, the Copeland Center features individuals who were psychotic at certain points in their lives, but who are presently are not on medication. Unmedicated former patients lead the training sessions.

Several high-profile groups have organized in this country to argue against forced treatment. Attorney James Gottstein has founded PsychRights. PsychRights sues on behalf of patients who are committed and forced to take medications. (PsychRights has also sued those who bill Medicare for off-label medications for children.) MindFreedom was founded by David Oaks. Both James Gottstein and David Oaks experienced psychosis in college as discussed in a web radio show from the MindFreedom website in March 2012. They are now very active competent persons who realized their considerable achievements without medications.

With the many high-profile shootings done by mentally ill individuals in this country, there is more public support for increasing involuntary treatment of those with mental illness. In fact, a bill (Helping Families in Mental Health Crisis Act) has been introduced in Congress to encourage more involuntary treatment (Carey, 2013). The passage of Kendra's Law in New York state was precipitated by a person with mental illness whose violence resulted in a terrible murder. In line with Kendra's Law, persons who are committed to outpatient treatment are more aggressively followed when they fail to present for their scheduled appointments. The system ensures that these individuals are medicated, often against their will. Other states have passed laws similar to the New York state law

(Appelbaum, 2005; Busch, Wilder, Van Dorn, Swartz, & Swanson, 2010; Swanson et al., 2013). An evaluation of Kendra's Law found that the costs to the state in terms of inpatient treatment and arrests eventuating in jail time have decreased since the passage of the law (Swanson et al., 2013). However, the evaluation of forced treatment did not consider the cost in terms of lost productivity and development of dementia in those complying with medications. Additionally, examination of whether compliance with medications increases or decreases violence has not been done. All the antidepressants carry black-box warnings for violence against self in young people.

In summary, there is a movement for ending forced treatment with antipsychotics. However, fierce opposition is to be expected. Presently, the newer antipsychotics (Seroquel and Abilify) are big money makers for the drug companies, with Abilify being the top-grossing drug in the United States (Lagnado, 2013). Sorting out the future policies will be controversial.

REFERENCES

American Psychiatric Association. (2013). *Diagnostic and statistical manual of mental disorders* (5th ed.). Washington, DC: Author.

Amminger, G. P., Schafer, M. R., Papageorgiou, K., Klier, C. M., Cotton, S. M., Harrigan, S. M.,...Berger, G. E. (2010). Long-chain omega-3 fatty acids for indicated prevention of psychotic disorders: A randomized, placebo-controlled trial. *Archives of General Psychiatry, 67*(2), 146–154.

Appelbaum, P. S. (2005). Assessing Kendra's law: Five years of outpatient commitment in New York. *Psychiatric Services, 56*(7), 791–792.

Arita, M., Bianchini, F., Aliberti, J., Sher, A., Chiang, N., Hong, S.,...Serhan, C. N. (2005). Stereochemical assignment, antiinflammatory properties, and receptor for the omega-3 lipid mediator resolvin e1. *Journal of Experimental Medicine, 201*, 713–722.

Arnedo, J., Svrakic, D. M., Romero-Zaliz, R., Hernández-Cuervo, H., Molecular Genetics of Schizophrenia Consortium, Fanous, A. H.,...Zwir, I. (2014). Uncovering the hidden risk architecture of the schizophrenias: Confirmation in three independent genome-wide association studies. *American Journal of Psychiatry, 172*(2), 139–153.

Arvindakshan, M., Ghate, M., Ranjekar, P. K., Evans, D. R., & Mahadik, S. P. (2003). Supplementation with a combination of omega-3 fatty acids and antioxidants (vitamins E and C) improves the outcome of schizophrenia. *Schizophrenia Research, 62*(3), 195–204.

Ballesteros, A., Summerfelt, A., Du, X., Jiang, P., Chiappelli, J., Tagamets, M.,...Hong, L. E. (2013). Electrophysiological intermediate biomarkers for oxidative stress in schizophrenia. *Clinical Neurophysiology, 124*(11), 2209–2215. doi:10.1016/j.clinph.2013.05.021

Bartos, M., Vida, I., & Jonas, P. (2007). Synaptic mechanisms of synchronized gamma oscillations in inhibitory interneuron networks. *Nature Reviews Neuroscience, 8*(1), 45–56.

Behrens, M. M., Ali, S. S., & Dugan, L. L. (2008). Interleukin-6 mediates the increase in NADPH-oxidase in ketamine model of schizophrenia. *Journal of Neuroscience, 28*(51), 13957–13966.

Behrens, M. M., & Sejnowski, T. J. (2009). Does schizophrenia arise from oxidative dysregulation of parvalbumin-interneurons in the developing cortex? *Neuropharmacology, 57*(3), 193–200.

Bentley, K. J., Walsh, J., & Farmer, R. L. (2005). Social work roles and activities regarding psychiatric medication: Results of a national survey. *Social Work, 50*(4), 295–303.

Berger, G. E., Proffitt, T. M., McConchie, M., Yuen, H., Wood, S. J., Amminger, G. P.,...McGorry, P. D. (2007). Ethyl-eicosapentaenoic acid in first-episode psychosis: A randomized, placebo-controlled trial. *Journal of Clinical Psychiatry, 68*(12), 1867–1875.

Berger, G. E., Wood, S. J., Wellard, R. M., Proffitt, T. M., McConchie, M., Amminger, G. P.,...McGorry, P. D. (2008). Ethyl-eicosapentaenoic acid in first-episode psychosis. A 1H-MRS study. *Neuropsychopharmacology, 33*(10), 2467–2473.

Berk, M., Copolov, D., Dean, O., Lu, K., Jeavons, S., Schapkaitz, I.,...Bush, A. I. (2008). N-acetyl cysteine as a glutathione precursor for schizophrenia—A double-blind, randomized, placebo-controlled trial. *Biological Psychiatry, 64*(5), 361–368.

Berk, M., Ng, F., Dean, O., Dodd, S., & Bush, A. I. (2008). Glutathione: A novel treatment target in psychiatry. *Trends in Pharmacological Science, 29*(7), 346–351.

Bitanihirwe, B. K., Lim, M. P., Kelley, J. F., Kaneko, T., & Woo, T. U. (2009). Glutamatergic deficits and parvalbumin-containing inhibitory neurons in the prefrontal cortex in schizophrenia. *BMC Psychiatry, 9*, 71. doi:10.1186/1471-244X-9-71

Bitanihirwe, B. K., & Woo, T. U. (2011). Oxidative stress in schizophrenia: An integrated approach. *Neuroscience and Biobehavioral Reviews, 35*(3), 878–893.

Bola, J. R., Lehtinen, K., Culberg, J., & Ciompi, L. (2009). Psychosocial treatment, antipsychotic postponement, and low-dose medication strategies in first-episode psychosis: A review of the literature. *Psychosis, 1*(1), 4–18.

Bola, J. R., & Mosher, L. R. (2003). Treatment of acute psychosis without neuroleptics: Two-year outcomes from the Soteria Project. *Journal of Nervous and Mental Disease, 191*(4), 219–229.

Brown, A. S., & Derkits, E. J. (2010). Prenatal infection and schizophrenia: A review of epidemiologic and translational studies. *American Journal of Psychiatry, 167*(3), 261–280.

Browne, S., Clarke, M., Gervin, M., Waddington, J. L., Larkin, C., & O'Callaghan, E. (2000). Determinants of quality of life at first presentation with schizophrenia. *British Journal of Psychiatry, 176*, 173–176.

Buka, S. L., Tsuang, M. T., & Lipsitt, L. P. (1993). Pregnancy/delivery complications and psychiatric diagnosis. A prospective study. *Archives of General Psychiatry, 50*(2), 151–156.

Busch, A. B., Wilder, C. M., Van Dorn, R. A., Swartz, M. S., & Swanson, J. W. (2010). Changes in guideline-recommended medication possession after implementing Kendra's law in New York. *Psychiatric Services, 61*(10), 1000–1005.

Cabungcal, J. H., Steullet, P., Kraftsik, R., Cuenod, M., & Do, K. Q. (2013). Early-life insults impair parvalbumin interneurons via oxidative stress: Reversal by N-acetylcysteine. *Biological Psychiatry, 73*(6), 574–582.

Cahalan, S. (2013). *Brain on fire: My month of madness*. New York, NY: Simon & Schuster.

Calarge, C. A., Zimmerman, B., Xie, D., Kuperman, S., & Schiechte, J. A. (2010). A cross-sectional evaluation of the effect of risperidone and selective serotonin reuptake inhibitors on bone mineral density in boys. *Journal of Clinical Psychiatry, 7*(3), 338–347.

Cani, P. D., Bibiloni, R., Knauf, C., Waget, A., Neyrinck, A. M., Delzenne, N. M., & Burcelin, R. (2008). Changes in gut microbiota control metabolic endotoxemia-induced inflammation in high-fat diet-induced obesity and diabetes in mice. *Diabetes, 57*, 1470–1481.

Carey, B. (2013, April 3). Mental health groups split on bill to overhaul care. *The New York Times*, p. A4.

Carter, C. J. (2006). Schizophrenia susceptibility genes converge on interlinked pathways related to glutamatergic transmission and long-term potentiation, oxidative stress and oligodendrocyte viability. *Schizophrenia Research, 86*(1–3), 1–14.

Casey, D. E. (2006). Implications of the CATIE trial on treatment: Extrapyramidal symptoms. *CNS Spectrum, 11*(Suppl. 7), 25–31.

Christensen, O., & Christensen, E. (1988). Fat consumption and schizophrenia. *Acta Psychiatrica Scandinavica, 78*(5), 587–591.

Cook, J. A., Copeland, M. E., Corey, L., Buffington, E., Jonikas, J. A., Curtis, L. C.,...Nichols, W. H. (2010). Developing the evidence base for peer-led services: Changes among participants following Wellness Recovery Action Planning

(WRAP) eduction in two statewide initiatives. *Psychiatric Rehabilitation Journal,* *34*(2), 113–120.

Corrigan, P. W., Mueser, K. T., Bond, G. R., Drake, R. E., & Solomon, P. (2008). *Principles and practice of psychiatric rehabilitation: An empirical approach.* New York, NY: Guilford Press.

Curley, A. A., Arion, D., Volk, D. W., Asafu-Adjei, J. K., Sampson, A. R., Fish, K. N., & Lewis, D. A. (2011). Cortical deficits of glutamic acid decarboxylase 67 expression in schizophrenia: Clinical, protein, and cell type-specific features. *American Journal of Psychiatry, 168*(9), 921–929.

Deo, A. J., Goldszer, I. M., Li, S., DiBitetto, J. V., Henteleff, R., Sampson, A.,...Sweet, R. A. (2013). PAK1 protein expression in the auditory cortex of schizophrenia subjects. *PLoS ONE, 8*(4), e59458. doi:10.1371/journal.pone.0059458

Dietrich-Muszalska, A., Malinowska, J., Olas, B., Glowacki, R., Bald, E., Wachowicz, B., & Rabe-Jablonska, J. (2012). The oxidative stress may be induced by the elevated homocysteine in schizophrenic patients. *Neurochemical Research, 37*(5), 1057–1062.

Do, K. Q., Cabungcal, J. H., Frank, A., Steullet, P., & Cuenod, M. (2009). Redox dysregulation, neurodevelopment, and schizophrenia. *Current Opinions in Neurobiology, 19*(2), 220–230.

Doischer, D., Hosp, J. A., Yanagawa, Y., Obata, K., Jonas, P., Vida, I., & Bartos, M. (2008). Postnatal differentiation of basket cells from slow to fast signaling devices. *Journal of Neuroscience, 28*(48), 12956–12968.

Dorph-Petersen, K. A., Pierri, J. N., Perel, J. M., Sun, Z., Sampson, A. R., & Lewis, D. A. (2005). The influence of chronic exposure to antipsychotic medications on brain size before and after tissue fixation: A comparison of haloperidol and olanzapine in macaque monkeys. *Neuropsychopharmacology, 30*(9), 1649–1661.

Eggan, S. M., Stoyak, S. R., Verrico, C. D., & Lewis, D. A. (2010). Cannabinoid CB1 receptor immunoreactivity in the prefrontal cortex: Comparison of schizophrenia and major depressive disorder. *Neuropsychopharmacology,* *35*(10), 2060–2071.

Emsley, R., Myburgh, C., Oosthuizen, P., & van Rensburg, S. J. (2002). Randomized, placebo-controlled study of ethyl-eicosapentaenoic acid as supplemental treatment in schizophrenia. *American Journal of Psychiatry, 159*(9), 1596–1598.

Erhardt, S., Olsson, S. K., & Engberg, G. (2009). Pharmacological manipulation of kynurenic acid: Potential in the treatment of psychiatric disorders. *CNS Drugs, 23*(2), 91–101.

Etminan, M., Heran, B., Carleton, B., & Brophy, J. (2014). Risperidone use and risk for gynecomastia in men [Letter to the editor]. *Journal of Clinical Psychopharmacology, 34*(5), 656–657. doi:10.1097/JCP.0000000000000182

Fenton, W. S., Dickerson, F., Boronow, J., Hibbeln, J. R., & Knable, M. (2001). A placebo-controlled trial of omega-3 fatty acid (ethyl eicosapentaenoic acid) supplementation for residual symptoms and cognitive impairment in schizophrenia. *American Journal of Psychiatry, 158*(12), 2071–2074.

Ferder, L., Ferder, M. D., & Inserra, F. (2010). The role of high-fructose corn syrup in metabolic syndrome and hypertension. *Current Hypertension Report, 12,* 105–112.

Fusar-Poli, P., & Berger, G. (2012). Eicosapentaenoic acid interventions in schizophrenia: Meta-analysis of randomized, placebo-controlled studies. *Journal of Clinical Psychopharmacology, 32*(2), 179–185.

Fusar-Poli, P., Smieskova, R., Kempton, M. J., Ho, B. C., Andreasen, N. C., & Borgwardt, S. (2013). Progressive brain changes in schizophrenia related to antipsychotic treatment: A meta-analysis of longitudinal MRI studies. *Neuroscience and Biobehavioral Reviews, 37*(8), 1680–1691.

Geddes, A. E., Huang, X. F., & Newell, K. A. (2011). Reciprocal signalling between NR2 subunits of the NMDA receptor and neuregulin1 and their role in schizophrenia. *Progress in Neuropsychopharmacology and Biological Psychiatry, 35*(4), 896–904.

Gianfrancesco, F., White, R., Wang, R.-H., & Nasrallah, H. A. (2003). Antipsychotic-induced type 2 diabetes: Evidence from a large health plan database. *Journal of Clinical Psychopharmacology, 23*(4), 328–335.

Gleeson, J. F., Cotton, S. M., Alvarez-Jimenez, M., Wade, D., Gee, D., Crisp, K.,...McGorry, P. D. (2013). A randomized controlled trial of relapse prevention therapy for first-episode psychosis patients: Outcome at 30-month follow-up. *Schizophrenia Bulletin, 39*(2), 436–448.

Godfrey, P. S., Toone, B. K., Carney, M. W., Flynn, T. G., Bottiglieri, T., Laundy, M.,...Reynolds, E. H. (1990). Enhancement of recovery from psychiatric illness by methylfolate. *Lancet, 336*(8712), 392–395.

Goff, D. C., Bottiglieri, T., Arning, E., Shih, V., Freudenreich, O., Evins, A. E.,...Coyle, J. (2004). Folate, homocysteine, and negative symptoms in schizophrenia. *American Journal of Psychiatry, 161*(9), 1705–1708.

Grace, A. A. (2012). Dopamine system dysregulation by the hippocampus: Implications for the pathophysiology and treatment of schizophrenia. *Neuropharmacology, 62*(3), 1342–1348.

Graham, K. L., Carson, C. M., Ezeoke, A., Buckley, P. F., & Miller, B. J. (2014). Urinary tract infections in acute psychosis. *Journal of Clinical Psychiatry 75*(4), 379–385. doi:10.4088/JCP.13m08469

Gysin, R., Kraftsik, R., Boulat, O., Bovet, P., Conus, P., Comte-Krieger, E.,...Do, K. Q. (2011). Genetic dysregulation of glutathione synthesis predicts alteration of plasma thiol redox status in schizophrenia. *Antioxidants and Redox Signaling, 15*(7), 2003–2010.

Gysin, R., Kraftsik, R., Sandell, J., Bovet, P., Chappuis, C., Conus, P.,...Do, K. Q. (2007). Impaired glutathione synthesis in schizophrenia: Convergent genetic and functional evidence. *Proceedings of the National Academy of Science of the United States of America, 104*(42), 16621–16626.

Haddad, P., M., & Anderson, I. M. (2002). Antipsychotic-related QTc prolongation, torsade de pointes and sudden death. *Drugs, 62*(11), 1649–1671.

Harrow, M., & Jobe, T. H. (2013). Does long-term treatment of schizophrenia with antipsychotic medications facilitate recovery? *Schizophrenia Bulletin, 39*(5), 962–965.

Harrow, M., Jobe, T. H., & Faull, R. N. (2012). Do all schizophrenia patients need antipsychotic treatment continuously throughout their lifetime? A 20-year longitudinal study. *Psychological Medicine, 42*(10), 2145–2155.

Hashimoto, T., Volk, D. W., Eggan, S. M., Mirnics, K., Pierri, J. N., Sun, Z.,... Lewis, D. A. (2003). Gene expression deficits in a subclass of GABA neurons in the prefrontal cortex of subjects with schizophrenia. *Journal of Neuroscience, 23*(15), 6315–6326.

Heins, M., Simons, C., Lataster, T., Pfeifer, S., Versmissen, D., Lardinois, M.,... Myin-Germeys, I. (2011). Childhood trauma and psychosis: A case-control and case-sibling comparison across different levels of genetic liability, psychopathology, and type of trauma. *American Journal of Psychiatry, 168*(12), 1286–1294.

Ho, B. C., Andreasen, N. C., Ziebell, S., Pierson, R., & Magnotta, V. (2011). Long-term antipsychotic treatment and brain volumes: A longitudinal study of first-episode schizophrenia. *Archives of General Psychiatry, 68*(2), 128–137.

Horrobin, D. F. (2003). Omega-3 fatty acid for schizophrenia [Comment letter]. *American Journal of Psychiatry, 160*(1), 188–189; author reply 189.

Howes, O. D., & Kapur, S. (2009). The dopamine hypothesis of schizophrenia: Version III—The final common pathway. *Schizophrenia Bulletin, 35*(3), 549–562.

Insel, T. (2013). *Director's blog: Antipsychotics: Taking the long view.* Retrieved from http://www.nimh.gov/about/director/2013/antipsychotics-taking-the-long-view.html

Jablensky, A. (1992). Schizophrenia: Manifestations, incidence and course in different cultures. *Psychological Medicine, 20*, Monograph, 1–95.

Johns, L. C., Nazroo, J. Y., Bebbington, P., & Kuipers, E. (2002). Occurrence of hallucinatory experiences in a community sample and ethnic variations. *British Journal of Psychiatry, 180*, 174–178.

Johnstone, E. C., Macmillan, J. F., Frith, C. D., Benn, D. K., & Crow, T. J. (1990). Further investigation of the predictors of outcome following first schizophrenic episodes. *British Journal of Psychiatry, 157*, 182–189.

Joy, C. B., Mumby-Croft, R., & Joy, L. A. (2000). Polyunsaturated fatty acid (fish or evening primrose oil) for schizophrenia [Review]. *Cochrane Database System Reviews,* (2), CD001257. doi:10.1002/14651858.CD001257

Kale, A., Naphade, N., Sapkale, S., Kamaraju, M., Pillai, A., Joshi, S., & Mahadik, S. (2010). Reduced folic acid, vitamin B12 and docosahexaenoic acid and increased homocysteine and cortisol in never-medicated schizophrenia patients: Implications for altered one-carbon metabolism. *Psychiatry Research, 175*(1–2), 47–53.

Kantrowitz, J. T., Hoptman, M. J., Leitman, D. I., Silipo, G., & Javitt, D. C. (2013, April 24). The 5% difference: Early sensory processing predicts sarcasm perception in schizophrenia and schizo-affective disorder. *Psychological Medicine,* 1–12. doi:10.1017/S0033291713000834

Kantrowitz, J. T., & Javitt, D. C. (2010a). N-methyl-d-aspartate (NMDA) receptor dysfunction or dysregulation: The final common pathway on the road to schizophrenia? *Brain Research Bulletin, 83*(3–4), 108–121.

Kantrowitz, J. T., & Javitt, D. C. (2010b). Thinking glutamatergically: Changing concepts of schizophrenia based upon changing neurochemical models. *Clinical Schizophrenia and Related Psychoses, 4*(3), 189–200.

Karry, R., Klein, E., & Ben Shachar, D. (2004). Mitochondrial complex I subunits expression is altered in schizophrenia: A postmortem study. *Biological Psychiatry, 55*(7), 676–684.

Katzung, B. G. (2013). Histamine, serotonin, & the ergot alkaloids. In B. G. Katzung, S. B. Masters, & A. J. Trevor (Eds.), *Basic and clinical pharmacology* (12th ed., pp. 273–293). New York, NY: McGraw Hill.

Kinney, J. W., Davis, C. N., Tabarean, I., Conti, B., Bartfai, T., & Behrens, M. M. (2006). A specific role for NR2A-containing NMDA receptors in the maintenance of parvalbumin and GAD67 immunoreactivity in cultured interneurons. *Journal of Neuroscience, 26*(5), 1604–1615.

Kirkpatrick, N., & Miller, B. J. (2013). Inflammation and schizophrenia. *Schizophrenia Bulletin, 39*(6), 1174–1179.

Konopaske, G. T., Dorph-Petersen, K. A., Pierri, J. N., Wu, Q., Sampson, A. R., & Lewis, D. A. (2007). Effect of chronic exposure to antipsychotic medication on cell numbers in the parietal cortex of macaque monkeys. *Neuropsychopharmacology, 32*(6), 1216–1223.

Konopaske, G. T., Dorph-Petersen, K. A., Sweet, R. A., Pierri, J. N., Zhang, W., Sampson, A. R., & Lewis, D. A. (2008). Effect of chronic antipsychotic exposure on astrocyte and oligodendrocyte numbers in macaque monkeys. *Biological Psychiatry, 63*(8), 759–765.

Labrie, V., & Roder, J. C. (2010). The involvement of the NMDA receptor D-serine/glycine site in the pathophysiology and treatment of schizophrenia. *Neuroscience and Biobehavioral Reviews, 34*(3), 351–372.

Lagnado, L. (2013, August 11). U.S. probes use of antipsychotic drugs on children. *Wall Street Journal.* Retrieved from http://online.wsj.com/article_email/SB10001424127887323477604578654130865413086574470

Lakhan, S. E., Caro, M., & Hadzimichalis, N. (2013). NMDA receptor activity in neuropsychiatric disorders. *Frontiers in Psychiatry, 4,* 52. doi:10.3389/fpsyt.2013.00052

Lane, H. Y., Chang, Y. C., Liu, Y. C., Chiu, C. C., & Tsai, G. E. (2005). Sarcosine or D-serine add-on treatment for acute exacerbation of schizophrenia: A randomized, double-blind, placebo-controlled study. *Archives of General Psychiatry, 62*(11), 1196–1204.

Lane, H. Y., Liu, Y. C., Huang, C. L., Chang, Y. C., Liau, C. H., Perng, C. H., & Tsai, G. E. (2008). Sarcosine (N-methylglycine) treatment for acute schizophrenia: A randomized, double-blind study. *Biological Psychiatry, 63*(1), 9–12.

Laugharne, J. D., Mellor, J. E., & Peet, M. (1996). Fatty acids and schizophrenia. *Lipids, 31*(Suppl.), S163–165.

Lavoie, S., Murray, M. M., Deppen, P., Knyazeva, M. G., Berk, M., Boulat, O.,...Do, K. Q. (2008). Glutathione precursor, N-acetyl-cysteine, improves mismatch negativity in schizophrenia patients. *Neuropsychopharmacology, 33*(9), 2187–2199.

Leucht, S., Tardy, M., Komossa, K., Heres, S., Kissling, W., Salanti, G., & Davis, J. M. (2012). Antipsychotic drugs versus placebo for relapse prevention in schizophrenia: A systematic review and meta-analysis. *Lancet, 379*(9831), 2063–2071.

Lewis, D. A., Curley, A. A., Glausier, J. R., & Volk, D. W. (2012). Cortical parvalbumin interneurons and cognitive dysfunction in schizophrenia. *Trends in Neuroscience, 35*(1), 57–67.

Li, X. F., Zheng, Y. L., Xiu, M. H., Chen da, C., Kosten, T. R., & Zhang, X. Y. (2011). Reduced plasma total antioxidant status in first-episode drug-naive patients with schizophrenia. *Progress in Neuropsychopharmacology and Biological Psychiatry, 35*(4), 1064–1067.

Linderholm, K. R., Skogh, E., Olsson, S. K., Dahl, M. L., Holtze, M., Engberg, G.,...Erhardt, S. (2012). Increased levels of kynurenine and kynurenic acid in the CSF of patients with schizophrenia. *Schizophrenia Bulletin, 38*(3), 426–432.

Lipska, B. K., & Weinberger, D. R. (2000). To model a psychiatric disorder in animals: Schizophrenia as a reality test. *Neuropsychopharmacology, 23*(3), 223–239.

Lipton, S. A., Kim, W. K., Choi, Y. B., Kumar, S., D'Emilia, D. M., Rayudu, P. V.,...Stamler, J. S. (1997). Neurotoxicity associated with dual actions of homocysteine at the N-methyl-D-aspartate receptor. *Proceedings of the National Academy of Sciences of the United States of America, 94*(11), 5923–5928.

Longden, E. (2013). *The voices in my head.* Retrieved from www.ted.com/talks/eleanor_longden_the_voices_in_my_head

Maidment, I. D. (2000). Are fish oils an effective therapy in mental illness—An analysis of the data. *Acta Psychiatrica Scandinavica, 102*(1), 3–11.

Marchbanks, R. M., Ryan, M., Day, I. N., Owen, M., McGuffin, P., & Whatley, S. A. (2003). A mitochondrial DNA sequence variant associated with schizophrenia and oxidative stress. *Schizophrenia Research, 65*(1), 33–38.

Marshall, M., & Rathbone, J. (2011). Early intervention for psychosis. *Schizophrenia Bulletin, 37*(6), 1111–1114.

McGorry, P., Alvarez-Jimenez, M., & Killackey, E. (2013). Antipsychotic medication during the critical period following remission from first-episode psychosis: Less is more. *JAMA Psychiatry, 70*(9), 898–899. doi:10.1001/jamapsychiatry.2013.264

McGrath, J. J., Burne, T. H., Feron, F., Mackay-Sim, A., & Eyles, D. W. (2010). Developmental vitamin D deficiency and risk of schizophrenia: A 10-year update. *Schizophrenia Bulletin, 36*(6), 1073–1078.

Meltzer, H. (2013). Antipsychotic agents and lithium. In B. G. Katzung, S. B. Masters, & A. J. Trevor (Eds.), *Basic and clinical pharmacology* (12 ed., pp. 501–520). New York, NY: McGraw Hill.

Meyer, U., Schwarz, M. J., & Muller, N. (2011). Inflammatory processes in schizophrenia: A promising neuroimmunological target for the treatment of negative/cognitive symptoms and beyond. *Pharmacological Therapy, 132*(1), 96–110.

Miller, B. J. (2014). Toward biological subtypes in schizophrenia: Potential role of NMDA-receptor antibodies. *Psychiatric Times, 31*(6), 1, 26.

Miller, B. J., Graham, K. L., Bodenheimer, C. M., Culpepper, N. H., Waller, J. L., & Buckley, P. F. (2013). A prevalence study of urinary tract infections in acute relapse of schizophrenia. *Journal of Clinical Psychiatry, 74*(3), 271–277.

MindFreedom Web Radio Show. (2012, March 10). Jim Gottstein, psychiatric survivor attorney activist, on MindFreedom. Retrieved from http://www.mindfreedom.org/campaign/media/radio/jim-gottstein-occupy-apa

Mittal, V. A., Ellman, L. M., & Cannon, T. D. (2008). Gene-environment interaction and covariation in schizophrenia: The role of obstetric complications. *Schizophrenia Bulletin, 34*(6), 1083–1094.

Morrision, A. P., Hutton, P., Shiers, D., & Turkington, D. (2012). Antipsychotics: Is it time to introduce patient choice? *British Journal of Psychiatry, 201*, 83–84.

Nitta, M., Kishimoto, T., Müller, N., Weiser, M., Davidson, M., Kane, J. M., & Correll, C. U. (2013). Adjunctive use of nonsteroidal anti-inflammatory drugs for schizophrenia: A meta-analytic investigation of randomized controlled trials. *Schizophrenia Bulletin, 39*(6), 1230–1241.

Peet, M. (2004). Nutrition and schizophrenia: Beyond omega-3 fatty acids. *Prostaglandins, Leukotrienes and Essential Fatty Acids, 70*(4), 417–422.

Peet, M., Brind, J., Ramchand, C. N., Shah, S., & Vankar, G. K. (2001). Two double-blind placebo-controlled pilot studies of eicosapentaenoic acid in the treatment of schizophrenia. *Schizophrenia Research, 49*(3), 243–251.

Peet, M., & Horrobin, D. F. (2002). A dose-ranging exploratory study of the effects of ethyl-eicosapentaenoate in patients with persistent schizophrenic symptoms. *Journal of Psychiatric Research, 36*(1), 7–18.

Pilowsky, L. S., Bressan, R. A., Stone, J. M., Erlandsson, K., Mulligan, R. S., Krystal, J. H., & Ell, P. J. (2006). First in vivo evidence of an NMDA receptor deficit in medication-free schizophrenic patients. *Molecular Psychiatry, 11*(2), 118–119.

Potvin, S., Stip, E., Sepehry, A. A., Gendron, A., Bah, R., & Kouassi, E. (2008). Inflammatory cytokine alterations in schizophrenia: A systematic quantitative review. *Biological Psychiatry, 63*(8), 801–808.

Powell, S. B., Sejnowski, T. J., & Behrens, M. M. (2012). Behavioral and neurochemical consequences of cortical oxidative stress on parvalbumin-interneuron maturation in rodent models of schizophrenia. *Neuropharmacology, 62*(3), 1322–1331.

Pramyothin, P., & Khaodhiar, L. (2010). Metabolic syndrome with the atypical antipsychotics. *Current Opinion in Endocrinology, Diabetes & Obesity, 17*(5), 460–466.

Pratt, C. W., Gill, K. J., Barrett, N. M., & Roberts, M. M. (2007). *Psychiatric rehabilitation* (2nd ed.). New York, NY: Academic Press.

Puri, B. K., & Richardson, A. J. (1998). Sustained remission of positive and negative symptoms of schizophrenia after treatment with eicosapentaenoic acid [letter]. *Archives of General Psychiatry, 55*, 188–189.

Rao, S. G., Williams, G. V., & Goldman-Rakic, P. S. (2000). Destruction and creation of spatial tuning by disinhibition: GABA(A) blockade of prefrontal cortical neurons engaged by working memory. *Journal of Neuroscience, 20*(1), 485–494.

Rapp, C. A., & Goscha, R. J. (2005). What are the common features of evidence-based practices? In R. E. Drake, M. R. Merrens, & D. W. Lynde (Eds.), *Evidence-based mental health practice* (pp. 189–215). New York, NY: Norton.

Reddy, R., Fleet-Michaliszyn, S., Condray, R., Yao, J. K., & Keshavan, M. S. (2011). Reduction in perseverative errors with adjunctive ethyl-eicosapentaenoic acid in patients with schizophrenia: Preliminary study. *Prostaglandins, Leukotrienes and Essential Fatty Acids, 84*(3–4), 79–83.

Robinson, D., Woerner, M. G., Alvir, J. M., Geister, S., Koreen, A., Sheitman, B.,…Liberman, J. A. (1999). Predictors of relapse following response from a first episode of schizophrenia or schizoaffective disorder. *Archives of General Psychiatry, 159*(3), 241–247.

Rodway, M., Vance, A., Watters, A., Lee, H., Bos, E., & Kaplan, B. J. (2012, November 9). Efficacy and cost of micronutrient treatment of childhood psychosis. *BMJ Case Reports.* pii: bcr2012007213; doi:10.1136/bcr-2012-007213

Samaha, A. N., Seeman, P., Stewart, J., Rajabi, H., & Kapur, S. (2007). "Breakthrough" dopamine supersensitivity during ongoing antipsychotic treatment leads to treatment failure over time. *Journal of Neuroscience, 27*(11), 2979–2986.

Schizophrenia Working Group for the Psychiatric Genomics Consortium. (2014). Biological insights from 108 schizophrenia-associated genetic loci. *Nature, 511*, 421–427.

Schwartz, M., & Schechter, R. (2011). Systemic inflammatory cells fight off neurodegenerative disease. *Nature Reviews: Neurology, 6*, 405–410.

Schwartz, T. L., Sachdeva, S., & Stahl, S. M. (2012). Glutamate neurocircuitry: Theoretical underpinnings in schizophrenia. *Frontiers in Pharmacology, 3*, 195. doi:10.3389/fphar.2012.00195

Seeman, P., Weinshenker, D., Quirion, R., Srivastava, L. K., Bhardwaj, S. K., Grandy, D. K., ... Tallerico, T. (2005). Dopamine supersensitivity correlates with D2High states, implying many paths to psychosis. *Proceedings of the National Academy of Sciences of the United States of America, 102*(9), 3513–3518.

Seikkula, J., Alakare, B., & Aaltonen, J. (2011). Long-term stability of acute psychosis outcomes in advanced community care: The western Lapland Project. *Psychosis, 1*, 1–13.

Seikkula, J., & Olson, M. E. (2003). The open dialogue approach to acute psychosis: Its poetics and micropolitics. *Family Process, 42*(3), 403–418.

Snyder, M. A., & Gao, W. J. (2013). NMDA hypofunction as a convergence point for progression and symptoms of schizophrenia. *Frontiers in Cellular Neuroscience, 7*, 31. doi:10.3389/fncel.2013.00031

Sorensen, H. J., Mortensen, E. L., Schiffman, J., Reinisch, J. M., Maeda, J., & Mednick, S. A. (2010). Early developmental milestones and risk of schizophrenia: A 45-year follow-up of the Copenhagen Perinatal Cohort. *Schizophrenia Research, 118*(1–3), 41–47.

Stahl, S. M. (2013). *Stahl's essential psychopharmacology: Neuroscientific basis and practical applications* (4th ed.). New York, NY: Cambridge University Press.

Steiner, J., Walter, M., Glanz, W., Sarnyai, Z., Bernstein, H-G., Vielhaber, S., ... Stoecker, W. (2013). Increased prevalence of diverse N-methyl-D-aspartate glutamate receptor antibodies in patients with an initial diagnosis of schizophrenia. *JAMA Psychiatry, 70*(3), 271–278.

Steullet, P., Cabungcal, J. H., Kulak, A., Kraftsik, R., Chen, Y., Dalton, T. P., ... Do, K. Q. (2010). Redox dysregulation affects the ventral but not dorsal hippocampus: Impairment of parvalbumin neurons, gamma oscillations, and related behaviors. *Journal of Neuroscience, 30*(7), 2547–2558.

Steullet, P., Neijt, H. C., Cuénod, & Do, K. Q. (2006). Synaptic plasticity impairment and hypofunction of NMDA receptors induced by glutathione deficit: Relevance to schizophrenia. *Neuroscience, 130*, 807–819.

Sullivan, P. F. (2005). The genetics of schizophrenia. *PLoS Medicine, 2*(7), e212. doi:10.1371/journal.pmed.0020212

Swanson, J. W., van Dorn, R. A., Swartz, M. S., Robbins, P. C., Steadman, H. J., McGuire, T. G., & Monahan, J. (2013). The cost of assisted outpatient treatment: Can it save states money? *American Journal of Psychiatry, 170*(12), 1423–1432.

Thompson, A., Nelson, B., & Yung, A. (2011). Predictive validity of clinical variables in the "at risk" for psychosis population: International comparison with results from the North American Prodrome Longitudinal Study. *Schizophrenia Research, 126*(1–3), 51–57.

Torrey, W. C., & Gorman, P. G. (2005). Closing the gap between what services are and what they could be. In R. E. Drake, M. R. Merrens, & D. W. Lynde (Eds.), *Evidence-based mental health practice* (pp. 167–187). New York, NY: Norton.

Tosic, M., Ott, J., Barral, S., Bovet, P., Deppen, P., Gheorghita, F., ... Do, K. Q. (2006). Schizophrenia and oxidative stress: Glutamate cysteine ligase modifier as a susceptibility gene. *American Journal of Human Genetics, 79*(3), 586–592.

Tsai, G., Lane, H. Y., Yang, P., Chong, M. Y., & Lange, N. (2004). Glycine transporter I inhibitor, N-methylglycine (sarcosine), added to antipsychotics for the treatment of schizophrenia. *Biological Psychiatry, 55*(5), 452–456.

Tsai, G. E., & Lin, P. Y. (2010). Strategies to enhance N-methyl-D-aspartate receptor-mediated neurotransmission in schizophrenia, a critical review and meta-analysis. *Current Pharmaceutical Design, 16*(5), 522–537.

van Os, J., & Kapur, S. (2009). Schizophrenia. *Lancet, 374*(9690), 635–645.

Volk, D. W., & Lewis, D. A. (2013). Prenatal ontogeny as a susceptibility period for cortical GABA neuron disturbances in schizophrenia. *Neuroscience, 248C*, 154–164.

Volman, V., Behrens, M. M., & Sejnowski, T. J. (2011). Downregulation of parvalbumin at cortical GABA synapses reduces network gamma oscillatory activity. *Journal of Neuroscience, 31*(49), 18137–18148.

Walker, E. F., Lewine, R. R., & Neumann, C. (1996). Childhood behavioral characteristics and adult brain morphology in schizophrenia. *Schizophrenia Research, 22*(2), 93–101.

Woo, T. -U. (2013). Neurobiology of schizophrenia onset. *Current Topics in Behavioral Neuroscience.* doi:10.1007/7854_2013_243

Wood, S. J., Berger, G. E., Wellard, R. M., Proffitt, T. M., McConchie, M., Berk, M., ... Pantelis, C. (2009a). Medial temporal lobe glutathione concentration in first episode psychosis: A 1H-MRS investigation. *Neurobiology of Disease, 33*(3), 354–357.

Wood, S. J., Yucel, M., Pantelis, C., & Berk, M. (2009b). Neurobiology of schizophrenia spectrum disorders: The role of oxidative stress. *Annals of the Academy of Medicine, Singapore, 38*(5), 396–396.

World Health Organization. (2015). *International statistical classification of diseases and related health problems, 10th revision (ICD-10).* Geneva, Switzerland: WHO. Retrieved from http://apps.who.int/classifications/icd10/browsee/2015

Wunderink, L., Nieboer, R. M., Wiersma, D., Sytema, S., & Nienhuis, F. J. (2013). Recovery in remitted first-episode psychosis at 7 years of follow-up of an early dose reduction/discontinuation or maintenance treatment strategy: Long-term follow-up of a 2-year randomized clinical trial. *JAMA Psychiatry 70*(9), 913–920. doi:10.1001/jamapsychiatry.2013.19

Ziv, Y., & Schwartz, M. (2008). Immune-based regulation of adult neurogenesis: Implications for learning and memory. *Brain, Behavior, and Immunity, 22*, 167–176.

7

Bipolar Disorders

This chapter examines bipolar disorders. We begin with a history of this disorder so that the dramatic differences in the prevalence of this disorder over time will make some sense. The rationale for the addition of the bipolar II category in 1994 to the *Diagnostic and Statistical Manual of Mental Disorders (DSM)* will be provided (American Psychiatric Association [APA], 1994). The case will be made that bipolar I and II share very little except for their common name. After discussing the history of the bipolar category, its neuroscience and genetics are reviewed. The neuroscience and genetics presentation diverges to cover bipolar I and the recently added bipolar II separately. Current pharmacological treatments and their outcomes are also reviewed. Because part of the rationale for early treatment of bipolar disorder derives from the kindling hypothesis, the case for kindling is reviewed. Finally, alternative, nontraditional treatments are covered.

HISTORY OF THE CONCEPT

Emil Kraepelin, the German psychiatrist famous for his descriptions of the patients in his asylum, did distinguish manic depression from schizophrenia. The primary differentiating factor, for him, was that those with manic depression recovered, whereas those with schizophrenia did not and frequently exhibited a trajectory of deterioration (Craddock, O'Donovan, & Owen, 2009; Kraepelin, 1919). In the *DSM-II*, schizophrenia and manic depression were both listed under psychoses. In the era of *DSM-II*, there was considerable diagnostic confusion, and Lawrence Kolb (1968), author of an authoritative text of that era, commented on the reliability problems across countries and time periods in the diagnoses of manic depression. Manic depression was very difficult to distinguish from schizophrenia. According to Kolb, if the family was wealthy, the patient was called manic depressive; if poor, the patient was labeled schizophrenic. With the *DSM-III* (APA, 1980), manic depression was moved from the psychosis section to the affective disorder section of the manual. Little rationale for moving manic depression from the psychosis section to the mood section was provided. Across studies, 47% to 90% of persons with bipolar I experience psychosis with hallucinations and delusions (F. K. Goodwin & Jamison, 2007, p. 53).

As defined in the *DSM-IV-TR* (American Psychiatric Association, 2000), bipolar I requires an episode of mania or a mixed episode (rapidly changing affect from negative to positive emotion within a given time period). Bipolar I does not require an episode of depression. Mania criteria are comparatively restrictive, requiring 1 week of elated, expansive, or irritable mood, with three or more of the following (or four or more of the following if irritability rather than expansive mood is present): inflated self-esteem, decreased need for sleep, pressured speech, flight of ideas or racing thoughts, distractibility, increased goal-directed activity, excessive involvement in risky but pleasurable activities. The manic episode must cause marked impairment in occupational activity or in interpersonal relationships in order to qualify as mania. The need for hospitalization or psychotic features precludes a diagnosis of hypomania.

In 1994, the *DSM-IV* added the category of bipolar II. In contrast to bipolar I, bipolar II requires having experienced an episode of major depression at some point in one's life plus an episode of hypomania. Hypomania requires only 4 days of an elevated or irritable mood with the same number of symptoms off the expansive-mood list, but with the caveat that none of the behaviors is severe enough to disrupt functioning.

In 2007, Merikangas et al., surveying a community sample, reported that the lifetime prevalence of bipolar I was 1% of the population; lifetime prevalence for bipolar II was 1.1%. In clinical settings, the percentage of persons being diagnosed with bipolar disorders has increased. With the addition of bipolar II, from the years 1999 to 2003, adult doctor visits yielding a diagnosis of bipolar disorder increased from 4.77% to 6.28% (Moreno et al., 2007).

Why Was Bipolar II Added?

At the time of the writing of the *DSM-IV* (APA, 1994), it was broadly acknowledged that antidepressant medications could precipitate mania. Allen Frances, the chairperson for the *DSM-IV* explained the rationale for including the category of bipolar II in the *DSM-IV* in 1994 (Frances & Jones, 2012), "We had to balance the fear that patients with bipolar disorder tendencies would be harmed iatrogenically if treated as routine unipolars (i.e., risking the dangers of receiving antidepressants without coverage with a mood stabilizer) against the concern that some patients who are really unipolar would be misidentified as having bipolar II disorder (and then receive unneeded mood stabilizers, which adds the burden of potentially quite harmful side effects)" (p. 474). At the time, Kupfer, Carpenter, and Frank (1988) wrote that those persons who had a history of a major depressive episode but had periods of hypomania suffered from a variant of major depression rather than from bipolar disorder. In contrast, Dunner (1993) argued that because those exhibiting features of bipolar II were midway between those with bipolar I and those with depression on the variable of family members with bipolar I, then those with hypomania should be considered variants of bipolar disorder. Dunner's side prevailed.

Who Was Right?

Frances and Jones (2012) cite studies finding that when persons meeting criteria for bipolar II are treated as unipolar depressed patients and are treated with antidepressants they are no more likely to exhibit mania than others. Thus, the reason for distinguishing the category of bipolar II has proven to be moot. There are other reasons for rejecting the idea that bipolar I and II share underlying commonalities. In studies attempting to identify gene variants predisposing to bipolar I and II, both fail to share the same risk factors. Vieta and Suppes (2008), who have published extensively on bipolar disorders, conclude, "in summary, from the genetic perspective, most investigators tend to think that bipolar II breeds true" (p. 166). Second, in a 13-year study of persons with bipolar disorder, Judd et al. (2003) concluded that those with bipolar I and those with bipolar II followed different trajectories.

Finally, there is the question of the likelihood of those with bipolar II experiencing a later episode of mania. Coryell et al. (1995) followed a clinical sample of persons (mean age = 36 years) with bipolar II and persons with unipolar depression for 10 years. Those with bipolar II were only slightly more likely to later exhibit mania than patients with unipolar depression (7.5% vs. 5.2%). Other predictors of conversion to mania were having a history of psychosis or a family history of bipolar I or schizoaffective disorder.

Young adulthood is the most likely period in which mania usually emerges (Duffy, Alda, Hajek, & Grof, 2009). The Longitudinal Investigation of Bipolar Spectrum Project, a large study conducted at several universities, provided an opportunity to determine the rate of conversion from bipolar II to bipolar I in a nonclinical, younger sample (mean age = 19 years). The risk of moving from bipolar II status to bipolar I was higher in a sample of younger college students than that found in the research with older adults in the Coryell et al. study. In a study by Alloy et al. (2012), 17.4% of those with bipolar II had experienced a manic episode at 4.5-year follow-up. Of the 25 individuals who developed a manic episode, more than half became psychotic. In the Alloy et al. sample, prior higher levels of depression, higher behavioral inhibition system (BIS) scores (the BIS is a measure of anxiety discussed in Chapter 2), impulsivity, and younger age of onset of mood disorder predicted the emergence of mania.

Retrospective reporting of adults with bipolar I finds that they more often identify depressive precursors rather than hypomania precursors as preceding the onset of their bipolar I diagnosis (Calabrese et al., 2006). In samples of young adults with early-onset depression (who were not assessed for hypomania), Goldberg, Harrow, and Whiteside (2001) found that 19% of those followed for 15 years developed mania. Questions remain about whether early hypomania or depression better predict the later emergence of mania. In a review by Fiedorowicz et al. (2011) of nine studies following samples of persons with unipolar depression, 7.5% did later develop mania. Predictors of later mania included family history of bipolar I, history of delusions, periods of decreased need for sleep, grandiosity, periods of enhanced goal-directed behavior, and periods of enhanced energy. Fifty-nine percent of those who developed mania had experienced the "hypomania" symptoms.

What to Conclude?

The issue of whether those who have experienced both episodes of major depression and hypomania should be treated as bipolar is important. As Frances and Jones pointed out, the medications used to treat bipolar disorders have more negative side effects than the medications for major depression. There can be a great cost to misclassification. The Alloy et al. study does suggest that the presence of hypomania does increase the probability of later developing mania. However, extrapolating from the Alloy et al. study, 82.6% will be false positives if bipolar II is regarded as a proxy for bipolar I. In older clinical samples, 92.5% of those meeting criteria for hypomania in the Coryell study and more than 75% of those with three or more symptoms of hypomania in the Fiedorowicz et al. analysis did not subsequently develop mania or hypomania as defined in the *DSM-IV* (APA, 1994). Coryell et al. (1995) concluded that bipolar II "is probably not simply a variant of bipolar I disorder or of a non-bipolar disorder, but is a separate and autonomous disorder" (p. 389). Perhaps those labeled bipolar II deserve the development of unique treatments rather than being lumped together with those labeled bipolar I, as commonly occurs in most pharmacological outcome studies (Thase et al., 2006).

BIPOLAR I

In the studies identifying genetic risk factors, the same genetic risk factors often emerge for bipolar I as for schizophrenia. Studies find that in the familial background of those with bipolar I there is an elevation in the numbers with schizophrenia; those with schizophrenia have an elevation in family members with bipolar I (Craddock et al., 2009; Lin & Mitchell, 2008; Thaker, 2008; Williams et al., 2011). In Chapter 6, the case for the core feature of schizophrenia being a dysfunction in fast-spiking gamma-aminobutyric acid (GABA) interneurons was made. Dysfunction of these GABA interneurons also is found in those with bipolar I (Benes & Berretta, 2001). As with schizophrenia, cognitive deficits have been noted in those with bipolar I (Murphy et al., 2001). In a review of the physiological findings of those with bipolar I, Berk et al. (2011a) list a host of abnormalities in those with bipolar I that have been detected in those with schizophrenia: inflammation and immune alterations, oxidative stress, and mitochondrial dysfunction. In a study of the children of parents with well-characterized bipolar I disorder, cognitive deficits and abnormal immune system function predicted those children in whom mania later emerged (S. E. Meyer et al., 2004; Padmos et al., 2008). It should be recalled that unusual thinking patterns are part of the constellation preceding the emergence of schizophrenia, and immune system anomalies are also found in those with schizophrenia.

There are additional areas of overlap between schizophrenia and those with bipolar I as well. Both those with schizophrenia and those with bipolar I display deficits on eye-tracking tasks (Lin & Mitchell, 2008). Both disorders share symptoms. Mood episodes occur in schizophrenia, and hallucinations and delusions emerge in half of those with bipolar I (Kerner, 2014; Lin & Mitchell, 2008). Thus, the overlap in the physiology underpinning schizophrenia and bipolar I is striking.

In Chapter 2, a discussion of the neurotransmitter dopamine was proffered. Dopamine is characterized as the neurotransmitter mediating motivated behavior and hallucinations. When found in excess, as occurs with unrestrained cocaine or amphetamine ingestion, excessive movement, excessive talking, excessive urgency about accomplishing a task, and an inability to sleep emerge. All of these are criteria for mania. This is circumstantial evidence implicating dopamine release in the nucleus accumbens as the proximal cause of the symptoms of mania. In schizophrenia, excess dopamine is the proximal cause of delusions and hallucinations. Neurologist Malon DeLong (Okun, Bakay, DeLong, & Vitek, 2003), who conducts surgery on patients with Parkinson's disease, observed that ablating nonmotor portions of the globus pallidus (a structure also known as the pallidum, which receives projections from the nucleus accumbens) induces mania (Nolte, 2008). Thus, the same structures implicated in psychosis are generally involved in manic behavior.

Although Kraepelin distinguished the disorders of manic depression and schizophrenia, some are questioning whether there is a basis for this distinction (Lichtenstein et al., 2009). In fact, in their review of the possible mechanisms underlying bipolar symptoms, Berk et al. (2011b) identify many of the same factors, which some of these same authors have argued, underlie symptoms of schizophrenia. At the end of their article, Berk et al. (2011b) reflect, "It is also becoming clearer that these pathways do not match the currently accepted *DSM-IV* classification" (p. 813). Berk et al. indicated that they were not yet prepared to challenge extant nosology in the *DSM*, which holds that bipolar disorder and schizophrenia are different disorders. However, challenges are likely to come in the future. Many now agree with Bleuer (Freud's contemporary) who characterized schizophrenia as really being "schizophrenias" (see Chapter 6). Perhaps bipolar behavior constitutes another variant reflecting excessive release of dopamine in the nucleus accumbens, which is secondary to the aberrant function of the fast-spiking GABA interneurons. For Kraepelin, the principle distinction between schizophrenia and bipolar I was that the latter got better. We return to whether this is still the case in a later section.

Does Depression Always Occur in Those With Mania?

The term *bipolar* implies that there are two poles to the disorder. The previous term for *bipolar, manic depression,* also implies that people who have exhibited mania experience periods of depression. However, the criteria for bipolar I in the *DSM* only require that an individual meet the criteria for a manic or mixed episode at some point in life. People who have experienced a mixed or manic episode do not always experience depression. Of those who have experienced mania, 25% to 33% never experience depression (Karkowski & Kendler, 1997; Kessler, Rubinow, Holmes, Abelson, & Zhao, 1997). Although some believe that depression follows a manic episode (Benazzi, 2002), the data are against this presumption. Vieta, Angst, Reed, Bertsch, and Haro (2009) followed 2,390 patients for 12 weeks and found that depression followed mania in only 5% of the cases. Haag, Heidorn, Haag, and Greil (1987) noted mania following depression as well as the reverse pattern.

Another assumption is also being challenged. Historically, both depression and mania were thought to be episodic. F. K. Goodwin and Jamison (2007) report that manic episodes emerge precipitously and last between 6 weeks and 6 months. In the predrug literature, according to F. K. Goodwin and Jamison (2007), an episode of depression was reported to last 11 weeks to 3 months, with the suicide rate (19%) being high for bipolar I disorder (Simpson & Jamison, 1999). In a later section, we evaluate current outcomes of bipolar I. As we look at current outcomes, bear in mind that before the advent of modern treatments, mania and depression were thought to be episodic, not permanent traits of the individual.

BIPOLAR II

Bipolar II is a new category introduced officially in 1994 with the publication of *DSM-IV* (APA, 1994). Consequently, a predrug-era literature does not exist. Bipolar II requires an episode of depression at some point during the life span along with meeting criteria for an episode of hypomania. Kessler et al. (2005) report that as much as 16% of the general population will experience an episode of major depression. Periods of hypomania are common in nonclinical samples (Udachina & Mansell, 2007; Wicki & Angst, 1991). Thus, many people can be anticipated to receive a diagnosis of bipolar II who might not have been diagnosed with bipolar disorder in the past. In fact, Berk and Dodd (2005) estimate the population prevalence of bipolar II to be 3% to 5%.

Studies of clinical samples of those with bipolar II suggest that they are much more likely to have comorbid disorders than are those with bipolar I. They are distinguished based on anxiety disorders, substance abuse disorders, and eating disorders. They are particularly more likely to meet criteria for borderline personality disorder (Berk & Dodd, 2005; Judd et al., 2003). (Persons with borderline personality are characterized by extreme moodiness, intolerance of being alone, suicidal gestures or self-mutilation, impulsivity, and intense angry outbursts.) The rate of suicide attempts is higher in bipolar II (24%) than in bipolar I (17%; Rihmer & Pestality, 1999).

Nonclinical College Student Samples of Bipolar II

The Longitudinal Investigation of Bipolar Spectrum Project at Temple University and University of Wisconsin has been collecting data for approximately 6 years on college students who meet criteria for bipolar II disorder. Meeting criteria for bipolar II was rigorously evaluated in the Longitudinal Investigation. Persons must have met criteria for an episode of hypomania and an episode of major depression. Several findings have emerged from this study. College students meeting criteria for bipolar II achieve high scores on the Carver and White paper–pencil measure of the Behavioral Activation Scale (Alloy et al., 2009a). (Recall from Chapter 2 that the BAS scale measures a propensity for strong responses in the appetitive areas of the brain.) Persons with bipolar II exhibit more substance abuse behaviors, but substance abuse risk is restricted to those with high scores on impulsivity and high scores on a fun-loving subscale of the BAS (Alloy et al., 2009b). In terms of school performance, those with bipolar II and with high scores on the BAS scale who are also high on impulsivity drop more classes and have lower grade point averages (GPAs; Nusslock, Alloy, Abramson, Harmon-Jones, & Hogan, 2008). Students with bipolar II have fewer routine activities in their schedules (Shen, Alloy, Abramson, & Sylvia, 2008). They exhibit more disruptions in their daily routines (Boland et al., 2012). Although routine disruptions can decrease sleep for everyone, those with bipolar II lose more sleep than others when their schedules are disrupted (Boland et al., 2012). During examination periods, the hypomanic behaviors of those with bipolar II increase, which is not mediated by less sleep (Nusslock, Abramson, Harmon-Jones, Alloy, & Hogan, 2007). The information on the sensitivity to disruptions in routine does have implications for treatment, which will be discussed later.

Harmon-Jones et al. (2008) sought to examine the relative brain activations of persons who were given difficult tasks. Basically, the researchers were evaluating how persons with hypomania respond to frustration. They compared students with elevations on both hypomania and depression scales with students who did not achieve high scores on either scale. Left-brain activity was assessed in response to increasing task difficulty for gaining reward. Those scoring high on both depression and hypomania scales exhibited stronger left-brain activity when working for reward. However, the increased left-brain activity was only present on tasks for achieving gain, not for avoiding punishment. In terms of mood of people working on the difficult tasks, greater left-brain activity was associated with self-report of anger and increased activation or arousal. Thus, rather than giving up in response to frustration, those with hypomania exhibited activation.

Other researchers have identified high school and college students with hypomanic behaviors *who have not been screened for having experienced an episode of major depression.* Because they have not met criteria for major depression, they could differ from the persons in the Longitudinal Investigation of Bipolar Spectrum Project. Studies suggest that those who score highly on the hypomania scale exhibit more self-reported positive emotion when watching various types of films (Gruber, Johnson, Oveis, & Keltner, 2008), report greater positive affect in response to reward, and are more self-confident (Johnson, Ruggero, & Carver, 2005). They expect higher levels of future success (T. Meyer & Krumm-Merabet, 2003), although they are not differentiated on expectation of better interpersonal relationships (Johnson & Carver, 2006).

On measures discussed in Chapter 2, those students achieving high scores on measures of hypomania appear to be doing well. They are higher on heart rate variability, that is, vagal tone (Gruber et al., 2008). After viewing positive material, they show a greater diminution in startle response than did normal controls (Sutton & Johnson, 2002). When provoked by a report that their tuition would be increased, they also display activation of the left prefrontal cortex (PFC), which is associated with approach rather than with withdrawal behavior (Harmon-Jones et al., 2002).

Summary

Data on genetics and on trajectories over time suggest that bipolar I and II are in fact distinct disorders. However, a small percentage of those meeting criteria for bipolar II will eventually become bipolar I. In clinical samples, those with bipolar II are particularly likely to exhibit comorbidity, especially with borderline personality disorder. In contrast to those with bipolar II who, by definition, have experienced at least one episode of major depression, the findings for persons meeting criteria for hypomania alone are relatively positive. Those with hypomania exhibit better vagal tone and respond robustly to positive stimuli. Even for those nonclinical sample subjects who also have high elevations on depression scales, given frustration or threat they increase the activity in the strong motivational areas of the brain. If those with hypomania are also high scorers on measures of impulsivity, then they face the risk of lower academic achievement and are more likely to abuse drugs. However, those with bipolar II who are not high scorers on impulsivity are not more likely to drop classes in school or abuse substances. There is a suggestion that those prone to hypomanic behaviors may be less prone to establishing regular schedules and may be more strongly impacted by disruptions in whatever daily routine they have.

TREATMENT

Must Pharmacological Treatment Be Initiated to Prevent Kindling?

Post (2007) proffered the kindling hypothesis of affective disorders. The kindling hypothesis was modeled on the ways that rodents responded to electrical stimulation of their brains. It was well established that if an animal receives a small amount of electrical stimulation to the brain over time, then subsequently a small dose of electrical stimulation can induce a seizure. In a kindled animal, the level of stimulation necessary for inducing a seizure is far less than that in a naive animal. After sufficient exposure to low levels of stimulation, seizures will occur spontaneously. The phenomenon of becoming more sensitive over time is referred to as kindling. Drawing an analogy to his model of seizure development, Post suggested that an experience of affective symptoms, either depressive symptoms or mania symptoms, "kindled" or changed the brain. By analogy to seizure kindling, symptoms of depression or mania would somehow change the brain. The alterations in the brain would make the brain much more vulnerable. The prediction was that the longer the duration of symptoms, the less likely a person would be to respond to treatment and that the periods of wellness in between illness episodes would be shorter. To summarize, those individuals with greater duration of symptomatic status would exhibit a worsening course.

F. K. Goodwin and Jamison (2007), in their classic book on bipolar disorders, evaluated whether the data support the kindling hypothesis. F. K. Goodwin and Jamison (2007) find that the duration of wellness intervals is shorter in those persons with bipolar disorders who have experienced more lifetime episodes of illness. However, they suggest that this does not necessarily support the kindling hypothesis. Many years ago, Slater (1938, as translated by Oepen, Baldessarini, Salvatore, & Slater [2004]) hypothesized that persons with bipolar I may each have a natural timing for mood episodes. Some persons will naturally cycle fast with many episodes in the course of a given time period; others will take a long time to complete a cycle, having only one episode within a time period. Assuming that an episode is constant across people, those with short cycles will exhibit shorter episodes of wellness.

Aggregating across individuals of the same age will yield an inverse correlation between number of episodes and duration of wellness intervals. This need not imply that more episodes within a time frame "cause" an inability to experience wellness (as would be implied by the kindling hypothesis). To properly evaluate the kindling hypothesis, one must examine whether the duration of wellness shortens with the ordinal value of the episode of illness. F. K. Goodwin and Jamison (2007, p. 152) concluded that the data fail to support the association of shorter duration of the wellness interval with ordinal value of the episode. After the first three episodes, the frequency of subsequent episodes is fairly consistent. Stated alternatively, the duration of wellness between episodes stabilizes (2007).

A second prediction of the kindling hypothesis is that a longer duration of untreated illness should make response to treatment less robust. Baldessarini and colleagues (Baethge et al., 2003: Baldessarini, Tondo, Baethge, & Batti, 2007) proffered data against another variant of the kindling hypothesis that treatment delay will lead to worse outcome. Baldessarini et al. (2007) conclude that delay in treatment seeking after illness does not increase the percentage of time with illness or increase the need for hospitalization.

Surprisingly, even Post's animal data do not support the theory that suppressing symptoms (seizure activity) with medication will block the process of kindling. Remember, the process of kindling the brain occurs as an animal is subjected to low levels of electrical stimulation of the brain. Post et al. have medicated animals with lamotrigine and carbamazepine, two drugs employed in the treatment of bipolar disorders, as the animals' brains were stimulated. Medicating animals with lamotrigene and carbamazepine while applying electrical activity to the animals' brains found that these drugs facilitate kindling (Postma, Krupp, Li, Post, & Weiss, 2000). Once the animal is kindled, then seizures will occur spontaneously. Spontaneous seizures can be suppressed with anticonvulsant drugs; however, over time, the drugs lose their efficacy. In order to reinstate drug efficacy, the animal must be taken off the drug and exposed to electrical stimulation *without* the presence of the drug (Post, 2004; Weiss, Clark, Rosen, Smith, & Post, 1995). Thus, in the animal work, suppressing symptoms with anticonvulsants did not seem to ameliorate the kindling process. Analogizing the animal-kindling phenomenon to those with human bipolar disorders, the kindling data offer little reason for believing that suppressing symptoms with a drug will in any way influence whatever mysterious process occurs in humans with bipolar disorders.

The kindling rationale for early treatment has been marshalled to support early treatment in children. Thus, the evidence against the kindling hypothesis is particularly relevant for the pharmacological treatment of children with possible bipolar disorder (see Chapter 9, on children).

The Pharmacological Treatments: Lithium, Anticonvulsants, and Atypical Antipsychotics

Lithium has been the mainstay for treatment of bipolar disorders since its discovery by Cade in 1949. No one knows how lithium works. However, it does decrease suicide and affective episodes. The side-effect profile of lithium includes cognitive slowing (Ghaemi, 2008; F. K. Goodwin & Jamison, 2007; Silva et al., 1992). Lithium induces weight gain in 20% of those taking the drug and 20% of patients develop diabetes insipidus (more loss of water through the kidney). Lithium can result in thyroid dysfunction (Chen & Silverstone, 1990; F. K. Goodwin & Jamison, 2007). On withdrawal, acceleration of mania can be expected (F. K. Goodwin, 1994). Lithium is a known teratogen, and heart valve defects in the fetus can occur if taken during pregnancy (F. K. Goodwin & Jamison, 2007).

A major concern for treatment with lithium is kidney dysfunction (Bendz, Aurell, & Lanke, 2001; Markowitz et al., 2000). In a sample of 74 patients treated with lithium for 20 years, 12 reached end-stage renal disease. Fifty percent exhibited impaired renal concentrating ability and frequent urination occurred in 20% of patients (Presne et al., 2003). Even when lithium is discontinued, once initiated, kidney damage can continue (Markowitz et al., 2000).

Anticonvulsants (valproate, carbamazepine, and lamotrigine) are used in the treatment of bipolar disorders. Anticonvulsants disrupt cognitive function (Loring & Meador, 2004). Valporate and carbamazepine can induce depression (Boylan, Devinsky, Barry, & Ketter, 2002) and carry warnings for suicidal ideation (FDA Alert, 2007). In a study by Isojärvi, Laatikainen, Pakarinen, Juntunen, and Myllylä (1993), 89% of young women taking valporate developed polycystic ovarian disease involving weight gain, facial-hair growth, and menstrual irregularities. Valporate increases the risk of hepatitis (Ghaemi & Ko, 2002). Lamotrigene carries a black-box warning for Stevens–Johnson syndrome (blistering on all external surfaces of the body) and an Food and Drug Administration (FDA) warning for aseptic meningitis (www.fda.gov, August 12, 2010). Both Stevens–Johnson syndrome and aseptic meningitis are life-threatening. The anticonvulsants are also associated with birth defects (F. K. Goodwin & Jamison, 2007, p. 816).

Atypical antipsychotics are used in the treatment of bipolar disorders. Their side effects are covered in Chapter 6. Antidepressant use in the treatment of depression in those with bipolar disorders remains controversial (Ghaemi, Hsu, Soldani, & Goodwin, 2003).

Both lithium and antipsychotics are associated with rebound withdrawal effects on discontinuation (see discussion in Chapter 6, Side Effects With Current Treatments; Suppes, Baldessarini, Faedda, & Tohen, 1991).

Efficacy of Pharmacological Treatment

As was stated at the beginning of this chapter, Kraepelin differentiated those with schizophrenia from bipolar disorders on the basis of whether they recovered. Those with schizophrenia followed a deteriorating course, whereas those with bipolar disorders recovered. Kraepelin (1899) observed that there were patients who experienced only one episode of mania and then fully recovered. Others experienced episodes every 20 years. Kraepelin's observations are consistent with Rennie's (1942) report on 208 patients treated between 1913 and 1916. Ninety-three percent of patients recovered from their initial episode and 23% did not ever relapse. Of those who did relapse, 30% remained remitted for at least 10 years with an average duration of relapse of 20 years.

Presently, psychotropic drugs are evaluated on the basis of 8-week studies (Oldham et al., 2011). There are numerous studies finding positive outcomes in the short term for drugs used to treat bipolar disorder. For the long term, outcomes in the modern era do not look nearly as positive for those with bipolar I as in the predrug era. Post et al. (2003) found that rapid cycling characterized 62.8% of their sample, with these individuals experiencing four or more mood episodes per year. Harrow, Goldberg, Grossman, and Meltzer (1990) found that 80% of those who recovered relapsed within 1.7 years. Functional recovery was not good.

Only 23% were continuously employed and another 35% were erratically employed. The longest follow-up study on those with bipolar I was the 13-year follow-up published by Judd et al. (2002). Judd et al. (2002) found that patients with bipolar I were symptomatic during 47% of the follow-up interval. Depressive symptoms occurred during an average of 31.9% of the weeks, manic symptoms occurred during an average of 8.9% of the weeks, mixed states occurred during an average of 5.9% of the weeks. Only 2.1% of the sample evidenced few symptoms throughout the follow-up period, whereas 9.6% of the sample was never symptoms free.

The National Institute of Mental Health (2006) funded a study to try to find better treatment protocols. The Systematic Treatment Enhancement Program for Bipolar Disorder (STEP-BD) was a very large study conducted during the years 1998 to 2005. The study investigated people who had been ill for a while, rather than examining those with newly emergent symptoms. At entry, 26.5% were in recovery, whereas 73.5% were not. Seventy-one percent of the sample had a diagnosis of bipolar I. The findings from this study are very consistent with the findings of others. STEP-BD began with 4,360 patients but had complete data for 2 years for only 1,469 of the patients. The researchers found that 58% of patients were able to achieve recovery (defined as an 8-week period with fewer than two symptoms). However, 48.5% of them relapsed within 2 years. Similar to the Judd et al. (2002) study, most of the relapses (70%) were depressive relapses (Perlis et al., 2004). Subsequently, the researchers conducted a smaller study (16 weeks with 66 participants) with those individuals who remained unresponsive to treatment in terms of their depressive symptoms. Treating the antidepressant-resistant patients with lamotrigine, inositol, or risperidone found that 23.8% responded to the lamotrigine, 17.4% responded to the inositol, and 4.6% responded to the risperidone, with response defined as no more than two depressive symptoms for 8 weeks. The authors concluded that "regardless of treatment assignment, the absolute rates of sustained recovery for 8 weeks were low, confirming the seriousness and persistence of treatment-resistant bipolar depression" (Nierenberg et al., 2006, p. 214).

The perceptions of the outcomes for bipolar I have changed over the years. In 1969, Winokur, Clayton, and Reich (1969, p. 21) concluded that there "was no basis to consider that manic depressive psychosis permanently affected those who suffered from it." Zarate, Tohen, Land, and Cavanagh (2000) noted the discrepancy between earlier days and current outcomes, "In the era prior to pharmacotherapy, poor outcome in mania was considered a relatively rare occurrence. However, modern outcome studies have found that a majority of bipolar patients evidence high rates of functional impairment" (p. 309).

Current Outcomes for Those With Bipolar II

Persons with bipolar II are treated with the same drugs that are used to treat bipolar I, and drugs studies lump together those with bipolar I and II in evaluating outcomes (Thase et al., 2006). There are studies suggesting what the likely outcomes are for those meeting criteria for bipolar II. Joffe, MacQueen, Marriott, and Trevor Young (2004) found that outcomes for those with bipolar II were about the same as outcomes for bipolar I. Following patients for an average of 170 weeks, Joffe et al. found that patients with bipolar II, like bipolar I, were symptom free half of the time. They did not differ from the patients with bipolar I in the duration of time spent experiencing depressive symptoms (which occurred 40.9% of the time). Joffe et al.'s findings contrast with Judd et al.'s findings. Following another sample, Judd et al. (2003) followed patients for up to 10 years. They found that those with bipolar II were less likely to return to prior levels of function than were those with bipolar I. Those with bipolar II spent a lesser period of time in wellness and spent more of their time experiencing depressive symptoms than those with bipolar I.

ALTERNATIVE TO DRUGS

Regular Routines

There are some alleles of genes coding for proteins that set up circadian rhythms for hormone production, sleepiness, and hunger production that are associated with the risk for psychosis (Benedetti et al., 2007; Mansour et al., 2006; Nievergelt et al., 2006). Nestler and colleagues (Roybal et al., 2007) expressed an allele for disrupted clock genes in the nucleus accumbens of rodents. The animals then exhibited manic behavior, displaying disruption in sleep and enhanced running-wheel activity. Others have noted that for people diagnosed with bipolar I, manic episodes are more likely to occur following schedule disrupting events (Malkoff-Schwartz et al., 1998).

Schedule disruption may create hypomania in even the "normal." In the Longitudinal Investigation of Bipolar Spectrum Project, Shen et al. (2008) found that disruptions in daily routine increase hypomania in all subjects, even normal controls. However, as mentioned previously, those with bipolar II were more sensitive to schedule disruptions. As part of the Longitudinal Investigation of Bipolar Spectrum Project, Boland et al. (2012) noted that those with bipolar II were more likely to experience schedule-disrupting events and were more responsive to these events in terms of losing more sleep.

Treatments have been developed for stabilizing circadian rhythms that result in longer duration of wellness for those with bipolar I (Frank et al., 2005). Social rhythm therapy involves helping people to establish regular routines for sleeping and eating. Interpersonal and social rhythm therapy has been applied to those with bipolar II. In a test of this treatment for 12 weeks and then an 8-week follow-up interval, 53% of those with bipolar II (11% of those who were medicated) witnessed a 50% drop in depression symptoms and 29% (33% of those who were medicated) were in full remission (Swartz, Frank, Frankel, Novick, & Houck, 2009). In a study in which those with bipolar II were randomized to treatment with an atypical antipsychotic or to interpersonal social rhythm therapy, no difference was found in outcome between the two groups at 12 weeks. In both groups, approximately 29% achieved a 50% drop in symptoms (Swartz, Frank, & Cheng, 2012). Thus, keeping a regular schedule for eating and sleeping improves outcome for both those with bipolar I and II.

Omega-3s

Noaghiul and Hibbeln (2003) reported epidemiological data finding that rates of bipolar disorder were lower in countries where fish consumption was higher. The specific pathways through which fish oil might impact mood and behavior are multiple. Omega-3s can be converted into resolvins, which place a brake on inflammation. Omega-3s are thus anti-inflammatory (see the Diet section in Chapter 4). Inflammation is not only implicated in depression but also in psychosis, whether due to bipolar disorder or schizophrenia (see Chapters 4 and 6). A Cochrane review (Montgomery & Richardson, 2009) located five studies that the reviewers evaluated as worthy of discussion. All studies evaluated omega-3s as adjunctive treatment. The Cochrane review concluded that omega-3s are efficacious in decreasing depressive symptoms. They noted that omega-3s have few negative effects with some gastric discomfort being a possible side effect.

N-Acetylcysteine

Magalhães et al. (2011) noted that excess free radicals (damaging molecules) have been implicated in bipolar disorder. As discussed in Chapter 6, N-acetylcysteine gets converted to glutathione, which will "mop up" free radicals. N-acetylcysteine has been evaluated as an adjunctive treatment for bipolar disorder. In a study by Berk et al. (2008) with random assignment, 37 were in the N-acetylcysteine group and 38 were in the placebo group for 24 weeks. Approximately 82% of each group were diagnosed with bipolar I, whereas the others met the criteria for bipolar II. The response rate (defined as a 50% reduction in depression scores) at 24 weeks was 51% for the N-acetylcysteine group compared to 18% on placebo. The N-acetylcysteine group also achieved higher ratings on daily functioning. In another study by Berk et al. (2011), bipolar patients, 71% of whom were bipolar I, were treated with add-on N-acetylcysteine for 8 weeks. Significant reductions in depressive symptomology and mania were achieved. Magalhães et al. (2011) analyzed the data for the subset of those with bipolar II from the Berk et al. study. Remission into the normal range on both the depression and manic symptom scales was achieved by six of seven individuals taking N-acetylcysteine but only two in the placebo group. Thus, N-acetylcysteine is promising for bipolar II as well as bipolar I.

N-Acetylcysteine is inexpensive and is not associated with appreciable side effects. However, intravenous administration can induce allergic reactions (Atkuri, Mantovani, Herzenberg, & Herzenberg, 2007).

WHERE HAVE WE BEEN AND WHERE ARE WE GOING?

The literature on bipolar disorders is difficult to evaluate because, over the years, the diagnostic criteria have changed rather dramatically. The addition of bipolar II is the most extreme deviation from the diagnostic criteria of the past. Many agree that bipolar II identifies a different population from those who are bipolar I. Another complicating factor is that antidepressants will induce mania, although risk factors for antidepressant-induced mania have not been identified. Whether those who display mania on antidepressants share any predisposing characteristics with those for whom mania develops spontaneously has not been examined.

With regard to bipolar I, evidence is beginning to emerge that the same underlying physiology predisposes to both bipolar I and schizophrenia. Clinically, it is very difficult to distinguish whether a person exhibiting psychosis stems from an underlying bipolar I or schizophrenia. Perhaps they share the same underlying physiology. In fact, many of the treatments (atypical antipsychotics, N-acetylcysteine, omega-3s) are efficacious for both disorders.

The treatment protocols for schizophrenia are being challenged. Although the antipsychotic drugs do make the voices go away, the long-term functional outcomes for those on antipsychotic drugs are worse (see Chapter 6, Current Treatments section). For bipolar I, the functional outcomes appear far bleaker than they were in the predrug era. All of the drugs used to treat bipolar I induce depressive symptoms. Lithium is associated with cognitive slowing. The anticonvulsants come with warnings for suicide. Antipsychotic drugs block dopamine, the neurotransmitter for motivation and energy. When recovered persons with bipolar I relapse, their relapses are most often depressive in nature (see summary of the STEP-BD study on page 277). An unanswered question is whether the lingering depressive symptoms would occur if bipolar I patients were free of the drugs to decrease psychosis. Attempts to counteract "mood stabilizers" with other chemicals in the STEP-BD study testify to the recalcitrance of the depressive symptoms.

Often those with bipolar I are first encountered when they display dramatic manic symptoms, which often include frank psychosis. Manic episodes last between 6 weeks and 6 months (F. K. Goodwin & Jamison, 2007). Perhaps if the mania were allowed to "run its course" long-term functional outcomes would be better, as they were in Kraepelin's day. Fortunately, there are other treatment options (omega-3s, N-acetylcysteine, stabilizing daily sleeping and eating cycles) that might be tried.

REFERENCES

Alloy, L. B., Abramson, L. Y., Walshaw, P. D., Gerstein, R. K., Keyser, J. D., Whitehouse, W. G.,...Harmon-Jones, E. (2009a). Behavioral approach system (BAS)-relevant cognitive styles and bipolar spectrum disorders: Concurrent and prospective associations. *Journal of Abnormal Psychology, 118*(3), 459–471.

Alloy, L. B., Bender, R. E., Wagner, C. A., Whitehouse, W. G., Abramson, L. Y., Hogan, M. E.,...Harmon-Jones, E. (2009b). Bipolar spectrum-substance use co-occurrence: Behavioral approach system (BAS) sensitivity and impulsiveness as shared personality vulnerabilities. *Journal of Personality and Social Psychology, 97*(3), 549–565.

Alloy, L. B., Uroševic, S., Abramson, L. Y., Jager-Hyman, S., Nusslock, R., Whitehouse, W. G., & Hogan, M. (2012). Progression along the bipolar spectrum: A longitudinal study of predictors of conversion from bipolar spectrum conditions to bipolar I and II disorders. *Journal of Abnormal Psychology, 121*(1), 16–27.

American Psychiatric Association. (1980). *Diagnostic and statistical manual of mental disorders* (3rd ed.). Washington, DC: Author.

American Psychiatric Association. (1994). *Diagnostic and statistical manual of mental disorders* (4th ed.). Washington, DC: Author.

American Psychiatric Association. (2000). *Diagnostic and statistical manual of mental disorders*, (4th ed., text rev.). Washington, DC: Author.

Atkuri, K. R., Mantovani, J. J., Herzenberg, L. A., & Herzenberg, L. A. (2007). N-Acetylcysteine—A safe antidote for cysteine/glutathione deficiency. *Current Opinion in Pharmacology, 7*(4), 355–359.

Baethge, C., Tondo, L., Bratti, I. M., Bschor, T., Bauer, M., Viguera, A. C., & Baldessarini, R. J. (2003). Prophylaxis latency and outcome in bipolar disorders. *Canadian Journal of Psychiatry, 48*(7), 449–457.

Baldessarini, R. J., Tondo, L., Baethge, C. J., Lepri, B., & Bratti, I. M. (2007). Effects of treatment latency on response to maintenance treatment in manic-depressive disorders. *Bipolar Disorders, 9*(4), 386–393.

Benazzi, R. (2002). Highly recurrent unipolar may be related to bipolar II. *Comprehensive Psychiatry, 43*(4), 263–268.

Bendz, H., Aurell, M., & Lanke, J. (2001). A historical cohort study of kidney damage in long-term lithium patients: Continued surveillance needed. *European Psychiatry, 16*(4), 199–206.

Benedetti, F., Dallaspezia, S., Fulgosi, M. C., Lorenzi, C., Serretti, A., Barbini, B., ... Smeraldi, E. (2007). Actimetric evidence that CLOCK 3111 T/C SNP influences sleep and activity patterns in patients affected by bipolar depression. *American Journal of Medical Genetics, 144B*(5), 631–635.

Benes, F. M., & Berretta, S. (2001). GABAergic interneurons: Implications for understanding schizophrenia and bipolar disorder. *Neuropsychopharmacology, 25*(1), 1–27.

Berk, M., Copolov, D. L., Dean, O., Lu, K., Jeavons, S., Schapkaitz, I., ... Bush, A. I. (2008). N-acetyl cysteine for depressive symptoms in bipolar disorder—A double-blind randomized placebo-controlled trial. *Biological Psychiatry, 64*(6), 468–475.

Berk, M., Dean, O., Cotton, S. M., Gama, C. S., Kapczinski, F., Fernandes, B. S., ... Malhi, G. S. (2011a). The efficacy of N-acetylcysteine as an adjunctive treatment in bipolar depression: An open label trial. *Journal of Affective Disorders, 135*(1–3), 389–394.

Berk, M., & Dodd, S. (2005). Bipolar II disorder: A review. *Bipolar Disorders, 7*(1), 11–21.

Berk, M., Kapczinski, F., Andreazza, A. C., Dean, O. M., Giorlando, F., Maes, M., ... Malhi, G. S. (2011b). Pathways underlying neuroprogression in bipolar disorder: Focus on inflammation, oxidative stress and neurotrophic factors. *Neuroscience and Biobehavioral Reviews, 35*(3), 804–817.

Boland, E. M., Bender, R. E., Alloy, L. B., Conner, B. T., Labelle, D. R., & Abramson, L. Y. (2012). Life events and social rhythms in bipolar spectrum disorders: An examination of social rhythm sensitivity. *Journal of Affective Disorders, 139*(3), 264–272.

Boylan, L. S., Devinsky, O., Barry, J. J., & Ketter, T. A. (2002). Psychiatric uses of antiepileptic treatments. *Epilepsy & Behavior, 3*(5S), 54–59.

Calabrese, J. R., Muzina, D. J., Kemp, D. E., Sachs, G. S., Frye, M. A., Thompson, T. R., ... Hirschfeld, R. M. (2006). Predictors of bipolar disorder risk among patients currently treated for major depression. *MedGenMed, 8*(3), 38.

Chen, Y., & Silverstone, T. (1990). Lithium and weight gain. *International Clinical Psychopharmacology, 5*(3), 217–225.

Coryell, W., Endicott, J., Maser, J. D., Keller, M. B., Leon, A. C., & Akiskal, H. S. (1995). Long-term stability of polarity distinctions in the affective disorders. *American Journal of Psychiatry, 152*(3), 385–390.

Craddock, N., O'Donovan, M. C., & Owen, M. J. (2009). Psychosis genetics: Modeling the relationship between schizophrenia, bipolar disorder, and mixed (or "schizoaffective") psychoses. *Schizophrenia Bulletin, 35*(3), 482–490.

Duffy, A., Alda, M., Hajek, T., & Grof, P. (2009). Early course of bipolar disorder in high-risk offspring: Prospective study. *British Journal of Psychiatry, 195*(5), 457–458.

Dunner, D. L. (1993). A review of the diagnostic status of "bipolar II" for the DSM-IV work group on mood disorders. *Depression, 1*, 2–10.

FDA Alert. (2007). *Information on carbamazepine.* Retrieved September 21, 2008, from http://www.fda.gov/cder/drug/infopage/carbamazine/default.htm

Fiedorowicz, J. G., Endicott, J., Leon, A. C., Solomon, D. A., Keller, M. B., & Coryell, W. H. (2011). Subthreshold hypomanic symptoms in progression from unipolar major depression to bipolar disorder. *American Journal of Psychiatry, 168*(1), 40–48.

Frances, A., & Jones, K. D. (2012). Bipolar disorder type II revisited. *Bipolar Disorders, 14*(5), 474–477.

Frank, E., Kupfer, D. J., Thase, M. E., Mallinger, A. G., Swartz, H. A., Fagiolini, A. M., … Monk, T. (2005). Two-year outcomes for interpersonal and social rhythm therapy in individuals with bipolar I disorder. *Archives of General Psychiatry, 62*(9), 996–1004.

Ghaemi, S. N. (2008). *Practical guides in psychiatry: Mood disorders* (2nd ed.). New York, NY: Lippincott Williams & Wilkins.

Ghaemi, S. N., Hsu, D. J., Soldani, F., & Goodwin, F. K. (2003). Antidepressants in bipolar disorder: The case for caution. *Bipolar Disorders, 5*(6), 421–433.

Ghaemi, S. N., & Ko, J. Y. (2002). Polypharmacy of bipolar disorder. In S. N. Ghaemi (Ed.), *Polypharmacy in psychiatry* (pp. 35–77). New York, NY: Marcel Dekker.

Goldberg, J. F., Harrow, M., & Whiteside, J. E. (2001). Risk for bipolar illness in patients initially hospitalized for unipolar depression. *American Journal of Psychiatry, 158*(8), 1265–1270.

Goodwin, F. K., & Jamison, K. R. (2007). *Manic-depressive illness: Bipolar disorders and recurrent depression* (2nd ed.). New York, NY: Oxford Press.

Goodwin, F. M. (1994). Recurrence of mania after lithium withdrawal. Implications for the use of lithium in the treatment of bipolar affective disorder. *British Journal of Psychiatry, 64,* 149–152.

Gruber, J., Johnson, S. L., Oveis, C., & Keltner, D. (2008). Risk for mania and positive emotional responding: Too much of a good thing? *Emotion, 8*(1), 23–33.

Haag, H., Heidorn, A., Haag, M., & Greil, W. (1987). Sequence of affective polarity and lithium response: Preliminary report on Munich sample. *Progress in Neuro-Psychopharmacology & Biological Psychiatry, 11*(2–3), 205–208.

Harmon-Jones, E., Abramson, L. Y., Nusslock, R., Sigelman, J. D., Urosevic, S., Turonie, L. D.,…Fearn, M. (2008). Effect of bipolar disorder on left frontal cortical responses to goals differing in valence and task difficulty. *Biological Psychiatry, 63*(7), 693–698.

Harmon-Jones, E., Abramson, L. Y., Sigelman, J., Bohlig, A., Hogan, M. E., & Harmon-Jones, C. (2002). Proneness to hypomania/mania symptoms or depression symptoms and asymmetrical frontal cortical responses to an anger-evoking event. *Journal of Personality and Social Psychology, 82*(4), 610–618.

Harrow, M., Goldberg, J. F., Grossman, L. S., & Meltzer, H. Y. (1990). Outcome in manic disorders. A naturalistic follow-up study. *Archives of General Psychiatry, 47*(7), 665–671.

Isojärvi, J. I., Laatikainen, T. J., Pakarinen, A. J., Juntunen, K. T., & Myllylä, V. V. (1993). Polycystic ovaries and hyperandrogenism in women taking valproate for epilepsy. *New England Journal of Medicine, 329*(19), 1383–1388.

Joffe, R. T., MacQueen, G. M., Marriott, M., & Trevor Young, L. (2004). A prospective, longitudinal study of percentage of time spent ill in patients with bipolar I or bipolar II disorders. *Bipolar Disorders, 6*(1), 62–66.

Johnson, S. L., & Carver, C. S. (2006). Extreme goal setting and vulnerability to mania among undiagnosed young adults. *Cognitive Therapy and Research, 30*(3), 377–395.

Johnson, S. L., Ruggero, C. J., & Carver, C. S. (2005). Cognitive, behavioral, and affective responses to reward: Links with hypomanic symptoms. *Journal of Social and Clinical Psychology, 24*(6), 894–906.

Judd, L. L., Akiskal, H. S., Schettler, P. J., Coryell, W., Maser, J., Rice, J. A., … Keller, M. B. (2003). The comparative clinical phenotype and long term longitudinal episode course of bipolar I and II: A clinical spectrum or distinct disorders? *Journal of Affective Disorders, 73*(1–2), 19–32.

Judd, L. L., Akiskal, H. S., Schettler, P. J., Endicott, J., Maser, J., Solomon, D. A., … Keller, M. B. (2002). The long-term natural history of the weekly symptomatic status of bipolar I disorder. *Archives of General Psychiatry, 59*(6), 530–537.

Karkowski, L. M., & Kendler, K. S. (1997). An examination of the genetic relationship between bipolar and unipolar illness in an epidemiological sample. *Psychiatric Genetics, 7*(4), 159–163.

Kerner, B. (2014). Genetics of bipolar disorder. *Application of Clinical Genetics, 7,* 33–42.

Kessler, R. C., Berglund, P., Demler, O., Jin, R., Merikangas, K. R., & Walters, E. E. (2005). Lifetime prevalence and age-of-onset distributions of DSM-IV disorders in the National Comorbidity Survey Replication. *Archives of General Psychiatry, 62*(6), 593–602.

Kessler, R. C., Rubinow, D. R., Holmes, C., Abelson, J. M., & Zhao, S. (1997). The epidemiology of DSM-III-R bipolar I disorder in a general population survey. *Psychological Medicine, 27*(5), 1079–1089.

Kolb, L. (1968). *Noyes' modern clinical psychiatry.* Philadelphia, PA: Saunders.

Kraepelin, E. (1899). *Manic-depressive insanity and paranoia* (R. M. Barclay , Trans.). Edinburgh, Scotland: E & S Livingstone. Retrieved from www.archive.org/details/manicdepressivei00kraeuoft

Kraepelin, E. (1919). *Dementia praecox and paraphrenia.* Edinburgh, UK: Livingstone.

Kupfer, D. J., Carpenter, L. L., & Frank, E. (1988). Is bipolar II a unique disorder? *Comprehensive Psychiatry, 29*(3), 228–236.

Lichtenstein, P., Yip, B. H., Björk, C., Pawitan, Y., Cannon, T. D., Sullivan, P. F., & Hultman, C. M. (2009). Common genetic determinants of schizophrenia and bipolar disorder in Swedish families: A population-based study. *Lancet, 373*(9659), 234–239.

Lin, P. I., & Mitchell, B. D. (2008). Approaches for unraveling the joint genetic determinants of schizophrenia and bipolar disorder. *Schizophrenia Bulletin, 34*(4), 791–797.

Loring, D. W., & Meador, K. J. (2004). Cognitive side effects of antiepileptic drugs in children. *Neurology, 62*(6), 872–877.

Magalhães, P. V., Dean, O. M., Bush, A. I., Copolov, D. L., Malhi, G. S., Kohlmann, K., ... Berk, M. (2011). N-acetyl cysteine add-on treatment for bipolar II disorder: A subgroup analysis of a randomized placebo-controlled trial. *Journal of Affective Disorders, 129*(1–3), 317–320.

Malkoff-Schwartz, S., Frank, E., Anderson, B., Sherrill, J. T., Siegel, L., Patterson, D., & Kupfer, D. J. (1998). Stressful life events and social rhythm disruption in the onset of manic and depressive bipolar episodes: A preliminary investigation. *Archives of General Psychiatry, 55*(8), 702–707.

Mansour, H. A., Wood, J., Logue, T., Chowdari, K. V., Dayal, M., Kupfer, D. J., ... Nimgaonkar, V. L. (2006). Association study of eight circadian genes with bipolar I disorder, schizoaffective disorder and schizophrenia. *Genes, Brain, and Behavior, 5*(2), 150–157.

Markowitz, G. S., Radhakrishnan, J., Kambham, N., Valeri, A. M., Hines, W. H., & D'Agati, V. D. (2000). Lithium nephrotoxicity: A progressive combined glomerular and tubulointerstitial nephropathy. *Journal of the American Society of Nephrology, 11*(8), 1439–1448.

Merikangas, K. R., Akiskal, H. S., Angst, J., Greenberg, P. E., Hirschfeld, R. M., Petukhova, M., & Kessler, R. C. (2007). Lifetime and 12-month prevalence of bipolar spectrum disorder in the National Comorbidity Survey replication. *Archives of General Psychiatry, 64*(5), 543–552.

Meyer, S. E., Carlson, G. A., Wiggs, E. A., Martinez, P. E., Ronsaville, D. S., Klimes-Dougan, B., ... Radke-Yarrow, M. (2004). A prospective study of the association among impaired executive functioning, childhood attentional problems, and the development of bipolar disorder. *Development and Psychopathology, 16*(2), 461–476.

Meyer, T., & Krumm-Merabet, C. (2003). Academic performance and expectations for the future for people putatively at risk for bipolar disorders. *Personality and Individual Differences, 35*, 785–796.

Montgomery, P., & Richardson, A. J. (2009). Omega-3 fatty acids for bipolar disorder. *Cochrane Library, 1*, 1–24.

Moreno, C., Laje, G., Blanco, C., Jiang, H., Schmidt, A. B., & Olfson, M. (2007). National trends in the outpatient diagnosis and treatment of bipolar disorder in youth. *Archives of General Psychiatry, 64*(9), 1032–1039.

Murphy, F. C., Rubinsztein, J. S., Michael, A., Rogers, R. D., Robbins, T. W., Paykel, E. S., & Sahakian, B. J. (2001). Decision-making cognition in mania and depression. *Psychological Medicine, 31*(4), 679–693.

National Institute of Mental Health. (2006). *Early findings from largest NIMH-funded research program on bipolar disorder begin to build evidence-base on best treatment options.* Retrieved from http://www.nimh.nih.gov//index.shtml

Nierenberg, A. A., Ostacher, M. J., Calabrese, J. R., Ketter, T. A., Marangell, L. B., Miklowitz, D. J.,...Sachs, G. S. (2006). Treatment-resistant bipolar depression: A STEP-BD equipoise randomized effectiveness trial of antidepressant augmentation with lamotrigine, inositol, or risperidone. *American Journal of Psychiatry, 163*(2), 210–216.

Nievergelt, C. M., Kripke, D. F., Barrett, T. B., Burg, E., Remick, R. A., Sadovnick, A. D.,...Kelsoe, J. R. (2006). Suggestive evidence for association of the circadian genes PERIOD3 and ARNTL with bipolar disorder. *American Journal of Medical Genetics, 141B*(3), 234–241.

Noaghiul, S., & Hibbeln, J. R. (2003). Cross-national comparisons of seafood consumption and rates of bipolar disorders. *American Journal of Psychiatry, 160*(12), 2222–2227.

Nolte, J. (2008). *The human brain: An introduction to its functional anatomy* (6th ed.). New York, NY: Elsevier.

Nusslock, R., Abramson, L. Y., Harmon-Jones, E., Alloy, L. B., & Hogan, M. E. (2007). A goal-striving life event and the onset of hypomanic and depressive episodes and symptoms: Perspective from the behavioral approach system (BAS) dysregulation theory. *Journal of Abnormal Psychology, 116*(1), 105–115.

Nusslock, R., Alloy, L. B., Abramson, L. Y., Harmon-Jones, E., & Hogan, M. E. (2008). Impairment in the achievement domain in bipolar spectrum disorders: Role of behavioral approach system hypersensitivity and impulsivity. *Minerva Pediatrica, 60*(1), 41–50.

Oepen, G., Baldessarini, R. J., Salvatore, P., & Slater, E. (2004). On the periodicity of manic-depressive insanity, by Eliot Slater (1938): Translated excerpts and commentary. *Journal of Affective Disorders, 78*(1), 1–9.

Okun, M. S., Bakay, R. A., DeLong, M. R., & Vitek, J. L. (2003). Transient manic behavior after pallidotomy. *Brain and Cognition, 52*(2), 281–283.

Oldham, J., Carlat, D., Friedman, R. W., Nierenberg, A. A., & Angell, M. (2011, August). The illusion of psychiatry: An exchange. *New York Review of Books,* LVIII, 82–84.

Padmos, R. C., Hillegers, M. H., Knijff, E. M., Vonk, R., Bouvy, A., Staal, F. J.,...Drexhage, H. A. (2008). A discriminating messenger RNA signature for bipolar disorder formed by an aberrant expression of inflammatory genes in monocytes. *Archives of General Psychiatry, 65*(4), 395–407.

Perlis, R. H., Miyahara, S., Marangell, L. B., Wisniewski, S. R., Ostacher, M., DelBello, M. P., ...; STEP-BD Investigators. (2004). Long-term implications of early onset in bipolar disorder: Data from the first 1000 participants in the Systematic Treatment Enhancement Program for Bipolar Disorder (STEP-BD). *Biological Psychiatry, 55*(9), 875–881.

Post, R. M. (2004). Neurobiology of seizures and behavioral abnormalities. *Epilepsia, 45*(Suppl. 2), 5–14.

Post, R. M. (2007). Kindling and sensitization as models for affective episode recurrence, cyclicity, and tolerance phenomena. *Neuroscience and Biobehavioral Reviews, 31*(6), 858–873.

Post, R. M., Denicoff, K. D., Leverich, G. S., Altshuler, L. L., Frye, M. A., Suppes, T.M., ...Nolen, W. A. (2003). Morbidity in 258 bipolar outpatients followed for one year with daily prospective ratings on the NIMH life chart method. *Journal of Clinical Psychiatry, 64*(6), 680–690.

Postma, T., Krupp, E., Li, X. L., Post, R. M., & Weiss, S. R. (2000). Lamotrigine treatment during amygdala-kindled seizure development fails to inhibit seizures and diminishes subsequent anticonvulsant efficacy. *Epilepsia, 41*(12), 1514–1521.

Presne, C., Fakhouri, F., Noël, L. H., Stengel, B., Even, C., Kreis, H., ...Grünfeld, J. P. (2003). Lithium-induced nephropathy: Rate of progression and prognostic factors. *Kidney International, 64*(2), 585–592.

Rennie, T. A. C. (1942). Prognosis in manic-depressive psychosis. *American Journal of Psychiatry, 149*, 1727–1729.

Rihmer, Z., & Pestality, P. (1999). Bipolar II disorder and suicidal behavior. *Psychiatric Clinics of North America, 22*(3), 667–673, ix–x.

Roybal, K., Theobold, D., Graham, A., DiNieri, J. A., Russo, S. J., Krishnan, V., ...McClung, C. A. (2007). Mania-like behavior induced by disruption of CLOCK. *Proceedings of the National Academy of Sciences of the United States of America, 104*(15), 6406–6411.

Shen, G. H., Alloy, L. B., Abramson, L. Y., & Sylvia, L. G. (2008). Social rhythm regularity and the onset of affective episodes in bipolar spectrum individuals. *Bipolar Disorders, 10*(4), 520–529.

Silva, R. R., Campbell, M., Golden, R. R., Small, A. M., Pataki, C. S., & Rosenberg, C. R. (1992). Side effects associated with lithium and placebo administration in aggressive children. *Psychopharmacology Bulletin, 28*(3), 319–326.

Simpson, S. G., & Jamison, K. R. (1999). The risk of suicide in patients with bipolar disorders. *Journal of Clinical Psychiatry, 60*(Suppl. 2), 53–56; discussion 75.

Suppes, T., Baldessarini, R. J., Faedda, G. L., & Tohen, M. (1991). Risk of recurrence following discontinuation of lithium treatment in bipolar disorder. *Archives of General Psychiatry, 48*(12), 1082–1088.

Sutton, S. K., & Johnson, S. J. (2002). Hypomanic tendencies predict lower startle magnitudes during pleasant pictures. *Psychophysiology, 39*, S80.

Swartz, H. A., Frank, E., & Cheng, Y. (2012). A randomized pilot study of psychotherapy and quetiapine for the acute treatment of bipolar II depression. *Bipolar Disorders, 14*(2), 211–216.

Swartz, H. A., Frank, E., Frankel, D. R., Novick, D., & Houck, P. (2009). Psychotherapy as monotherapy for the treatment of bipolar II depression: A proof of concept study. *Bipolar Disorders, 11*(1), 89–94.

Thaker, G. (2008). Psychosis endophenotypes in schizophrenia and bipolar disorder. *Schizophrenia Bulletin, 34*(4), 720–721.

Thase, M. E., Macfadden, W., Weisler, R. H., Chang, W., Paulsson, B., Khan, A., Calabrese, J. R., & BOLDER II Study Group. (2006). Efficacy of quetiapine monotherapy in bipolar I and II depression: A double-blind, placebo-controlled study (the BOLDER II study). *Journal of Clinical Psychopharmacology, 26*(6), 600–609.

Udachina, A., & Mansell, W. (2007). Cross-validation of the Mood Disorders Questionnaire, the Internal State Scale, and the Hypomanic Personality Scale. *Personality and Individual Differences, 42*, 1539–1549.

Vieta, E., Angst, J., Reed, C., Bertsch, J., & Haro, J. M.; EMBLEM Advisory Board. (2009). Predictors of switching from mania to depression in a large observational study across Europe (EMBLEM). *Journal of Affective Disorders, 118*(1–3), 118–123.

Vieta, E., & Suppes, T. (2008). Bipolar II disorder: Arguments for and against a distinct diagnostic entity. *Bipolar Disorders, 10*(1, Pt. 2), 163–178.

Weiss, S. R., Clark, M., Rosen, J. B., Smith, M. A., & Post, R. M. (1995). Contingent tolerance to the anticonvulsant effects of carbamazepine: Relationship to loss of endogenous adaptive mechanisms. *Brain Research, 20*(3), 305–325.

Wicki, W., & Angst, J. (1991). The Zurich Study. X. Hypomania in a 28- to 30-year-old cohort. *European Archives of Psychiatry and Clinical Neuroscience, 240*(6), 339–348.

Williams, H. J., Craddock, N., Russo, G., Hamshere, M. L., Moskvina, V., Dwyer, S., . . . O'Donovan, M. C. (2011). Most genome-wide significant susceptibility loci for schizophrenia and bipolar disorder reported to date cross-traditional diagnostic boundaries. *Human Molecular Genetics, 20*(2), 387–391.

Winokur, G., Clayton, P. J., & Reich, T. (1969). *Manic depressive illness.* St. Louis, MO: Mosby.

Zarate, C. A., Tohen, M., Land, M., & Cavanagh, S. (2000). Functional impairment and cognition in bipolar disorder. *Psychiatric Quarterly, 71*(4), 309–329.

8

Addictions

This chapter covers drug addiction. There are too many addictive substances to provide in-depth coverage for each specific chemical. However, the neuroscience of addiction is the same for all of these substances. The story on how to treat those who want to stop using these chemicals is also generic. This chapter considers addiction generally without reference to the specific chemical to which an addiction develops.

The chapter begins with the neuroscience of addiction. The story on how addictive chemicals change the brain is presented. Research on brain changes with addiction does provide useful information on when recovering persons are more susceptible to relapse. The story on brain changes also is helpful in appreciating the extent to which addiction really is a "loss of control."

Much of the history of the neuroscience of addiction derives from work on animals. In humans, the motivation for chemical use sometimes mirrors the way in which compulsion develops in animals. However, other pathways to heavy use of chemicals are also possible. Following the presentation of understanding based on animal work, consideration of the heterogeneity of addictive patterns in people is discussed. This section concludes with some of the findings on genetic variations associated with the risk of addiction to drugs of abuse.

The latter section of the chapter considers treatment. Specific information on how to screen and initiate treatment is provided. Motivational interviewing approaches and the transtheoretical model of change are discussed and contrasted with the 12-step model on how to approach clients. Subsequently, interventions for maintaining abstinence are reviewed. The efficacy of pharmaceutical and nonpharmaceutical treatments is discussed. In the final section, some reflections on drug policy laws are proffered.

NEUROSCIENCE OF ADDICTION

The definition of *addiction* has changed. In earlier times, pharmacologists defined *addiction* in terms of tolerance and withdrawal. The idea was that some homeostatic mechanism would kick in to counter the effect of the drug. This meant that more of the drug would be required to experience the effect of the drug when taken for the first time (tolerance). If the drug was discontinued abruptly, the homeostatic mechanism would still be in play and extreme physiology, opposite to the effect of the drug, would be manifested (withdrawal). Withdrawal symptoms were believed to compel continued use of the drug. Compulsion to use a substance captures the essence of what constitutes addiction in most people's minds. As more data accrued, the homeostasis explanation as a basis for compulsion was challenged. Many drugs that are associated with clear physiological withdrawal phenomena, such as lithium, antipsychotics, and antidepressants, fail to induce compulsive use. Thus, the body's fight to return to physiological homeostasis does not appear to explain compulsive drug use.

In the 1980s, Wise and Bozarth (1987) recognized that all drugs that lead to compulsive-use patterns induce the release of dopamine into the shell of the nucleus accumbens from neurons whose cell bodies are in the ventral tegmental area. These drugs include alcohol, opiates, nicotine, cocaine, and amphetamines. The nucleus accumbens and the ventral tegmental area along with dopamine constituted the focus of investigation of researchers attempting to explain why compulsion to use chemicals develops.

The Process of Becoming Addicted: Drug Sensitization

If an animal is allowed to continue to work for administration of a drug, such as cocaine, over time the animal exhibits sensitization to the chemical. The level of dopamine released into the nucleus accumbens with successive administration of cocaine or amphetamine increases over time. The animal's behavior reflects the increase in dopamine release. The animal is increasingly more active and more vigilant (Berridge & Robinson, 1998; Robinson & Berridge, 2008). Eventually, the animal may display stereotypic behavior, such as picking at its skin, given a strong stimulant. The animal also increases the rate of its lever pressing for the drug as drug exposure continues.

It Is Not About Pleasure

When animals have an opportunity for copulation or are given access to food, dopamine is released in the nucleus accumbens. The animal becomes more active, moving about to a greater degree (locomotion) when the opportunity for copulation or feeding is presented. Because natural rewards are associated with dopamine release, an initial hypothesis was that dopamine release mediated pleasure. As discussed in Chapter 2 (references in Neurons and Neurotransmitters, dopamine section), this hypothesis was discredited by the work of Kent Berridge and colleagues. To quickly recap, three facts argued against the idea that dopamine is the neurotransmitter of pleasure. Dopamine is released as an animal works to avoid shock, which is aversive. Dopamine is released as the animal is working toward a reward but not during consumption of the reward. If the dopamine neurons in the ventral tegmental area are removed, the animal will appear to enjoy the food if force fed. However, the animal will no longer work for the food (see Chapter 2, Dopamine section).

The current view of dopamine's function is that dopamine lowers the subjective cost of effort; dopamine makes hard work seem easy (Font et al., 2008; Niv, Daw, Joel, & Dayan, 2007; Salamone & Correa, 2002; Salamone, Correa, Farrar, & Mingote, 2007). Others have characterized the dopamine circuitry as the wanting system, not the liking system (Berridge, Robinson, & Aldridge, 2009). With this new appreciation of the function of dopamine, explanation of the addictive process changed. Given continued use of an addicting drug, the animal works harder for the chemical, although the animal may not necessarily be enjoying the experience.

Dopamine does make the animal more vigilant with increased capacity for making connections and learning. The dopamine circuitry has been labeled the "incentive salience system" because the animal is prepared to distinguish or discern the optimal routes for finding the reward. When the animal is lever pressing for cocaine, what the animal learns is to administer more of the drug. Additionally, the animal learns to strongly associate the environmental cues with the availability of the drug. The environmental cues become conditioned stimuli, which will elicit drug-seeking behavior and more vigorous "working toward." The animal's "working toward" is the animal model equivalent of compulsive drug use.

Historically, many have believed that all motivation can be explained by working for pleasure or working to avoid pain. The characterization of the dopaminergic mesolimbic system (projections from the ventral tegmental area to the nucleus accumbens) has offered a new view of motivation. Sometimes people work very hard because they have no choice. The brain's motivational system can operate independent of the affective consequences. This makes sense from an evolutionary standpoint. Parents, both human and animal, work very hard to protect and feed their offspring even when this behavior fails to be pleasurable and sometimes even produces pain (e.g., when arising in the middle of the night to feed a newborn). In fact, there are receptors for chemicals in the nucleus accumbens associated with mating and caring for the young (Young, Lim, Gingrich, & Insel, 2001). Thus, the motivational system plays a major role in preservation of the species. Activation of the motivational system leaves no room for choice. Addicting chemicals highjack the brain's motivational system, the system designed for the preservation of the species.

The Brain Is Being Changed

As addicting drugs capture the brain's motivational system, the brain is changed in recognizable ways. The nucleus accumbens of animals that have been addicted are different in many ways from those of drug-naive animals. For example, the synapses per dendrite on the neurons are increased (Kalivas, Peters, & Knackstedt, 2006; Kalivas, Volkow, & Seamans, 2005).

Researchers know that an animal's working for a drug can be "extinguished" if the drug is no longer delivered when the animal lever presses. Eventually, the animal quits working for the drug. However, several conditions (discussed later) can get the animal to once again work for the drug. Kalivas et al. (2005, 2006; Knacksted & Kalivas, 2009) were interested in knowing what accounts for relapse to drug use after an animal's working for the drug has been extinguished. They honed in on a difference that could explain a return to compulsive drug taking. When an animal perceives the availability of the drug or other stimuli that have been previously associated with drug delivery, neurons, whose cell bodies are in the prefrontal cortex (PFC), release glutamate into the nucleus accumbens. In addicted animals, the amount of glutamate released by the PFC neurons is greater than that in a naive animal.

The Break on Glutamate and Dopamine
Release in the Nucleus Accumbens

Kalivas et al. searched for an explanation for the greater amount of glutamate that was released in addicted animals. Kalivas et al. showed that in addicted animals, the extra-synaptic levels of glutamate (i.e., glutamate in the area outside the synaptic cleft) were lower than those in drug-naive animals. The function of the extra-synaptic glutamate is to occupy autoreceptors on the axons from the PFC neurons and serve as a breaking mechanism on the amount of glutamate released. Addicted animals lack a breaking mechanism.

The next task was to explore how restoration of the breaking mechanism might be achieved. Glial cells are a source of the extra-synaptic glutamate. Kalivas et al. showed that by getting the glial cells to release more extra-synaptic glutamate, the addicted animal would no longer work for the cocaine when cues suggesting access were presented. This discovery led to the development of pharmaceuticals that can increase glutamate release from the glial cells to decrease drug seeking (Kalivas, 2005; Kalivas & Volkow, 2005; Kalivas et al., 2003; McFarland, Lapish, & Kalivas, 2003; Moussawi et al., 2009). In a subsequent section, we look at the pharmaceutical intervention based on this discovery to decrease relapse.

In order to induce a previously addicted animal that has undergone extinguishment to again work for the drug, both glutamate and dopamine are necessary. However, the interface between these two neurotransmitter systems is not yet known. Nevertheless, it is clear that they are connected. If the level of extra-synaptic glutamate is restored, not only is the animal less susceptible to relapse, but the animal's sensitized behavior, which reflects augmented release of dopamine, is erased. That is, the animal does not display enhanced locomotion to a stimulant relative to a drug-naive animal (Steketee & Kalivas, 2011).

When Are Addicts More Vulnerable to Relapse?

After an animal learns to lever press for cocaine, as previously discussed, the lever pressing can be extinguished. To recap, extinction involves allowing the animal to lever press without the delivery of cocaine. The animal eventually stops lever pressing. Several procedures reliably reinstate the lever pressing: exposing the animal to shock, exposing the animal to the cues that were present when cocaine was delivered, and providing a small amount of cocaine (Kalivas et al., 2005). Making the animal hungry has also been found to reinstate drug seeking (Adler et al., 2000; Cummings, Naleid, & Lattemann, 2007).

The conditions under which animals relapse do correspond to the human literature on when people relapse. Across all types of drugs, people are more vulnerable to relapse when they are in a bad mood, analogous to the state of a shocked animal. Returning to an environment where drugs were used in the past will also induce cravings (Littrell, 2011). In the Goals of Treatment section, this information will be relevant to the prevention of relapse.

Additional discoveries increased the appreciation of how powerful relapse precipitants can be. Childress and colleagues (Goldstein et al., 2009) flashed images of cocaine paraphernalia on a screen below the exposure time threshold for awareness. Cocaine addicts responded with more craving and activation in brain reward areas, such as the nucleus accumbens (also called the ventral striatum), even though they did not know why they were experiencing these cravings. The rapidity of the response suggested that drug-seeking behavior can take addicts by surprise. Craving elicited by conditioned stimuli can occur even without awareness of the stimuli. Because of their lack of awareness, addicts may not have time to mount a defense. In fact, dopamine projections also go to the dorsal striatum where automatic behaviors reside (Belin & Everitt, 2008; Everitt et al., 2008; Yin & Knowlton, 2006).

Understanding Addiction

The animal models of addiction do have implications for humans who use drugs compulsively. Given exposure to precipitating cues, dopamine is released and craving is experienced. It is automatic. Alcoholics

Anonymous (AA) characterizes addiction as a disease. The word *disease* usually implies an automatic process that does not vary much regardless of the cultural context. (Colds have the same symptoms regardless of culture.) Drug addiction has the same characteristics across species and cultures.

The research on dopamine offers a different perspective as to why addicts use. Dopamine is about being motivated and ready to learn. Exposure to dopamine-agonist drugs captures the person's motivation system. The addicted use because their motivational systems have been highjacked. They do not necessarily experience pleasure or relief from pain when using their drug. Addicts use because they are compelled to do so. As they say in AA, there is a "loss of control." The automatic nature of the process of addiction is confirmed by observation of Parkinson's-disease patients. Treatment of Parkinson's disease involves provision of dopamine agonist drugs. When Parkinson's patients are given dopamine-agonists, many develop gambling and sexual compulsions (Bostwick, Hecksel, Stevens, Bower, & Ahlskog, 2009; Stamey & Jankovic, 2008). Thus, even when dopamine agonists are provided outside the context of drug-seeking behavior, motivation systems can be highjacked.

What About Free Will?

The notion that addicts are compelled to find and use their drug raises the issue of free will. Neuroscientist Mike Gazzaniga (2011) had access to a particular population of patients, which enabled findings relevant to the issue of free will. Some people with intractable epilepsy have the connections linking the two hemispheres of the brain (the corpus callosum) severed by surgery in order to limit the spread of the seizure. The daily function of these individuals is not disturbed. However, these patients provide an opportunity for neuroscientists to investigate how the brain works. Gazzaniga worked with split-brain patients. The information from the right visual field is processed by the left side of the brain. Information from the left visual field is processed by the right side of the brain. The ability to speak is located in the left hemisphere; so talking about actions can only be about material processed in the right visual field. Gazzaniga sent different imagery to each visual field. Gazzaniga asked the individual to select which tool went with the image on the screen. Chicken claws were presented in the right visual field. Snow was seen in the left visual field. The person pointed to the picture of a shovel on the desk after seeing the snow in the left visual field. However, when Gazzaniga asked the left hemisphere why the shovel was selected, the individual, who only was consciously aware of the chicken claw images, answered the chicken shed needed cleaning. For Gazzaniga, the experiment illustrated that people frequently discover their motivations by observing themselves and then drawing inferences about why they did something after they have acted. After the fact, people can find a plausible explanation for their choices after observing their own behavior. Gazzaniga extrapolates from these observations. Human behavior is elicited by environmental stimuli and we make up a story, after the fact, about plausible motivations for our actions.

Gazzaniga (2011) suggests that most human behavior is elicited by environmental cues often outside of awareness of the person who is behaving. Gazzaniga's perspective is consistent with the work on priming. In fact, exposure to environmental cues can raise particular thoughts or behaviors in the hierarchy of options. For example, seeing a group of slowly walking geriatric persons influences a person to walk more slowly himself or herself, although he or she may not realize why he or she is behaving in this fashion (Aarts & Dijksterhuis, 2000; Bargh & Chartrand, 1999; Bargh, Gollwitzer, Lee-Chai, Barndollar, & Trotschel, 2001). Although all of these findings challenge the notion of free will, there are other perspectives on the issue. Gazzaniga (2011) does believe that people do have free will. People have the capacity to select the cues they will have in their environment. By selecting the cues properly, one can make sure the desired behaviors are triggered. This view of where individuals have control has implications for how recovery is possible, which will be covered in a later section.

Do Addicts Use Because They Are in Pain?

Koob (2013) and Koob et al. (2014) have been exponents of the view that relapse occurs because addicts are in a state of distress–dysphoria and using substances allows escape from this negative state. Koob marshals evidence that during the course of any bout of heavy drug administration, anxiety-promoting molecules will build up and will be particularly aversive when not offset by the chemical effects of the drug of choice. Koob also suggests that even during extended periods of abstinence, these aversive molecules can be increased by drug cues. Similar to Koob's thinking, Volkow et al. (Goldstein & Volkow, 2002; Volkow, Fowler, & Wang, 2004) suggest that cocaine addicts have impaired capacity for experiencing response to natural reinforcers, and thus are in a state of relative lack of motivation when not under the influence of their drug of choice. Volkow et al. base this hypothesis on brain scans of cocaine addicts, which show cocaine addicts display less activation in the ventral striatum (where the nucleus accumbens is located) in response to natural reinforcers than do nonaddicted individuals (de Acros, Verdejo, Peralta, Sanchez-Barrera, & Perez-García, 2004; Garavan et al., 2000).

The hypotheses raised by Koob and Volkow offer a fairly pessimistic assessment of the prospects for future wellness among abstinent addicts. There are reasons to doubt their hypotheses. Anyone who attends AA meetings knows that most recovering people are cheerful folks who like to laugh. With regard to the data, the imaging work cited by Volkow was of addicts with varying duration of abstinence. During withdrawal, dopamine reserves are low (Knoblich et al., 1992; Leyton, 2007; Schulteis & Koob, 1996). During this time, addicts are less responsive to rewards, including cocaine (Leyton, 2007). Moreover, Koob (see Koob et al., 2014) has shown that during drug withdrawal, addicts fail to electrically stimulate areas of the brain, which would raise dopamine levels. Dopamine reserves take a long time to replenish as evidenced by the fact that visual responses controlled by dopamine (yellow–blue color discriminations) are aberrant long after sobriety (Desai, Roy, Brown, & Smelson, 1997; Roy, Roy, Williams, Weinberger, & Smelson, 1997). Alcoholics in early sobriety are often depressed and lethargic, possibly reflecting low levels of dopamine. It takes several weeks before their early lethargy clears. However, most do get better. In fact, Marc Schuckit suggests waiting a week or 2 before making a decision about whether an alcoholic in early sobriety who appears to be depressed is actually suffering from major depression (Littrell, 1991a; Schuckit & Tapert, 2004).

Additional questions exist about the type of distress that will motivate drug seeking. Recall that drug seeking is fueled by dopamine release, which energizes behavior and promotes vigilance to motivational cues. In animals, exposure to shock and short-term social defeat motivate drug taking. As stated earlier, shock increases dopamine release in the nucleus accumbens (Berridge & Robinson, 1998). But given the conditions of uncontrollable shock (the learned-helplessness paradigm), the lateral habenula will suppress release of dopamine into the nucleus accumbens (see Chapter 2). Consistent with this line of reasoning, Miczek, Nikulina, Shimamoto, and Covington (2011) found that short-term defeat motivates drug seeking; with prolonged defeat, dopamine in the nucleus accumbens is downregulated and the animals quit working for a stimulant drug and lose their preference for sugar. The defeated animal is not a motivated animal. Extrapolating from this, severe stress may fail to result in drug-seeking behavior.

With regard to drug use during the withdrawal period from drugs, some people use drugs to "get well." However, dopamine reserves are low during drug withdrawal (Treadway & Zald, 2011). During the state of withdrawal, strong motivation for anything, including seeking drugs, may not occur. Consistent with this, Harriet de Witt and colleagues (Bedi et al., 2011) found an "incubation of craving" effect. The further away from the initial withdrawal period after smoking cessation, the greater the craving. The "wanting system," as assessed by dopamine release, is not very active during withdrawal. Aggressive drug seeking requires a strong, dopaminergic "wanting system." During withdrawal, the motivational system is down.

Substance Abusers Are a Heterogeneous Population

The research on addiction in animals examined how exposure to chemicals changes the brain so that drug seeking becomes compulsive. For the most part, this research did not examine variations in rodent genes that might make some animals more vulnerable than others. For many addicts, drug seeking is fueled by a strong motivation (dopamine) system. However, humans probably can vary in the neurochemical motivations to use drugs. Neuroscientist Carl Hart's (2013) research suggests that many of his inner-city addicts are not compelled by drug stimuli. Hart (2013) argues that many poor African Americans use drugs because the alternatives for ways to attain gratification are so bleak. They use to escape. For this type of client, improving alternatives may be required if the recovery strategy is to be effective.

In the early literature on alcoholism, a distinction was made between primary alcoholics and secondary alcoholics. Primary alcoholics do not have a major mental disorder that precedes their heavy drinking. For primary alcoholics, drinking may develop in the context of a pretty positive existence. Researchers have looked at college-age predictors of alcoholism at age 40 years in males. In a particular study, the best college-age predictor of alcoholism at age 40 years was the MacAndrew Alcoholism Scale from the Minnesota Multiphasic Personality Inventory as assessed during college (Kammeier, Hoffman, & Loper, 1973). The MacAndrew Alcoholism Scale captures an extroverted personality who likes fun and excitement (sensation seeking; Littrell, 1991a; MacAndrew, 1981). Extroversion is a strong correlate of positive affect (Watson, Clark, McIntyre, & Hamaker, 1992). Under stressful conditions, extroverted, sensation seekers are less likely to exhibit dysphoria than other persons (Smith, Ptacek, & Smoll, 1992). Thus, prior to the initiation of their heavy drinking, primary alcoholics were cheerful people.

Primary alcoholics are more likely to have a family history of alcoholism (Littrell, 1991a). Primary alcoholics are more likely to conform to the pattern of addiction consistent with greater activation of the dopamine system in response to alcohol. For example, sons of alcoholics who develop their own heavy-drinking pattern are much less sedated or intoxicated by alcohol than the offspring of nonalcoholics (Littrell, 1991b; Schuckit, 1994, 2014). Studies of biological children of alcoholics fail to find elevated rates of anxiety or depressive disorders, although they are more likely to develop alcoholism (Schuckit, 1994). However, absolute statements regarding whether children of alcoholics are not generally distinguished on measures of distress cannot be made. Research on children of alcoholics does find that they are distressed when hardships occur in their home environments (Littrell, 1991a).

In contrast to primary alcoholism, secondary alcoholism is preceded by major depression or another major mental illness. Secondary alcoholism is less likely to be associated with a family history of alcoholism. In males, about 80% of a group of alcoholics were primary alcoholics and 20% were secondary alcoholics. In females, the numbers are reversed with 80% being secondary alcoholics. These findings do have implications for treatment (Littrell, 1991a). The secondary alcoholics will require attention to their primary disorder (depression, posttraumatic stress disorder [PTSD], etc.) for treatment to decrease drinking to be effective. Once they quit drinking, secondary alcoholics may need to address other mental health disorders. In contrast, once they quit drinking, primary alcoholics are more likely to be free of mood disorders.

Genetic Predisposition

According to Hasin, Stinson, Ogburn, and Grant (2007), who used the *Diagnostic and Statistical Manual of Mental Disorders*, Fourth Edition (*DSM-IV*; American Psychiatric Association, 1994) criteria, there is a lifetime prevalence of alcoholism for 12.5% of the population. Estimates of the population prevalence for addiction to other drugs are harder to gauge, given that data are harder to collect. Researchers suggest that heritability accounts for about 60% of risk for addiction to alcohol and other drugs (Kreek, Bart, Lilly, LaForge, & Nielsen, 2005; Kreek, Nielsen, Butelman, & LaForge, 2005). Researchers have identified alleles and personality traits associated with risk for drug addiction. In both humans and rodents, hyperactivity and impulsivity increase the speed of developing compulsive drug use (Belin, Mar, Dalley, Robbins, & Everitt, 2008; Verdejo-García, Lawrence, & Clark, 2008). Poor impulse control at age 10 to 12 years is a correlate of drug use at age 19 years (Tarter, 2003). Alleles of the dopamine receptors and the dopamine transporters predict both substance abuse and hyperactivity in humans (Brewer & Portenza, 2008) and animals (Everitt et al., 2008). Volkow et al. focus on the D2 receptor. Persons with lower levels of D2 receptors evaluate cocaine more positively and they are more impulsive (Dalley et al., 2007; Volkow et al., 2004). D2 receptors are relevant to neuronal functioning not only in the ventral striatum, where the nucleus accumbens is found, but also to areas in the brain involved in regulation (Volkow et al., 2004). Genetic risk factors seem to be associated with a stronger dopaminergic system and a weaker self-regulation system. In the Goals of Treatment section, we consider how to strengthen self-regulation.

HOW TO APPROACH CLIENTS

Is Breaking Down Denial Relevant?

An assumption from the Big Book of AA (Alcoholics Anonymous, 2001) is that alcoholics deny that they have a drinking problem. According to the denial hypothesis, alcoholics refuse to admit that they have a problem with substance abuse. E. Jellinek, who authored the influential *The Disease Concept of Alcoholism* in 1960, proffered the notion that denial fueled the progression of alcoholism. Jellinek waffled between two positions: alcoholics will quit drinking once they admit they are alcoholics; or in contrast, acknowledgment of alcoholism is required for sobriety but is not sufficient for sobriety. Given the central role of denial, it was understandable why many therapists affiliated with AA who read the Big Book and are familiar with Jellinek's work believe that it is vital to "break down denial" (Littrell, 1991a).

In recent years, there has been little investigation into the question of whether alcoholics deny. Investigation of the validity of the denial assumption was contributed by earlier researchers. The results from research examining the basic assumption that alcoholics deny have been mixed. On the "they don't deny side," Cooper, Sobell, Maisto, and Sobell (1980) found that alcoholics overreport their misdeeds while drinking relative to official California records. Alcoholics do not deny specific events that occurred in the past while they were drinking, although they are not very accurate about how much they have had to drink (Babor, Stephens, & Marlatt, 1987; Czarnecki, Russell, Cooper, & Salter, 1990). On the other hand, alcoholics identify the development of their problem drinking at a later time point than do their relatives (Leonard, Dunn, & Jacob, 1983; Orford, 1973) and they view themselves as having more control over their drinking than do their relatives (Orford & Keddie, 1986).

There is also research examining how self-labeling relates to outcome. In fact, those who embrace the label "alcoholic" at the beginning of treatment have worse outcomes than those who do not (Orford, 1973; Moberg, Krause, & Klein, 1982; Rossi, Stach, & Bradley, 1963). This does not necessarily imply that self-labeling causes the worse outcome. Rather, those with extreme drinking problems are more likely to know who they are (Helzer & Pryzbeck, 1988), and initial drinking severity predicts worse outcome. There is also research suggesting that admission of alcoholism is not a requirement for sobriety. Mark and Linda Sobell, along with their colleagues, find that 75% of those alcoholics who become sober do so outside of treatment and AA (Sobell, Cunningham, & Sobell, 1996; Sobell, Sobell, Toneatto, & Leo, 1993). Some people quit without even considering the question of whether they are alcoholic (Tuchfeld, 1981).

The critical factor in motivating a change in drinking behavior is desire for a change. Research on AA members finds that the best predictive factors for sobriety of a menu of possible factors are wanting to be sober, a view of former drinking as harmful, and self-confidence (self-efficacy) about being able to maintain sobriety. In these studies, belief in the disease concept and applying the label "alcoholic" to oneself were not predictive of successful outcome (Morgenstern, Bux, Labouvie, Blanchard, & Morgan, 2002; Morgenstern et al., 2003; Morgenstern, Labouvie, McCrady, Kahler, & Frey, 1997; Muench & Morgenstern, 2007).

For those who believe that alcoholics deny, confronting denial is a logical next step. There are studies examining the efficacy of confrontation with alcoholics. An early study was done in an employment context in which alcoholics were threatened with job loss if they did not enter treatment. In terms of getting alcoholics to enter treatment, listening to their excuses and talking about what to expect from treatment resulted in more people entering treatment than did threatening them with consequences and describing their negative behavior (Trice & Beyer, 1984). The concept behind the popularized "interventions," which is the title of an Emmy award–winning TV program, also entails confrontation. During interventions, family members describe the addict's embarrassing behavior and then threaten them with consequences if they fail to agree to treatment. In fact, data suggest that interventions work less well than gentler approaches in getting addicts into treatment and in helping them to achieve sobriety (Meyers, Miller, Smith, & Tonigan, 2002; W. R. Miller, Meyers, Smith, & Tonigan, 1999). The developers of motivational interviewing (described in greater detail in the next section) analyzed what actually happened during intake interviews in order to ascertain which processes are associated with better outcome. When the therapist confronts, then the client argues and defends his or her position of denial. In fact, clients argued less when the therapist did not confront. The longer the clients argued, the greater the likelihood of a negative outcome (Glynn & Moyers, 2010; Martin, Christopher, Houck, & Moyers, 2011; W. R. Miller, Benefield, & Tonigan, 1993; Moyers, Martin, Houck, Christopher, & Tonigan, 2009). Thus, various evaluations of confrontation suggest that confrontation may not be the best way to approach individuals.

From an observer perspective, looking at the lives of some alcoholics who continue drinking despite the obvious devastation does raise the question, "why don't they stop?" In social psychology, there is a formula for motivation: motivation = (valuing the goal) × (self-efficacy). Research has investigated whether self-efficacy is the missing factor for some alcoholics who continue drinking. An early study done at a Veterans Administration hospital involved getting the alcoholics very drunk and then videotaping their drunken comportment. Then the researchers showed the films to the alcoholics. Although many were repulsed and vowed to stay sober, they more often dropped out of treatment, although they also later attended more AA meetings (Schaefer, Sobell, & Mills, 1971; Schaefer, Sobell, & Sobell, 1972). One possible explanation for the increase in leaving treatment was that the alcoholics lacked confidence in changing their behavior and it was just too distressing to keep on trying. Self-efficacy regarding sobriety is a big predictor of eventual success (Ilgen, McKellar, & Tiet, 2005; Ilgen & Moos, 2005; Ilgen, Tiet, Finney, & Moos, 2006). In early sobriety, helping to convince addicts that change is possible may be a good strategy to begin with.

New Approaches: Transtheoretical Models of Change and Motivational Interviewing

Although early thinking about addiction regarded breaking down denial as key, new perspectives have emerged in the field. The transtheoretical model of change was introduced by Prochaska, Norcross, and Diclemente (1994) who studied the process through which persons make any major shift in life course. These researchers found that people spend a great deal of time contemplating change before making a commitment and taking action. They suggested that clients should be approached in keeping with the stage at which they are positioned. Rushing the process could provoke resistance.

At the University of New Mexico, Bill Miller and colleagues (W. R. Miller & Rollnick, 2013) have developed the approach of motivational interviewing. The approach is very consistent with Carl Rogers's reflective-listening strategy. The detailed questions the therapist asks about the client's daily life are designed to reveal ambivalence about his or her current drinking or drug use. The therapist listens to what the client is stating and paraphrases the emotional tone and content of what the client has said. The idea is to get the client to convince himself or herself that change is desirable.

With motivational interviewing, the therapist's job is to reflect back the client's concern. Advice is only given after asking the client's permission. Information, perhaps about a client's liver scores or other health indicators, is only provided after the client agrees to listen. If any resistance is met, the therapist quickly steps back (roll with resistance). Motivational interviewers avoid confrontation because when clients hear themselves arguing against the therapist, clients solidify their positions. If the client resists, the therapist retreats, for example, by changing the subject. The therapist waits for the next opportunity to reflect the client's own ambivalence. The therapist's task is to help the client make the case for sobriety. During the interview, the client does most of the talking and the therapist's questions can direct where the client focuses.

David Rosengren's (2009) book is an excellent resource for learning the motivational interviewing techniques. Asking about how the client perceives the therapist is very consistent with the motivational interviewing philosophy. Scott D. Miller (www.scottdmiller.com), a psychologist who conducts workshops internationally, has short assessment forms available on his website. The forms invite the client to provide feedback to the therapist. If the therapist receives negative ratings from the client, a discussion with the client, soliciting help in how to be more effective, should occur. Such discussions promote client engagement.

What Level of Drug Consumption Should Be Changed?

For many addiction counselors, the question of drinking-pattern goals never comes up. Generally, clients are mandated into treatment by some authority after a commission of a crime, a threat of job loss, or the threat of divorce. Usually, the mandating party expects sobriety. Very rarely do clinicians employed in treatment centers engage in questioning whether an individual should identify a controlled-drinking goal, as opposed to embracing sobriety. However, given that behavioral health clinicians will be employed in primary care settings in the future, helping clients decide whether to attempt controlled use versus abstinence with regard to a particular substance may be the task.

People who receive DUIs (legal charges for driving under the influence) may or may not be alcoholics. Prevention Research Institute (PRI) is an organization that has a good track record of working, in several states, with people who have been convicted of driving under the influence. Those at PRI have developed a strategy for assisting individuals to make conscious decisions about a desirable pattern of drinking. At court-mandated seminars, the PRI people present information on the risks to health at various levels of drinking. During the PRI program, levels of safe drinking graduated according to risk attributable to familial genetics, are proffered. The PRI staff suggests that the safe level of drinking for those without hereditary risk are two drinks per day for men and one drink for women. Then participants are asked to select their safe-drinking-level goals. The program is very collaborative. A PRI approach could be adapted to a primary care health setting. People can be invited to review their current behavior in light of information regarding the health consequences of drinking. They can be assisted in identifying their own goals.

For people working in primary care, identifying alcoholism or drug addiction can be problematic because definitions keep changing. At one point, the WHO's definition of an alcoholic was "someone who continues to drink despite a problem" (Littrell, 1991a). (The WHO offered no definition of what constituted "a problem.") The National Institute on Alcohol Abuse and Alcoholism (NIAAA, 2014) recommends that levels of alcohol consumption should not exceed two standard drinks a day for men and one drink per day for women. (A drink is 12 oz. of 0.4% alcohol beer; 1.25 oz. of 40% hard liquor; or 12 oz. of 4% wine). Presumably, those exceeding these limits should change their pattern. However, ambiguity remains on the frequency with which these limits are exceeded for defining a problem. There are guidelines specifying levels of safe drinking. However, hard-and-fast rules for diagnosing problematic drinking are not available.

Identifying the level of drinking that is healthy is difficult. In fact, drinking at low to moderate levels is associated with better health. Alcohol increases high-density lipoproteins, which protects against cardiovascular disease. Recent studies from neurologists find that drinking at moderate levels (defined as less than 36 g with a standard drink being 15 g/day) is associated with less age-related memory decline (Sabia et al., 2014; Stampfer, Kang, Chen, Cherry, & Grodstein, 2005). In terms of health effects, fatty liver occurs at around five drinks per day. Drinking in excess of four drinks on any one occasion should be avoided because at this level hangovers can occur. Functioning is impaired during hangovers. Holiday heart, an arrhythmic heartbeat, can occur after heavy intoxication. Blackouts (memory loss for a period of time even when function might not have been obviously impaired) are disconcerting (Ling, Stephens, & Heffernan, 2010; Littrell, 1991b; Rehm, 2011). In helping clients assess their current drinking, questions can be asked about blackouts and average levels of consumption. If an individual is drinking in the heavy range, an extant threat to health can be identified on blood tests by examining liver enzyme scores and blood work (Littrell, 1991b; Rehm, 2011). Feedback on lab values can help the client to make decisions.

Newly emerging changes in drug laws reflect the shifting consensus on what constitutes a problem. In Colorado, Washington, Oregon, and Alaska, recreational marijuana use is legal and in many other states medical marijuana is legal. We do not yet know the public health consequences of these changes. In the United States, opiate agonists (buprenorphine and methadone) are legal and considered to be treatment. As discussed in Chapter 4, buprenorphine is being tested as a treatment for depression in Israel. Smoking cessation is desirable, but the jury is still out on nicotine nasal spray, nicotine patches, and Snus, a nicotine preparation marketed in Sweden. New forms of legal hallucinogens (e.g., bath salts) keep emerging on the Internet; the street drug ketamine is being tested as an antidepressant. Amphetamine use is considered a problem if it is a street drug, but amphetamines are a treatment for adults with attention deficit hyperactivity disorder (ADHD). In our society, there is considerable ambiguity (ambivalence) regarding drug use.

The Wisdom of Initial Sobriety

At some point, clients who are motivated to make a change will probably consider what their goals should be. In Europe, therapists work with people who want to learn how to control drink. (Control drinking means establishing drinking levels that do not result in social or physical problems.) If the client cannot maintain drinking at the level the client has chosen, then the targets are changed. Often initial control-drinking goals change to abstinence goals. However, even if an abstinence plan is later amended to permit some drinking, there is wisdom in an initial period of abstention. In a study carried out in Europe, Nordstrom and Berglund (1987) examined how long it took to become a nonproblematic drinker by studying two groups: those who purposefully tried to abstain for 4 to 5 years or those who never tried to abstain. In achieving a nonproblematic-drinking status, the initial abstention group took 2 years, whereas the never-abstain group took 16 years. The Nordstrom and Berglund study is heuristic. For those wishing to modify their drinking behavior, initial abstention offers a wise course.

At AA meetings, it is generally assumed that those who choose to attend a meeting are probably alcoholics. Little time is spent evaluating whether newcomers actually have a problem. The AA assumption is that all alcoholics can never drink again without risking severe harm. In AA, the goal is abstinence from all mood- and mind-altering chemicals. Even with this rather clear goal in AA, people never seemed to question the cigarettes and the coffee at every meeting. The AA "cross-addiction" prediction is that using any mood-altering chemical will facilitate relapse to one's drug of choice. According to AA dogma, a person who is addicted to one substance is addicted to all substances. In terms of empirical support for cross-addiction, the major overlapping categories are alcohol and cigarettes. If a person is a heavy drinker, chances are that the person is a two-pack-per-day smoker. Eighty-eight percent of alcoholics are heavy smokers (Batel, Pessione, Maitre, & Rueff, 1995; Littleton, Barron, Prendergast, & Nixon, 2007). With regard to cross-addiction between alcoholism and other chemicals, there is less support. A study by Stinson et al. (2006) found that only 13% of those with an alcohol disorder abused other substances. Cross-addiction with tranquilizers was least likely to occur.

With regard to smoking crack cocaine, often people develop a compulsive-use pattern of cocaine ingestion in a matter of months or even weeks. Some have long histories of drinking in moderation. They are hard to convince that abstinence from alcohol is a desirable goal. There are data on whether use of one substance will jeopardize abstention from another substance. If a recovering cocaine addict was not a heavy drinker prior to addiction to cocaine, then drinking in moderation probably will not jeopardize cocaine abstention (McKay, Alterman, Rutherford, Cacciola, & McLellan, 1999). However, many cocaine abusers also abuse alcohol. The issue needs to be assessed along with clarification regarding how NIAAA defines *heavy drinking*.

INITIAL ENGAGEMENT

There are some initial screening questions that can be helpful in alerting when a further evaluation should be conducted. Questions such as, "Have you ever felt you needed to cut down?" "Has anyone ever been annoyed by your drinking?" "Have you ever felt guilty about your drinking?"

"Have you ever purposefully changed your drinking pattern?" are good openers (CAGE Questionnaire; http://niaaa.nih.gov/publications/ AssessingAlcohol/InstrumentPDFs/16_CAGE.pdf). The questions from the Alcohol Use Disorders Identification Test (http://pubs.niaaa.nih.gov/ publications/aa65/AA65.html) are provided in the Appendix, as are the questions from the CAGE Questionnaire, another assessment device, which are frequently used for screening. Additional screening tools can be obtained through niaaa.nih.gov/publications, drugabuse.gov, or sam-sha.gov. However, getting honest answers may require establishing some rapport.

Blood work can identify those who require additional assessment. However, to obtain information for an assessment as well as for recruiting clients into a collaborative process of maximizing health, the worker must be diligently searching for the client's perspectives and concerns during the interview. In line with motivational interviewing, taking a nonjudgmental approach is useful. Everyone has a story to tell with regard to alcohol, even nondrinkers have a reason for deciding not to drink. It is critical to find out the details about when a person drinks and what he or she is doing while drinking. It is important to notice when the client seems ambivalent about past behavior around substance use and to reflect back the ambivalence. It is important to learn what the client is proud of and what the client cares about. Learning about resources that might promote change and obstacles that can interfere with change are important objectives for an initial engagement. Often motivational interviewers use a values exercise in which the client identifies those people and life goals that he or she cares about. Then the client is asked to evaluate how substance use comports with his or her values.

If the client and the worker agree that there is reason for concern about substance abuse, the next task is planning for the immediate future. It is important to emphasize the client's choice. Even if a client agrees to attend some treatment program that requires a commitment to sobriety throughout the treatment process, clients should understand that the eventual decision about which goal to embrace belongs to them. Attending treatment is an opportunity to think about the role that drugs have played in one's life, to identify future life goals, and to determine whether substances fit in with these goals, and if so, how.

If a client is referred to an outside facility (e.g., an AA meeting), it is important to help the client envision the process. Having the client visualize the process serves two goals. First, reservations or mistaken beliefs about what will happen can be addressed. Second, the availability heuristic of Tversky and Kahneman (1974), for which they won the Nobel prize, avers that events that a person has concretely imagined are more likely to be seen as probable. Thus, if I can imagine myself doing something, I will be more likely to believe I can do it. My sense of efficacy will be changed; self-efficacy predicts behavior. Specific research testing this idea shows that having people imagine themselves carrying out a plan increases the likelihood that they will follow through (Littrell & Magel, 1991). Thus, having the client envision the process of attending a particular meeting is a good strategy.

Assessing Detox Requirements

If your assessment suggests that an individual is a heavy substance user, it is important to find out about the time and amount of last use. Alcohol, barbiturates, and benzodiazepines are the drugs associated with lethal withdrawal symptoms, such as seizures or delirium tremens. If a person has been a regular daily consumer of a tranquilizer for over a 3-week period, he or she should be medically evaluated. A person who has consumed eight to nine drinks the previous night, particularly if he or she exhibits a tremor on reaching for something, should be medically evaluated. These are rough estimates that will vary with the status of the client. However, very recent heavy consumption does justify evaluation of the person's blood pressure. Providing benzodiazepines for outpatient detoxification of alcoholics can often be accomplished safely (Blondell, 2005).

Assessing Level of Care

The American Society of Addiction Medicine (ASAM) has published guidelines for levels of care for those in need of treatment of addictions. For those who are homeless, lacking in social support, or who are a threat to themselves or others, inpatient programs are recommended (Mee-Lee & Shulman, 2011). For others, outpatient programs have been found to be as successful as inpatient programs, although enhancing outpatient treatment with case management services will be beneficial for some (Committee to Identify Research Opportunities in the Prevention and Treatment of Alcohol-Related Problems, Institute of Medicine, 1990; Littrell, 1991a; McLellan et al., 1999; Weisner & Schmidt, 1996). In fact, outpatient programs offer the benefit of having patients practice new ways of behaving in the same environment in which these new ways of behaving will be needed. Thus, treatment is more likely to generalize to the home environment. However, if an individual has friends who will encourage heavy consumption, then inpatient treatment does have an advantage. If a person drinks during outpatient treatment, then treating him or her as an inpatient may be a better option and offers a backup strategy.

Empirical research has offered some other bottom lines on what works. In terms of treatment efficacy, duration of aftercare matters. Follow-up visits maximize the probability that treatment benefits will be sustained (Carroll et al., 2011; Littrell, 1991a). Mandated treatment is as effective as voluntary treatment, probably because alcoholics often get convinced of the wisdom of change in the course of treatment (N. S. Miller & Flaherty, 2000; Wild, Roberts, & Cooper, 2002). Talking with alcoholics about the threats to health in their heavy drinking can result in a reduction in consumption and can enhance the efficacy of later treatment (Littrell, 1991a; McQueen, Howe, Allan, Mains, & Hardy, 2011).

GOALS OF TREATMENT

In group treatment and AA meetings, the client hears the stories of others who do want to change their lives. In the modal treatment centers in this country, information is provided about the nature of the addiction process. Clients often are given an opportunity to complete a "first step" in which they review in detail the specifics of the role that substances have played in their life. Through this process, most people make decisions about their goals with regard to substances. This is the point at which many choose abstinence.

Relapse Prevention

Even in those who make a commitment to sobriety, maintaining the commitment is often difficult. As discussed in the Neuroscience of Addiction section, cravings can be elicited by environmental cues. In fact, work with human subjects on relapsing finds that drug cues do increase relapse events (Connors, Longabaugh, & Miller, 1996; Lowman, Allen, Stout, & the Relapse Research Group, 1996; W. R. Miller, Westerberg, Harris, & Tonigan, 1996; Zywiak et al., 2006). The client can find himself or herself seeking his or her substance without having gone through a deliberate decision-making process. Research also suggests strategies for countering the automaticity of drug cures. Priming involves arranging the environment to cue behavior. Research suggests that if another goal is primed, then the cognitive availability of an opposing goal declines (Shah, Friedman, & Kruglanski, 2002). Just as drug paraphernalia can cue craving, reminders of sobriety (e.g., a copy of the Alcoholics Anonymous Big Book on the table) can cue motivation for sobriety. The way to combat the automaticity of drug seeking is to arrange the environment to trigger sobriety-promoting behavior. Involvement in AA provides many "triggers" for staying sober. The day becomes centered around going to meetings. At AA meetings, members collect tangible reminders of their sobriety. Chips representing various lengths of sobriety are distributed. People carry sobriety chips in their pockets, which makes salient the importance of sobriety. Active AA members are surrounded by primes for staying sober.

Developing a plan for staying sober increases the likelihood of adhering to one's goal. Gollwitzer, Fujita, and Oettingen (2004) have researched the process of how people stick to plans. The more specific the plan, the more likely it is to be carried out. Identifying obstacles and ways to combat the obstacles further increases the probability that the plan will be adhered to. People in recovery need to make specific plans for attending meetings to support sobriety. For most people in recovery, plans for resisting people who might encourage use is helpful. Envisioning oneself carrying out these plans will make them seem more probable and will increase self-efficacy. Talking to family members and spouses about the type of help they can provide is helpful.

Sometimes previous drug-using companions can be cues for drug use. Developing friends who support sobriety maximizes the probability of success. Consistent with this, Project MATCH, the big government-funded study evaluating treatments for alcoholism, found that for those without sober friends, AA was particularly helpful (Longabaugh, Wirtz, Zweben, & Stout, 1998; Project MATCH Research Group, 1998). If AA is not a compatible choice, then other avenues for establishing friendships that will support sobriety should be pursued.

In AA, members are advised to avoid being hungry, angry, lonely, or tired. (This is the HALT acronym.) The AA advice is very consistent with empirical findings on relapse. When animals whose drug seeking has been extinguished are distressed or hungry, they are more likely to reinstate level pressing for drug. Work investigating the conditions under which human addicts relapse suggests that being in a negative mood is indeed a strong cue for relapse (Connors et al., 1996; Lowman et al., 1996). Thus, support systems for helping to allay stress should be developed.

Developing Self-Regulation

In Chapter 2, the brain structures involved in dampening the strength of impulses were discussed. Several researchers have found that regulation of impulses can be an issue for some persons who abuse substances. Warren Bickel and colleagues (Bickel & Marsch, 2001; Bickel et al., 2007) found that impulsivity and the tendency to value immediate rewards over long-term rewards characterize many substance abusers. Antoine Bechara also assesses impulsivity. He developed the Iowa gambling task to identify persons who make risky choices and persons who fail to learn to avoid previously punished choices. Some substance abusers perform poorly on these types of tasks (Verdejo-García & Bechara, 2009). Thus, developing the brain's capacity for self-regulation may be relevant for some.

A particular study further established the relevance of developing regulatory control for increasing the probability of maintaining abstinence. Berkman, Falk, and Lieberman (2011) did brain scans of a group of individuals who were about to quit smoking. The scans were taken as these individuals performed the "go–no go" task. The "go–no go" task asks the individual to lever press when a particular letter appears on the screen but to refrain from pressing when particular low-frequency letters are presented. The researchers identified those individuals with more or less activity in the right ventrolateral PFC (the regulation area discussed in Chapter 2) as they performed the "go–no go" task. During the early-smoking-abstention phase, Lieberman contacted people about every 2 hours and recorded when they experienced cravings and then, in the next 2-hour block, whether they succumbed to the craving. The level of ventrolateral PFC activity as assessed during the "go–no go" task predicted outcome. Those with greater ventrolateral PFC during the "go–no go" task were able to resist temptation to smoke.

Strategies for increasing regulatory strength are available. Research suggests that the process of self-regulation involves the engagement of the parasympathetic nervous system (Ahern et al., 2001; Allen, Matthews, & Kenyon, 2000; Hansen, Johnsen, Sollers, Stenvik, & Thayer, 2004; Hansen, Johnsen, & Thayer, 2003; Ingjaldsson, Laberg, & Thayer, 2003). An increase in average level of heart rate variability during a day is a correlate of increased self-regulatory capacity. In contrast, momentary decreases in heart rate variability (a measure of parasympathetic nervous system [PNS] activity) are correlated with lapses in self-regulation (Segerstrom & Solberg Nes, 2007). In Chapter 4, ways to increase heart rate variability (HRV; vagal tone) were covered. These include consuming more omega-3s, being with trusted others, exercise, and meditation. In fact, with regard to maintaining abstinence goals, meditation does decrease relapses, which are associated with increased HRV (Bowen et al., 2014; Libby, Worhunsky, Pilver, & Brewer, 2012).

Baumeister and colleagues (Baumeister, Bratslavsky, Muraven, & Tice, 1998; Baumeister, Gailliot, DeWall, & Oaten, 2006; Baumeister, Vohs, & Tice, 2007; Vohs & Baumeister, 2004) have studied regulatory control as well. Baumeister's research suggests that regulatory capacity is like a muscle: level of capacity can be developed through practice; however, for any one time period, it is a limited resource. For any given moment in time, taxing regulatory capacity will lower one's capacity for regulation on the next task. It has been shown, for example, that spending a great deal of effort working on math problems will vitiate one's capacity for resisting the temptation to eat a cookie.

Baumeister's research has identified other short-term drainers of regulatory capacity. Fatigue vitiates regulatory capacity. Having low blood sugar or being sleep deprived can lower self-regulatory capacity (Gailliot, 2008; Gailliot et al., 2007). As stated previously, being stressed and being hungry are states that trigger dopamine release from the ventral tegmental area (VTA) and thus can be expected to increase craving (Abizaid et al., 2006; Adler et al., 2000; Cummings et al., 2007; Jerlhag et al., 2007; Kalivas et al., 2005). Those conditions that vitiate regulatory capacity are very consistent with relapse precipitants identified in the addiction literature. Plans for arranging life to avoid these states will maximize the probability of staying sober (Littrell, 2010).

Dealing With Abstinence Violation Syndrome

Relapses are common in early sobriety. The late Alan Marlatt coined the term "abstinence violation syndrome" to describe how a violation of one's commitment to sobriety can lead to guilty feelings that further precipitate more drinking (Littrell, 1991a). Careful planning for how to counter abstinence violation syndrome can shorten the duration of a relapse. Envisioning how to get quickly back on track following a lapse can prevent a "lapse" from becoming a "relapse." Writing a letter to one's self detailing the positive feelings about sobriety, to be read in the event of relapse, can be helpful. Reminding oneself that periods of sobriety have been achieved can bolster self-efficacy. As a backup strategy, giving a friend permission to contact the individual if he or she should fail to come to an AA meeting might prove helpful.

Pharmaceutical Treatments

A number of drugs intended to decrease relapses are on the market. Antabuse (disulfiram) blocks the breakdown of acetaldehyde (a metabolite of alcohol) to vinegar. With Antabuse in the body, drinking alcohol will result in the accumulation of acetaldehyde, a noxious substance, in the body. If the client drinks with Antabuse in the body, he or she will be quite nauseated. For clients who might drink on impulse, Antabuse offers a short-term coping strategy that allows recovering alcoholics to develop better coping skills (Littrell, 1991b).

Naltrexone (Vivitrol) is longer acting than naloxone (Narcan). Both naltrexone and naloxone are antagonists at opiate receptors. In Chapter 2, the role of natural endorphins in increasing activity in the nucleus accumbens was covered. Naloxone will block the opiate-induced increase of the dopamine release. Naloxone has shown efficacy in decreasing relapse to various types of drug use. Unfortunately, however, because naloxone downregulates the nucleus accumbens, not only is desire for drug use decreased but so is the desire for natural rewards. People who take it also become lethargic and apathetic. Moreover, naloxone does increase stress (Eisenberger & Cole, 2012; Littrell, 2001).

Acamprosate (Campral) is a drug that targets glutamate signaling. It is used to prevent the craving for alcohol (DeWitte, Littleton, Parot, & Koob,

2005). N-acetylcysteine is a drug that was identified in Kalivas's work on how addictive chemicals change the brain. N-acetylcysteine operates at a protein complex called the glutamate–cystine exchanger, which is located on the cell wall of glial cells. It causes the glial cells to release more glutamate into the extra-synaptic space in the nucleus accumbens, which then dampens the glutamate signal in the nucleus accumbens (see The Brain Is Being Changed section on Kalivas's research). N-acetylcysteine has shown efficacy in reducing the craving for cocaine, cannabis, and nicotine. Its big advantage over other pharmacological interventions is that it has minimal side effects; however, preliminary results have not been uniformly supported (Littrell, 2011; McClure, Gipson, Malcolm, Kalivas, & Gray, 2014). It is sold in health food stores.

Chantix (varenicline) is a drug that is a partial agonist at the nicotinic acetylcholine receptor. It is used to decrease craving during the process of smoking cessation (Lüscher, 2013). Although Chantix does increase the probability of success, only 40% achieve abstinence at 3 months (McClure et al., 2014). As discussed in Chapter 3, Nicotine section, Chantix is associated with violence. Antidepressants (Wellbutrin) and nicotine patches or nicotine gum are also used to facilitate smoking cessation.

Efficacy of Treatment

Project MATCH was a large multisite study funded by the federal government in the 1980s. It contrasted the efficacy of three approaches: motivational enhancement/motivational interviewing, the 12-step approach, and cognitive behavioral therapy. All approaches resulted in lower levels of problematic drinking. For those whose friends encouraged heavy drinking, the 12-step approach worked better (Longabaugh et al., 1998; Project MATCH Research Group, 1998). For those who were angry about being in treatment, motivational interviewing worked better (Project MATCH Research Group, 1997, 1998). Good therapeutic alliance and client self-efficacy both emerged as strong predictors of positive outcome in Project MATCH. A good therapeutic alliance means that the therapist and client agreed on the problem definition and the goals and strategies for achieving success (Ilgen et al., 2006).

Fletcher (2012), in her book *Inside Rehab*, describes her investigation into how the substance abuse treatment industry functions in this country.

What she describes comports well with my experiences in the field and those of my colleagues. Across treatment programs, whether they be at the costly rehab programs, such as the Betty Ford Center, or the halfway house funded through donations, there is not much difference in the approach or the psychoeducational material. All treatment centers almost everywhere show the obligatory Father Martin *Chalk Talk on Alcoholism*. Everyone reads daily devotional material published by Hazelden. Where there is some variation is the degree to which therapists respect and listen to clients and adapt procedures to the individual needs of clients. More tailoring to each client's needs is better. Fletcher recommends investigating the philosophy of particular programs before enrolling. The same approach can be used for AA. AA meetings vary a lot, so if a person is not comfortable, he or she should go to another. As they say in AA, "take what you can use, and leave the rest."

REFLECTIONS ON U.S. DRUG POLICY

Overdoses from prescription drugs are now reaching epidemic numbers. Deaths from prescription drugs outnumber those from street drugs (Association of State and Territorial Health Officials, 2008). The Drug Enforcement Administration considers prescription drugs to be the nation's leading drug problem (Schwarz, 2014). Despite the legal drugs being the bigger threat to the nation's health, America imprisons more people than any other nation on Earth. Most of these incarcerations are for drug crimes and the bulk of those who are convicted are minorities (Alexander, 2010). Ironically, the drugs for which these individuals are incarcerated can be acquired legally. Amphetamine is prescribed for ADHD. Although heroin is illegal, buprenorphine and methadone are considered to be treatments, with leaders at the Centers for Disease Control and Prevention (CDC) and National Institute on Drug Abuse (NIDA) being strong advocates for its use (Volkow, Frieden, Hyde, & Cha, 2014). (Under the Drug Addiction Treatment Act of 2000, after 8 hours of training, physicians can prescribe buprenorphine for patients in their private practices.)

Sometimes it is difficult to say whether the legal version of a drug that shares the same mechanism as the street drug is better or worse than the street drug. Both buprenorphine and methadone are agonists at mu-opioid receptors, as is heroin. Buprenorphine, methadone, and heroin are addictive substances and can cause respiratory depression and death if taken in large amounts. Arguably, heroin is better in terms of long-term effects on the body than methadone. Methadone can induce cardiac arrhythmias that can require a pacemaker (Barbhaiya, Seewald, & Hanon, 2011). This does not occur with heroin. Methadone is associated with more severe withdrawal symptoms than heroin (Gossop & Strang, 1991). Perhaps the history of various drugs in this country does more to explain why one chemical is legal and the other is not than can be explained by the pharmacological properties of various drugs (Musto, 1973, 2002). In Europe, opiate addicts are given a choice of treatment with buprenorphine, methadone, or heroin (Strang, Groshkova, & Metrebian, 2012). Even when drugs, such as opiate agonists, are legalized, a street market may continue to exist because pharmaceuticals (e.g., OxyContin) are much more expensive than street heroin. However, in countries where access to drugs is legalized, street trafficking does decline (Strang et al., 2012).

As mentioned previously, many states allow medical marijuana and Colorado, Washington, Oregon, and Alaska allow recreational marijuana for adults. Ketamine, a street drug, and buprenorphine are being investigated as treatments for depression. It is puzzling that some people are locked up for many years for exchanging the same chemicals that are legally acquired through prescription. Perhaps it is time for this nation to rethink its drug policies.

REFERENCES

Aarts, H., & Dijksterhuis, A. (2000). Habits as knowledge structures: Automaticity in goal directed behavior. *Journal of Personality and Social Psychology, 78*, 53–63.

Abizaid, A., Liu, Z-.W., Andrews, Z. B., Shanabrough, M., Borok, E., Elsworth, J. D.,…Hovarth, T. L. (2006). Ghrelin modulates the activity and synaptic input organization of midbrain dopamine neurons while promoting appetite. *Journal of Clinical Investigation, 116*(12), 3229–3239.

Adler, C. M., Elman, I., Weisenfeld, N., Kestler, L., Pickar, D., & Breier, A. (2000). Effect of acute metabolic stress on striatal dopamine release in healthy volunteers. *Neuropsychopharmacology, 22*, 545–550.

Ahern, G. L., Sollers, J. J., Lane, R. D., Labiner, D. M., Herring, A. M., Weinand, W. E.,…Thayer, J. F. (2001). Heart rate and heart rate variability changes in the intracarotid sodium amobarbital test. *Epilepsia, 42*, 912–921.

Alcoholics Anonymous. (1976). *Alcoholics Anonymous: The story of how many thousands of men and women have recovered from alcoholism.* New York, NY: Alcoholic Anonymous World Services.

Alexander, M. (2010). *The New Jim Crow: Mass incarceration in the age of colorblindness*. New York, NY: The New Press.

Allen, M. T., Matthews, K. A., & Kenyon, K. L. (2000). The relationships of resting baroreflex sensitivity, heart rate variability and measures of impulse control in children and adolescents. *International Journal of Psychophysiology, 37*, 185–194.

American Psychiatric Association. (1994). *Diagnostic and statistical manual of mental disorders* (4th ed.). Washington, DC: Author.

Association of State and Territorial Health Officials. (2008). *Prescription drug overdose: State health agencies respond*. Retrieved from http://www.astho.org/Programs/Prevention/Injury-and-Violence-Prevention/_Materials/Prescription-Drug-Overdose/

Babor, T. F., Stephens, R. S., & Marlatt, G. A. (1987). Verbal report methods in clinical research on alcoholism: Response bias and its minimization. *Journal of Studies on Alcohol, 48*, 410–424.

Barbhaiya, C. R., Seewald, R. M., & Hanon, S. (2011). QT prolongation and arrhythmia risk in methadone maintenance treatment. *Journal of Innovations in Cardiac Rhythm Management, 2*, S66–S68.

Bargh, J. A., & Chartrand, T. L. (1999). The unbearable automaticity of being. *American Psychologist, 54*, 462–479.

Bargh, J. A., Gollwitzer, P. M., Lee-Chai, A., Barndollar, K., & Trotschel, R. (2001). The automated will: Nonconscious activation and pursuit of behavioral goals. *Journal of Personality and Social Psychology, 81*(6), 1014–1027.

Batel, P., Pessione, F., Maître, C., & Rueff, B. (1995). Relationship between alcohol and tobacco dependencies among alcoholics who smoke. *Addiction, 90*(7), 977–980.

Baumeister, R. F., Bratslavsky, E., Muraven, M., & Tice, D. M. (1998). Ego depletion: Is the active self a limited resource? *Journal of Personality and Social Psychology, 74*(5), 1252–1265.

Baumeister, R. F., Gailliot, M., DeWall, C. N., & Oaten, M. (2006). Self-regulation and personality: How interventions increase regulatory success, and how depletion moderates the effects of traits on behavior. *Journal of Personality, 74*, 1773–1801.

Baumeister, R. F., Vohs, K. D., & Tice, D. M. (2007). The strength of the self-control. *Current Directions in Psychological Science, 16*, 351–355.

Bedi, G., Preston, K. L., Epstein, D. H., Heishman, S. J., Marrone, G. F., Shaham, Y., & de Wit, H. (2011). Incubation of cue-induced cigarette craving during abstinence in human smokers. *Biological Psychiatry, 69*(7), 708–711.

Belin, D., & Everitt, B. J. (2008). Cocaine seeking habits depend upon dopamine-dependent serial connectivity linking the ventral with the dorsal striatum. *Neuron, 57*, 432–441.

Belin, D., Mar, A., Dalley, J. W., Robbins, T. W., & Everitt, B. J. (2008). High impulsivity predicts the switch to compulsive cocaine-taking. *Science, 320*, 1352–1354.

Berkman, E. T., Falk, E. B., & Lieberman, M. D. (2011). In the trenches of real-world self-control: Neural correlates of breaking the link between craving and smoking. *Psychological Science, 22*(4), 498–506.

Berridge, K. C., & Robinson, T. E. (1998). What is the role of dopamine in reward: Hedonic impact, reward learning, or incentive salience. *Brain Research Review, 28*, 309–369.

Berridge, K. C., Robinson, T. E., & Aldridge, J. W. (2009). Dissecting components of reward: "Liking," "wanting," and learning. *Current Opinion in Pharmacology, 9*, 65–73.

Bickel, W. K., & Marsch, L. A. (2001). Toward a behavioral economic understanding of drug dependence: Delay discounting processes. *Addiction, 96*, 73–86.

Bickel, W. K., Miller, M. L., Yi, R., Kowal, B. P., Lindquist, D. M., & Pitcock, J. A. (2007). Behavioral and neuroeconomics of drug addiction: Competing neural systems and temporal discounting processes. *Drug and Alcohol Dependence, 90*(Suppl. 1), S85–S91.

Blondell, R. D. (2005). Ambulatory detoxification of patients with alcohol dependence. *American Family Physician, 71*(3), 495–502.

Bostwick, J. M., Hecksel, K. A., Stevens, S. R., Bower, J. H., & Ahlskog, J. E. (2009). Frequency of new-onset pathologic compulsive gambling or hypersexuality after drug treatment of idiopathic Parkinson disease. *Mayo Clinic Proceedings, 84*(4), 310–316.

Bowen, S., Witkiewitz, K., Clifasefi, S. L., Grow, J., Chawla, N., Hsu, S. H., . . . Larimer, M. E. (2014). Relative efficacy of mindfulness-based relapse prevention, standard relapse prevention, and treatment as usual for substance use disorders: A randomized clinical trial. *JAMA Psychiatry, 71*(5), 547–556.

Brewer, J. A., & Potenza, M. N. (2008). The neurobiology and genetics of impulse control disorders: Relationships to drug addictions. *Biochemical Pharmacology, 75*, 63–75.

Carroll, K. M., Ball, S. A., Jackson, R., Martino, S., Petry, N. M., Stitizer, M. L., . . . Weiss, R. D. (2011). Ten take home lessons from the first ten years of the CTN and ten recommendations for the future. *American Journal of Drug and Alcohol Abuse, 37*(5), 275–282.

Committee to Identify Research Opportunities in the Prevention and Treatment of Alcohol-Related Problems, Institute of Medicine. (1990). *Prevention and treatment of alcohol problems: Research opportunities.* Washington, DC: The National Academies Press.

Connors, G. J., Longabaugh, R., & Miller, W. R. (1996). Looking forward and looking back to relapse: Implications for research and practice. *Addiction, 91*, S191–S196.

Cooper, A. M., Sobell, M. B., Maisto, S. A., & Sobell, L. C. (1980). Criterion intervals for pretreatment drinking measures in treatment evaluation. *Journal of Studies on Alcohol, 41*, 1186–1195.

Cummings, D. E., Naleid, A. M., & Lattemann, D. P. F. (2007). Ghrelin: A link between energy homeostasis and drug abuse? *Addiction Biology, 12,* 1–5.

Czarnecki, D. M., Russell, M., Cooper, M. L., & Salter, D. (1990). Five-year reliability of self-reported alcohol consumption. *Journal of Studies on Alcohol, 51,* 68–76.

Dalley, J. W., Fryer, T. D., Brichard, L., Robinson, E. S. J., Theobald, D. E. H., & Laane, K. (2007). Nucleus accumbens D2/3 receptors predict trait impulsivity and cocaine reinforcement. *Science, 315*(5816), 1267–1270.

de Acros, F., Verdejo, A., Peralta, M. I., Sanchez-Barrera, M., & Perez-García, M. (2004). Experience of emotions in substance abusers exposed to images containing neutral, positive, and negative affective stimuli. *Drug and Alcohol Dependence, 76,* 159–167.

Desai, P., Roy, A., Brown, S., & Smelson, D. (1997). Impaired color vision in cocaine-withdrawn patients. *Archives of General Psychiatry, 54*(8), 696–699.

DeWitte, P., Littleton, J., Parot, P., & Koob, G. (2005). Neuroprotective and absti-nence-promoting effects of acamprosate. *CNS Drugs, 19*(6), 517–537.

Drug Addiction Treatment Act, Pub. L. No. 106–310 § 3501. (2000).

Eisenberger, N. I., & Cole, S. W. (2012). Social neuroscience and health: Neurophysiological mechanisms linking social ties with physical health. *Nature Neuroscience, 15*(5), 669–674.

Everitt, B. J., Belin, D., Economidou, D., Pelloux, Y., Dalley, J. W., & Robbins, T. W. (2008). Neural mechanisms underlying the vulnerability to develop compul-sive drug-seeking habits and addiction. *Philosophical Transactions of the Royal Society, B, 363,* 3125–3135.

Father Martin (Speaker). (1972). *Chalk talk on alcoholism.* Retrieved from Fathermartinmedia.org

Fletcher, A. M. (2012). *Inside rehab: The surprising truth about addiction treatment.* New York, NY: Penguin Group.

Font, L., Mingote, S., Farrar, A. M., Pereira, M., Worden, L., Stopper, C., ... Salamone, J. D. (2008). Intra-accumbens injections of the adenosine A2A agonist CGS 21680 affect effort-related choice behavior in rats. *Psychopharmacology, 199,* 515–526.

Gailliot, M. T. (2008). Unlocking the energy dynamics of executive functioning: Linking executive functioning to brain glycogen. *Perspectives on Psychological Science, 3,* 245–263.

Gailliot, M. T., Baumeister, R. F., DeWall, C. N., Maner, J. K., Plant, E. A., & Tice, D. M. (2007). Self-control relies on glucose as a limited energy source: Willpower is more than a metaphor. *Journal of Personality and Social Psychology, 92,* 325–336.

Garavan, H., Pankiewicz, J., Bloom, A., Cho, J. K., Sperry, L., & Ross, T. J. (2000). Cue-induced cocaine craving: Neuroanatomical specificity for drug users and drug stimuli. *American Journal of Psychiatry, 157,* 1789–1798.

Gazzaniga, M. (2011). *Who's in charge: Free will and the science of the brain.* New York, NY: HarperCollins.

Glynn, L. H., & Moyers, T. B. (2010). Chasing change talk: The clinician's role in evoking client language about change. *Journal of Substance Abuse Treatment, 39*, 65–70.

Goldstein, R. Z., Craig, A. D., Bechara, A., Garavan, H., Childress, A. R., Paulus, M. P., & Volkow, N. D. (2009). The neurocircuitry of impaired insight in drug addiction. *Trends in Cognitive Science, 12*, 372–380.

Goldstein, R. Z., & Volkow, N. D. (2002). Drug addiction and its underlying neurobiological basis: Neuroimaging evidence for the involvement of the frontal cortex. *American Journal of Psychiatry, 159*, 1642–1652.

Gollwitzer, P. M., Fujita, K., & Oettingen, G. (2004). Planning and the implementation of goals. In R. F. Baumeister & K. D. Vohs (Eds.), *Handbook of self-regulation: Research, theory, and applications* (pp. 221–228). New York, NY: Guilford Press.

Gossop, M., & Strang, J. (1991). A comparison of the withdrawal responses of heroin and methadone addicts during detoxification. *British Journal of Psychiatry, 158*, 697–699.

Hansen, A. L., Johnsen, B. H., Sollers, J. J. 3rd, Stenvik, K., & Thayer, J. F. (2004). Heart rate variability and its relation to prefrontal cognitive function: The effects of training and detraining. *European Journal of Applied Physiology, 93*(3), 263–272.

Hansen, A. L., Johnsen, B. H., & Thayer, J. F. (2003). Vagal influence on working memory and sustained attention. *International Journal of Psychophysiology, 48*, 263–274.

Hart, C. (2013). *High price: A neuroscientist's journey of self-discovery that challenges everything you know about drugs and society.* New York, NY: HarperCollins.

Hasin, D. S., Stinson, F. S., Ogburn, E., & Grant, B. F. (2007). Prevalence, correlates, disability, and comorbidity of DSM-IV alcohol abuse and dependence in the United States. *Archives of General Psychiatry, 64*(7), 830–842.

Helzer, J. E., & Pryzbeck, T. R. (1988). The co-occurrence of alcoholism and other psychiatric disorders in the general population and its impact on treatment. *Journal of Studies on Alcohol, 49*, 219–224.

Ilgen, M., McKellar, J., & Tiet, Q. (2005). Abstinence self-efficacy and abstinence 1 year after substance use disorder treatment. *Journal of Consulting and Clinical Psychology, 73*(6), 1175–1180.

Ilgen, M., & Moos, R. (2005). Deterioration following alcohol-use disorder treatment in Project MATCH. *Journal of Studies on Alcohol, 66*(4), 517–525.

Ilgen, M., Tiet, Q., Finney, J., & Moos, R. H. (2006). Self-efficacy, therapeutic alliance, and alcohol-use disorder treatment outcomes. *Journal of Studies on Alcohol, 67*(3), 465–472.

Ingjaldsson, J. T., Laberg, J. C., & Thayer, J. F. (2003). Reduced heart rate variability in chronic alcohol abuse: Relationship with negative mood, chronic thought suppression, and compulsive drinking. *Biological Psychiatry, 54*(12), 1427–1436.

Jellinek, E. M. (1960). *The disease concept of alcoholism.* New Brunswick, NJ: Hillhouse Press.

Jerlhag, E., Egecioglu, E., Dickson, S. L., Douhan, A., Svensson, L., & Engel, J. A. (2007). Ghrelin administration into tegmental areas stimulates locomotor activity and increases extracellular concentration of dopamine in the nucleus accumbens. *Addiction Biology, 12*(1), 6–16.

Kalivas, P. W. (2005). How do we determine which drug-induced neuroplastic changes are important? *Nature Neuroscience, 8*(11), 1440–1439.

Kalivas, P. W., McFarland, K., Bowers, S., Szumlinski, K., Xi, K. X., & Baker, D. (2003). Glutamate transmission and addiction to cocaine. *Annals of the New York Academy of Sciences, 1003,* 169–175.

Kalivas, P. W., Peters, J., & Knackstedt, L. (2006). Animal models and brain circuits in drug addiction. *Molecular Interventions, 6*(6), 339–344.

Kalivas, P. W., Volkow, N., & Seamans, J. (2005). Unmanageable motivation in addiction: A pathology of prefrontal-accumbens glutamate transmission. *Neuron, 45,* 647–650.

Kalivas, P. W., & Volkow, N. D. (2005). The neural basis of addiction: A pathology of motivation and choice. *American Journal of Psychiatry, 162,* 1403–1413.

Kammeier, M. L., Hoffman, H., & Loper, R. G. (1973). Personality characteristics of alcoholics as college freshman and at time of treatment. *Quarterly Journal of Studies on Alcohol, 34,* 390–399.

Knackstedt, L. A., & Kalivas, P. W. (2009). Glutamate and reinstatement. *Current Opinion in Pharmacology, 9,* 59–64.

Knoblich, G., Curtis, D., Faustman, W. O., Zarcone, V., Stewart, S., Mefford, I., & King, R. (1992). Increased CSF HVA with craving in long-term abstinent cocaine abusers. *Biological Psychiatry, 32,* 96–100.

Koob, G. F. (2013). Addiction is a reward deficit and stress surfeit disorder. *Frontiers in Psychiatry, 4*(Article 72), 1–18.

Koob, G. F., Buck, C. L., Cohen, A., Edwards, S., Park, P. E., Schlosburg, J. E.,…George, O. (2014). Addiction as a stress surfeit disorder. *Neuropharmacology, 76*(Pt. B), 370–382.

Kreek, M. J., Bart, G., Lilly, C., LaForge, K. S., & Nielsen, D. A. (2005). Pharmacogenetics and human molecular genetics of opiate and cocaine addictions and their treatments. *Pharmacological Review, 57*(1), 1–26.

Kreek, M. J., Nielsen, D. A., Butelman, E. R., & LaForge, K. S. (2005). Genetic influences on impulsivity, risk taking, stress responsivity and vulnerability to drug abuse and addiction. *Nature Neuroscience, 8*(11), 1450–1457.

Leonard, K., Dunn, N. J., & Jacob, T. (1983). Drinking problems of alcoholics: Correspondence between self and spouse reports. *Addictive Behaviors, 8,* 369–373.

Leyton, M. (2007). Conditioned and sensitized responses to stimulant drugs in humans. *Progress in Neuropsychopharmacology and Biological Psychiatry, 31,* 1601–1613.

Libby, D. J., Worhunsky, P. D., Pilver, C. E., & Brewer, J. A. (2012). Meditation-induced changes in high-frequency heart rate variability predict smoking outcomes. *Frontiers in Human Neuroscience, 6*(Article 54), 1–8.

Ling, J., Stephens, R., & Heffernan, T. M. (2010). Cognitive and psychomotor performance during alcohol hangover. *Current Drug Abuse Reviews, 3,* 80–87.

Littleton, J., Barron, S., Prendergast, M., & Nixon, S. J. (2007). Smoking kills (alcoholics)! Shouldn't we do something about it? *Alcohol and Alcoholism, 42*(3), 167–173.

Littrell, J. (1991a). *Understanding and treating alcoholism: An empirically based clinician's handbook for the treatment of alcoholism.* Hillsdale, NJ: Lawrence Erlbaum.

Littrell, J. (1991b). *Understanding and treating alcoholism: Biological, psychological, and social aspects of alcohol consumption and abuse.* Hillsdale, NJ: Lawrence Erlbaum.

Littrell, J. (2001). What neurobiology has to say about why people abuse alcohol and other drugs. *Journal of Social Work Practice in the Addictions, 1,* 23–40.

Littrell, J. (2010). Perspectives emerging from neuroscience on how people become addicted and what to do about it. *Journal of Social Work Practice in the Addictions, 10,* 229–256.

Littrell, J. (2011). How addiction happens, how change happens, and what social workers need to know to be effective facilitators of change. *Journal of Evidence-Based Social Work Practice, 8*(5), 469–486.

Littrell, J., & Magel, D. (1991). The influence of self-concept on change in client behavior. *Research in Social Work Practice, 1,* 46–67.

Longabaugh, R., Wirtz, P. W., Zweben, A., & Stout, R. L. (1998). Network support for drinking. Alcoholics Anonymous and long-term matching effects. *Addiction, 93,* 141–158.

Lowman, C., Allen, J., Stout, R L., & The Relapse Research Group. (1996). Replication and extension of Marlatt's taxonomy of relapse precipitants: Overview of procedures and results. *Addiction, 91,* S51–S71.

Lüscher, C. (2013). Drugs of abuse. In B. G. Katzung, S. B. Masters, & A. J. Trevor (Eds.), *Basic and clinical pharmacology* (12th ed., pp. 565–580). New York, NY: McGraw Hill.

MacAndrew, C. (1981). What the MAC scale tells us about men alcoholics. An interpretive review. *Journal of Studies on Alcohol, 42,* 604–625.

Martin, T., Christopher, P. J., Houck, J. M., & Moyers, T. B. (2011). The structure of client language and drinking outcomes in Project MATCH. *Psychology of Addictive Behaviors, 25*(3), 439–445.

McClure, E. A., Gipson, C. D., Malcolm, R. J., Kalivas, P. W., & Gray, K. M. (2014). Potential role of N-acetylcysteine in the management of substance use disorders. *CNS Drugs, 28*(2), 95–106.

McFarland, K., Lapish, C. C., & Kalivas, P. W. (2003). Prefrontal glutamate release into the core of the nucleus accumbens mediates cocaine-induced reinstatement of drug-seeking behavior. *Journal of Neuroscience, 23*(8), 3531–3537.

McKay, J. R., Alterman, A. I., Rutherford, M. J., Cacciola, J. S., & McLellan, A. T. (1999). The relationship of alcohol use to cocaine relapse in cocaine dependent patients in an aftercare study. *Journal of Studies on Alcohol, 60*, 76–80.

McLellan, A. T., Hagan, T. A., Levine, M., Meyers, K., Gould, F., Bencivengo, M., . . . Jaffe, J. (1999). Does clinical case management improve outpatient addiction treatment. *Drug and Alcohol Dependence, 55*, 91–103.

McQueen, J., Howe, T. E., Allan, L., Mains, A. L., & Hardy, V. (2011). Brief interventions for heavy alcohol users admitted to general hospital wards [Review]. *Cochrane Library, 8*. Retrieved from http://www.thecochranelibrary.com

Mee-Lee, D., & Shulman, G. D. (2011). The ASAM placement criteria and matching patients to treatment. In C. A. Cavacuiti (Ed.), *Principles of addiction medicine: The essentials*. New York, NY: Lippincott Williams & Wilkins.

Meyers, R. J., Miller, W. R., Smith, J. E., & Tonigan, J. S. (2002). A randomized trial of two methods for engaging treatment-refusing drug users through concerned significant others. *Journal of Consulting and Clinical Psychology, 70*(5), 1182–1185.

Miczek, K. A., Nikulina, E. M., Shimamoto, A., & Covington, H. E. III. (2011). Escalated or suppressed cocaine reward, tegmental BSNF and accumbal dopamine due to episodic or continuous social stress in rats. *Journal of Neuroscience, 31*(27), 9848–9857.

Miller, N. S., & Flaherty, J. A. (2000). Effectiveness of coerced addiction treatment (alternative consequences): A review of the clinical research. *Journal of Substance Abuse Treatment, 18*, 9–16.

Miller, W. R., Benefield, R. G., & Tonigan, J. S. (1993). Enhancing motivation for change in problem drinking: A controlled comparison of two therapist styles. *Journal of Consulting and Clinical Psychology, 61*(3), 455–461.

Miller, W. R., Meyers, R. J., Smith, J. E., & Tonigan, J. S. (1999). Engaging the unmotivated in treatment for alcohol problems: A comparison of three strategies for intervention through family members. *Journal of Consulting and Clinical Psychology, 67*(3), 688–697.

Miller, W. R., & Rollnick, S. (2013). *Motivational interviewing* (3rd ed.). New York, NY: Guilford Press.

Miller, W. R., Westerberg, V. S., Harris, R. J., & Tonigan, J. S. (1996). What predicts relapse? Prospective testing of antecedent models. *Addiction, 91*, S155–S171.

Minnesota Multiphasic Personality Inventor-2. (1989, 2001-revised, updated 2003 and 2009). Minneapolis, MN: University of Minnesota Press. Distributor: Pearson Assessments.

Moberg, D. P., Krause, W. K., & Klein, P. E. (1982). Posttreatment drinking behavior among inpatients from an industrial alcoholism program. *International Journal of the Addictions, 17*, 549–567.

Morgenstern, J., Bux, D. A., Labouvie, E., Blanchard, K. A., & Morgan, T. I. (2002). Examining mechanisms of action in 12-step treatment: The role of 12-step cognitions. *Journal of Studies on Alcohol, 63*(6), 665–672.

Morgenstern, J., Bux, D. A., Labouvie, E., Morgan, T., Blanchard, K. A., & Muench, F. (2003). Examining mechanisms of action in 12-step community outpatient treatment. *Drug and Alcohol Dependence, 72*(3), 237–247.

Morgenstern, J., Labouvie, E., McCrady, B. S., Kahler, C. W., & Frey, R. M. (1997). Affiliation with Alcoholics Anonymous after treatment: A study of its therapeutic effects and mechanisms of action. *Journal of Consulting and Clinical Psychology, 65*(5), 768–777.

Moussawi, K., Pacchioni, A., Moran, M., Olive, M. F., Gass, J. T., Lavin, A., & Kalivas, P. W. (2009). N-acetylcysteine reverses cocaine-induced metaplasticity. *Nature Neuroscience, 12*(2), 182–189.

Moyers, T. B., Martin, T., Houck, J. M., Christopher, P. J., & Tonigan, J. S. (2009). From in-session behaviors to drinking outcomes: A causal chain for motivational interviewing. *Journal of Consulting and Clinical Psychology, 77*(8), 1113–1124.

Muench, F., & Morgenstern, J. (2007). Reducing past harm appraisals during treatment predicts worse substance use outcome. *Alcoholism: Clinical and Experimental Research, 31*(10, Suppl.), 67s–70s.

Musto, D. F. (1973). *The American disease: Origins of narcotic control.* New York, NY: Oxford University Press.

Musto, D. F. (2002). Introduction: Opiate, cocaine, cannabis, and other drugs. In D. Musto (Ed.), *Drugs in America: A documentary history* (pp. 183–193). New York, NY: New York University Press.

National Institute on Alcohol Abuse and Alcoholism. (2014). *Drinking levels defined.* Retrieved from http://www.niaaa.nih.gov/alcohol-health/overview-alcohol-consumption/moderate-binge-drinking

Niv, Y., Daw, N. D., Joel, D., & Dayan, P. (2007). Tonic dopamine: Opportunity costs and the control of response vigor. *Psychopharmacology, 191*, 507–520.

Nordstrom, G., & Berglund, M. (1987). A prospective study of successful long-term adjustment in alcohol dependence: Social drinking versus abstinence. *Journal of Studies on Alcohol, 48*, 229–235.

Orford, J. (1973). A comparison of alcoholics whose drinking is totally uncontrolled and those whose drinking is mainly controlled. *Behavior Research and Therapy, 11*, 565–576.

Orford, J., & Keddie, A. (1986). Abstinence or controlled drinking in clinical practice: Implications at initial assessment. *Addictive Behaviors, 11*, 71–86.

Prochaska, J. O., Norcross, J. C., & DiClemente, C. C. (1994). *Changing for good: A revolutionary six-stage program for overcoming bad habits and moving your life positively forward.* New York, NY: HarperCollins.

Project MATCH Research Group. (1997). Matching alcoholism treatment to client heterogeneity: Project MATCH post-treatment-drinking outcomes. *Journal of Studies on Alcohol, 58,* 7–29.

Project MATCH Research Group. (1998). Matching alcoholism treatments to client heterogeneity. Project MATCH three-year drinking outcomes. *Alcoholism: Clinical and Experimental Research, 22,* 1300–1311.

Rehm, J. (2011). The risks associated with alcohol use and alcoholism. *Alcohol Research Health, 34*(2), 135–143.

Robinson, T. E., & Berridge, K. C. (2008). The incentive sensitization theory of addiction: Some current issues. *Philosophical Transactions of the Royal Society, B, 363,* 3137–3146.

Rosengren, D. B. (2009). *Building motivational interviewing skills: A practitioner workbook.* New York, NY: Guilford Press.

Rossi, J. J., Stach, A., & Bradley, N. J. (1963). Effects of treatment of male alcoholics in a mental hospital: A follow-up study. *Quarterly Journal of Studies on Alcohol, 24,* 91–108.

Roy, M., Roy, A., Williams, J., Weinberger, L., & Smelson, D. (1997). Reduced blue cone electroretinogram in cocaine-withdrawn patients. *Archives of General Psychiatry, 54*(2), 153–156.

Sabia, S., Elbaz, A., Britton, A., Bell, S., Dugravot, A., Shipley, M.,…Singh-Manoux, A. (2014). Alcohol consumption and cognitive decline in early old age. *Neurology, 82,* 332–339.

Salamone, J. D., & Correa, M. (2002). Motivational views of reinforcement: Implications for understanding the behavioral functions of the nucleus accumbens dopamine. *Behavioural Brain Research, 137,* 3–25.

Salamone, J. D., Correa, M., Farrar, S., & Mingote, S. M. (2007). Effort-related functions of nucleus accumbens dopamine and associated forebrain circuits. *Psychopharmacology, 191,* 461–482.

Schaefer, H. H., Sobell, M. B., & Sobell, L. C. (1972). Twelve month follow-up of hospitalized alcoholics given self-confrontation experiences via videotape. *Behavior Therapy, 3,* 283–285.

Schaefer, H. H., Sobell, M. B., & Mills, K. C. (1971). Some sobering data on the use of self-confrontation with alcoholics. *Behavior Therapy, 2,* 28–39.

Schuckit, M. A. (1994). Low level of response to alcohol as a predictor of future alcoholism. *American Journal of Psychiatry, 151*(2), 184–189.

Schuckit, M. A. (2014). A brief history of research on the genetics of alcohol and other drug use disorders. *Journal of Studies on Alcohol and Drugs, 75*(Suppl. 17), 59–67.

Schuckit, M. A., & Tapert, S. (2004). Alcohol. In M. Galanter & H. D. Kleber (Eds.), *Textbook of substance abuse treatment* (3rd ed., pp. 151–166). Washington, DC: American Psychiatric Press.

Schulteis, G., & Koob, G. F. (1996). Reinforcement processes in opiate addiction: A homeostatic model. *Neurochemical Research, 21,* 1437–1454.

Schwarz, S. (2014, May 11). Hooked. *The New York Times Magazine*, pp. 21–25, 40, 48–49.

Segerstrom, S. C., & Solberg Nes, L. (2007). Heart rate variability reflects self-regulatory strength, effort, and fatigue. *Psychological Science, 18*, 275–281.

Shah, J. Y., Friedman, R. S., & Kruglanski, A. W. (2002). Forgetting all else: On the antecedents and consequences of goal shielding. *Journal of Personality and Social Psychology, 83*(6), 1261–1280.

Smith, R. E., Ptacek, J. T., & Smoll, F. L. (1992). Sensation seeking, stress, and adolescent injuries: A test of stress buffering, risk-taking, and coping skills hypotheses. *Journal of Personality and Social Psychology, 62*, 1016–1024.

Sobell, L. C., Cunningham, J. A., & Sobell, M. B. (1996). Recovery from alcohol problems with and without treatment: Prevalence in two population surveys. *American Journal of Public Health, 86*(7), 966–972.

Sobell, L. C., Sobell, M. B., Toneatto, T., & Leo, G. I. (1993). What triggers the resolution of alcohol problems without treatment? *Alcoholism: Clinical and Experimental Research, 17*(2), 217–224.

Stamey, W., & Jankovic, J. (2008). Impulse control disorders and pathological gambling in patients with Parkinson disease. *Neurologist, 14*(2), 89–99.

Stampfer, M. J., Kang, J. H., Chen, J., Cherry, R., & Grodstein, F. (2005). Effects of moderate alcohol consumption on cognitive function in women. *New England Journal of Medicine, 352*(3), 245–253.

Steketee, J. D., & Kalivas, P. W. (2011). Drug wanting: Behavioral sensitization and relapse to drug-seeking behavior. *Pharmacological Reviews, 63*(2), 348–365.

Stinson, F. S., Grant, B. F., Dawson, D. A., Ruan, W. J., Huang, B., & Saha, T. (2006). Comorbidity between DSM-IV alcohol and specific drug use disorders in the United States. *Alcohol Research and Health, 29*(2), 94–106.

Strang, J., Groshkova, T., & Metrebian, N. (2012). New heroin-assisted treatment. *EMCDDA Insights. European Monitoring Centre for Drugs and Drug Addiction.* ISSN 1606–1683. Retrieved from www.emcdda.europa.eu/attachements.cfm/att_154996_EN-Heroin%20Insight.pdf

Tarter, R. E. (2003). Neurobehavioral disinhibition in childhood predicts early age onset of substance use disorder. *American Journal of Psychiatry, 160*, 1078–1085.

Treadway, M. T., & Zald, D. H. (2011). Reconsidering anhedonia in depression: Lesson for translational neuroscience. *Neuroscience and Biobehavioral Reviews, 35*(3), 537–555.

Trice, H. M., & Beyer, J. M. (1984). Work-related outcomes of the constructive-confrontation strategy in a job-based alcoholism program. *Journal of Studies on Alcohol, 45*, 393–404.

Tuchfeld, B. S. (1981). Spontaneous remission in alcoholics: Empirical observations and theoretical implications. *Journal of Studies on Alcohol, 42*, 626–641.

Tversky, A., & Kahneman, D. (1974). Judgments under uncertainty: Heuristics and biases. *Science, 1985*, 1124–1131.

Verdejo-García, A., & Bechara, A. (2009). A somatic-marker theory of addiction. *Neuropharmacology, 56*(Suppl. 1), 48–62.

Verdejo-García, A. J., Lawrence, A. J., & Clark, L. (2008). Impulsivity as a vulnerability marker for substance-use disorders: Review of the findings from high-risk research, problem gamblers and genetic association studies. *Neuroscience and Biobehavioral Reviews, 32,* 777–810.

Vohs, K. D., & Baumeister, R. F. (2004). Understanding self-regulation: An introduction. In R. F. Baumeister & K. D. Vohs (Eds.), *Handbook of self-regulation: Research, theory, and application* (pp. 1–12). New York, NY: Guilford Press.

Volkow, N. D., Fowler, J. S., & Wang, G. J. (2004). The addicted human brain viewed in the light of imaging studies: Brain circuits and treatment strategies. *Neuropharmacology, 47*(Suppl. 1), 3–13.

Volkow, N. D., Frieden, T. R., Hyde, P. S., & Cha, S. S. (2014). Medication-assisted therapies—Tackling the opioid-overdose epidemic. *New England Journal of Medicine, 370,* 2063–2066.

Watson, D., Clark, L. A., McIntrye, C. W., & Hamaker, S. (1992). Affect, personality, and social activity. *Journal of Personality and Social Psychology, 63,* 1011–1025.

Weisner, C., & Schmidt, L. A. (1996). Rethinking access to alcohol treatment. In M. Galanter (Ed.), *Recent developments in alcoholism: Service research in the era of managed care* (pp. 107–156). Washington, DC: American Society of Addiction Medicine.

Wild, T. C., Roberts, A. B., & Cooper, E. L. (2002). Compulsory substance abuse treatment: An overview of recent findings and issues. *European Addiction Research, 8,* 84–93.

Wise, R. A., & Bozarth, M. A. (1987). A psychomotor stimulant theory of addiction. *Psychological Review, 94,* 469–492.

World Health Organization. (1952). *Expert Committee on Mental Health. Alcoholism Subcommittee, second report* (WHO Technical Report Serial No. 48). Geneva: [no. 5543].

Yin, H. H., & Knowlton, B. J. (2006). Addiction and learning in the brain. In R. W. Wiers & W. Stacy (Eds.), *Handbook of implicit cognition and addictions* (pp. 167–184). Thousand Oaks, CA: Sage.

Young, L. J., Lim, M. M., Gingrich, B., & Insel, T. R. (2001). Cellular mechanisms of social attachment. *Hormones and Behavior, 40,* 133–138.

Zywiak, W. H., Stout, R. L., Longbaugh, R., Dyck, I., Connors, G. J., & Maisto, S. A. (2006). Relapse-onset factors in Project MATCH: The relapse questionnaire. *Journal of Substance Abuse Treatment, 31,* 341–345.

9

Children

This chapter covers psychiatric diagnoses that might be applied to children seen in primary care: pediatric bipolar disorder, major depression, attention deficit hyperactivity disorder (ADHD), and posttraumatic stress disorder (PTSD). The diagnoses are discussed in the context of the neuroscience explaining the disorder. The efficacy of current pharmacological treatments along with explanations regarding how they impact physiology are reviewed. Side effects are considered. PTSD is included in the discussion of the treatment of children in foster care. Nonpharmacological treatments for those behaviors that are problematic in a classroom are included in the Attention Deficit Hyperactivity Disorder section. Alternatives to drugs administered for distress in the children themselves are considered at the end of the chapter.

RISE IN MEDICATING CHILDREN

Seven percent of American adolescents are taking some form of psychotropic medication. A total of 3.9% take an antidepressant, 2.8% take a stimulant, 0.8% take anxiolytics, 0.5% take antipsychotics, and 0.4% take mood stabilizers (Olfson, He, & Merikangas, 2013). Among younger children, 3.5% are taking a stimulant (Zuvekas & Vitiello, 2012) and the Centers for Disease Control and Prevention (CDC) has documented the rise of medicating children aged 2 and 3 years (Schwarz, 2014). According to Olfson, Blanco, Wang, Laje, and Correll (2014), for children younger than 13 years, 13.5% of office visits to physicians, including psychiatrists and other specialists, resulted in a mental health diagnosis and 15.42% were given a prescription for a psychotropic drug: 9.15% were for stimulants, 1.73% for antipsychotics, 1.95% for antidepressants, 4.63% for anxiolytics, and 1.0% for a mood stabilizer. For adolescents, 18.73% of office visits to physicians, including psychiatrists and other specialists, resulted in a mental health diagnosis and 20.40% were given a prescription for a psychotropic drug: 9.16% were for stimulants, 3.81% for antipsychotics, 8.26% for antidepressants, 4.13% for anxiolytics, and 2.71% for a mood stabilizer. The rise in prescriptions for antipsychotic drugs is particularly steep among economically disadvantaged children. Poor children are more likely to receive a prescription of a psychotropic drug on an initial visit than are more affluent children. A study of 16 state Medicaid programs in 2007 found that 1.6% of children younger than 19 years were receiving antipsychotic drugs (Medicaid Medical Directors Learning Network and Rutgers Center for Education and Research on Mental Health Therapeutics, 2010).

PEDIATRIC BIPOLAR DISORDER

Prior to the 1990s, there was a widespread agreement that bipolar disorder did not emerge prior to puberty (Anthony & Scott, 1960; Goodwin & Jamison, 2007; Loranger & Levine, 1978). Then, in the 1990s, Joseph Biederman, a full professor of child psychiatry at Harvard University, and his colleagues began arguing that symptoms of conduct disorder and hyperactivity were early signs of bipolar disorder (see Biederman et al., 2000, 2003). Pediatric bipolar disorder was the least frequent diagnosis for hospitalized children in 1996; by 2004, it was the most frequent diagnosis (Blader & Carlson, 2007). (As discussed in Chapter 1, Biederman was investigated by Senator Charles Grassley's Senate committee for receiving large amounts of undeclared money from the pharmaceutical industry.)

In order to bolster their claim that the children they were diagnosing as "bipolar" were correctly diagnosed, Biederman et al. examined the diagnostic status of the parents of these children. Biederman et al. found that many of the parents of the children they had diagnosed with pediatric bipolar disorder also met criteria for bipolar disorder (see review of studies in Littrell & Lyons, 2010a; Wozniak, Biederman, Mundy, Mennin, & Faraone, 1995). In fact, the logic behind the strategy employed by Biederman et al. is based on tenuous assumptions.

The 1994 addition of bipolar II to the *Diagnostic and Statistical Manual of Mental Disorders*, 4th Edition (*DSM-IV*; American Psychiatric Association [APA], 1994) allowed Biederman et al. to adduce evidence that children with pediatric bipolar have parents who have a bipolar pedigree. As discussed in Chapter 7 on bipolar disorder, in the section titled Why Was Bipolar II Added?, there is little reason for believing that bipolar I and bipolar II share the same biological basis. Experts on bipolar disorder find that the genetics for bipolar I and bipolar II are distinct. In the articles on the diagnostic status of the parents of children with pediatric bipolar, Biederman et al. failed to provide information on the percentage of parents who were bipolar I versus bipolar II, nor did they provide information on whether the parents had been hospitalized or displayed classic signs of bipolar disorder (such as spending sprees, hearing voices, grandiose behavior). Thus, the type of bipolar disorder the parents had was never identified and it cannot be concluded that the "bipolar" children have parents with bipolar I. What the studies suggest is that parents and children may share the trait of being energetically exuberant at times.

The profile of adults with bipolar I differs dramatically from the behavioral pattern of children being diagnosed as having pediatric bipolar disorder. Akiskal et al. (2000), leading experts on bipolar disorder, describe persons with bipolar disorder as "warm, people-seeking or extroverted...articulate and eloquent" (p. 12). Promiscuity is a component of manic episodes, which again requires some social skills (Duke & Hochman, 1991). In contrast, children being diagnosed with pediatric bipolar disorder are oppositional, defiant, and prone to violent outbursts (Biederman et al., 2000, 2003; Geller et al., 1995). Biederman et al. describe one of their child patients (Faraone, Biederman, Mennin, Wozniak, & Spencer, 1997): "He exhibited violent outbursts, threatened to kill family members, used vulgar language, and verbalized graphic sexual ideation and graphic sexual action (e.g., rubbing his genitals in public)" (p. 1381). Others find that children with pediatric bipolar disorder exhibit poor social skills and school functioning (Geller et al., 2000; Tillman et al., 2003). Thus, the behaviors characterizing adults with bipolar I differ dramatically from the behaviors exhibited by children who are given the pediatric bipolar diagnosis.

Adult bipolar disorder and childhood bipolar disorder are not only qualitatively different, but the duration of an "episode" is also very different. Mania in adults is episodic, with a return to competent function between episodes. An episode of mania typically lasts 6 weeks to 6 months (Goodwin & Jamison, 2007). Episodes of mania in pediatric bipolar disorder last over 3 years (Craney & Geller, 2003; Tillman et al., 2003). Consistent with other studies, in a large sample of children with bipolar spectrum disorder, Birmaher et al. (2009) report a mean duration of 123.7 weeks for the first episode.

Children being diagnosed as exhibiting "pediatric bipolar" disorder can also be compared to the children of parents who have exhibited a classical bipolar I pattern. There are several research cohorts of children of parents with classic bipolar I disorder that have been followed from grade-school age into early adulthood (see Littrell & Lyons, 2010a for a review). Duffy, Alda, Hajek, and Grof's (2009) cohort is representative of longitudinal studies of children of parents with classical bipolar I disorder. These studies offer additional reasons for doubting whether children currently being diagnosed with pediatric bipolar disorder are the same as persons with classic bipolar I patterns. In the "children-of-bipolar I-parents" cohorts, with high genetic loading for bipolar I disorder, some did develop bipolar disorder themselves. In the Duffy et al. cohort, the children were free of dramatic symptoms until late adolescence. The first episode of a mood disorder was depression, which emerged at a mean age of 17 years. Episodes of depression lasted an average of 6.1 months. When mania did emerge, an episode lasted an average of 1.7 months. Thus, when psychiatric disturbances were seen in those children of parents with bipolar I, the symptoms were qualitatively different from the symptoms in those children currently being diagnosed with pediatric bipolar disorder.

In the Duffy et al. longitudinal cohort study, for those children in whom manic depression emerged, an episode of depression preceded the emergence of mania. Anne Duffy's findings are very consistent with retrospective studies of adults with bipolar I (see Chapter 7, Who Was Right? section) who report that prior to the emergence of a manic episode, they experienced depressive symptoms. In the literature written prior to the pediatric epidemic, the assumption was that bipolar I disorder manifested in early adulthood. Akiskal et al. (1985), prolific contributors to the literature on bipolar illness, concluded "bipolar disorder often begins insidiously in late childhood, adolescence and early adulthood with relatively minor oscillations in mood, most characteristically depressive in nature" (p. 1002).

The Push to Medicate

Kiki Chang and colleagues have been proponents of medicating those exhibiting features of pediatric bipolar disorder (Chang, 2010; Chang,

Howe, Gallelli, & Miklowitz, 2006; Chang & Kowatch, 2007). They refer to Robert Post's notion of kindling and suggest that suppressing symptoms can arrest the kindling process. As discussed in Chapter 7 on bipolar disorder, there is very little evidence to support the existence of a kindling process in bipolar disorder. Moreover, in laboratory studies of kindling seizures (the disorder on which the kindling hypothesis is based), suppressing seizures with drugs does not alter the kindling process. The studies of children with pediatric bipolar disorder who were medicated fail to suggest that early treatment alters long-term outcomes. Geller, Tillman, Bolhofner, and Zimerman (2008) reported on their sample of children with bipolar disorder for whom treatment began at grade-school age and who had reached age 18 years. Although 87.8% had recovered from mania, 73.3% later relapsed. Birmaher et al. followed their sample of children who had been treated for bipolar disorder for 4 years. On average, they were symptomatic for 60% of the follow-up interval; 62.5% relapsed with a mean of 72 weeks following recovery (Birmaher et al., 2006, 2009). In an 8-year follow-up study of 55 children who had been hospitalized for severe mania, 91% experienced at least one relapse, 38% attempted suicide, and 36% transitioned to a diagnosis of schizophrenia spectrum disorder. Treatment with classical antipsychotics was a predictor of poorer outcome in the 8-year follow-up study (Consoli et al., 2014). These findings can be contrasted to the findings in community samples, where most of the children grew out of their childhood mania (Cicero, Epler, & Sher, 2009; Lewinsohn, Klein, & Seeley, 2000). Although it should be noted that Lewinsohn et al. (2000) found that some who were said to be exhibiting symptoms of bipolar disorder at a young age were later diagnosed with antisocial personality disorder and borderline personality disorder.

Side Effects of the Drugs

The side effects of the drugs used to treat bipolar disorder were covered in Chapter 7, "Bipolar Disorders." There are particular concerns about these medications for children. Dickstein et al. (2009) have questioned the efficacy of lithium for reducing bipolar symptoms in children aged 7 to 17 years. In children medicated with lithium, 60% exhibit side effects, including confusion, slurred speech, ataxia, bed-wetting, abdominal discomfort, nausea, and vomiting (Hagino et al., 1995). The fact that lithium is associated with impaired renal concentrating ability in 50% of persons when examined for over 20 years should be particularly concerning for children (Presne et al., 2003). If lithium treatment is initiated at age 6 years, by age 26 years, end-stage renal disease is a significant risk.

Children are at a higher risk of developing the Stevens–Johnson syndrome (life-threatening blistering all over the body) when taking lamotrigine/Lamictal than are adults (Ghaemi & Martin, 2007). Carbamazepine/Tegretol causes impairment on learning and memory tasks (Banu et al., 2007).

As covered in Chapter 6 in the section titled Side Effects With Current Treatments, antipsychotic drugs cause considerable shrinkage of the cortex. Children are at a greater risk of metabolic side effects and weight gain when taking atypical antipsychotic drugs than are adults (Correll & Carlson, 2006; Ratzoni et al., 2002).

The Status of the Diagnosis

The diagnosis of pediatric bipolar disorder was not included in the *DSM-5* (APA, 2013), although no minimal age requirement was added to the adult category. The category of temper dysregulation disorder was added to the *DSM-5*. Presumably, children being diagnosed with pediatric bipolar disorder are better described under the category of temper dysregulation disorder.

MAJOR DEPRESSION

Efficacy of Antidepressants

Children do become depressed. They can have punishing interpersonal problems; they are responsive to the troubles of their parents. The Food and Drug Administration (FDA) has approved fluoxetine/Prozac for the treatment of depression in children. However, the efficacy of antidepressants for the treatment of depression in children is, at best, minimal. Goodman, Murphy, and Storch (2007) noted that only 3 of 15 studies submitted to the FDA evaluating antidepressants in children achieved significant results. Jureidini et al. (2004) conducted a meta-analysis of six published randomized controlled studies evaluating antidepressants in children. Of the six studies, only two were found positive. Jureidini et al. reported, "On 42 reported measures, only 14 showed a statistical advantage for an antidepressant. None of the 10 measures relying on patient reported or parent reported outcomes showed a significant advantage for an antidepressant, so that claims for effectiveness were based entirely on ratings by doctors" (p. 880). In terms of the effect size in the two positive studies, the effect-size value (0.26) was small. Jureidini et al. further explained, "the effect size of 0.26 is equivalent to a very modest 3 to 4 point difference on the scale, which has a range of possible scores from 17 to 113" (p. 880).

The Treatment of Adolescents with Depression Study (TADS) was the largest study of antidepressant treatment of children. It was a government-funded study involving 13 academic centers and 327 adolescents aged 12 to 17 years. Adolescents were randomly assigned to cognitive behavioral therapy (CBT), fluoxetine/Prozac, or a combination. Treatment was evaluated at 12 weeks. In terms of treatment response (defined as a 50% drop in symptoms) at 12 weeks, 73% exhibited a response in the combination group, 62% achieved a response in the Prozac group, and 48% achieved a response in the CBT group. By week 24, the groups did not differ in their response to treatment, and 81% to 86% could be counted as responders. Where the big differences were seen were in the relapse rates. Of those who were categorized as responders at 12 weeks, by 36 weeks, 3.1% had relapsed in the CBT group compared to 25.9% in the Prozac group and 11.5% in the combination group (March et al., 2007; Rohde et al., 2008). (Because drugs were continued in the Prozac and combination groups, the relapses were not explained by drug withdrawal.) Kennard et al. (2009) reported on remission rates in the TADS study (not scoring in the depressed range). By 36 weeks, 64% of the CBT group had recovered, 60% of the combinatoin group had recovered, and 55% of the Prozac group had recovered. The authors acknowledged that, as in adults, the rates of remission without treatment are high with most recovering by 1 year, although they did not report on outcomes in the placebo group.

Side Effects

Antidepressants carry an FDA black-box warning for suicidal ideation in children and adolescents (FDA, 2007). In fact, the TADS study (March et al., 2007) did find that suicidal ideation more often emerged in the drug-treatment groups. By 36 weeks, suicide-associated events occurred in 14.7% of the Prozac group, 8.4% of the combination group, and 6.3% of the CBT group. Most events occurred within the first 12 weeks. The numbers at 12 weeks were 11% in the Prozac group, 4.7% in the combination group, and 4.5% in the CBT group.

Because the TADS study was a manipulated variable, random-assignment study, it offers legitimate evidence that antidepressant treatment induces the emergence of suicidal ideation in adolescents. Data pertinent to the risk of suicidal ideation in adolescents outside of treatment versus in treatment were provided by a study by Nock et al. (2013). The study was retrospective. Nock et al. assessed 6,483 adolescents between the ages of 13 and 18 years recruited from the general population. Of this group, 12% reported only suicidal ideation, 4.0% had planned a suicide, and 4.0% had attempted suicide. Eventually, most of those with suicidal behavior outcomes (planned suicide or attempt) were engaged in treatment at some point in the study (94.2%). The surprise was that most were already in treatment prior to the emergence of the suicidal behavior. According to the authors, "These analyses reveal that most suicidal adolescents (55.3–73.2% across outcomes) receive some form of treatment before the onset of their suicidal behavior—most often mental health or school-based services" (p. 8). Unfortunately, the type of treatment, pharmacotherapy or psychotherapy, was not reported. A surprise finding was that the children whose parents had not gone to college were statistically less likely to experience suicidal behavior.

Antidepressants can precipitate mania and young people are at increased risk (Goldstein et al., 1999; Martin et al., 2004). In addition to antidepressants, stimulants can precipitate manic behavior in children (Delbello et al., 2001; Ghaemi, Hsu, Soldani, & Goodwin, 2003; Martin et al., 2004; Spetie & Arnold, 2007). Antidepressants carry a warning for agitation in children and adolescents (*Physicians' Desk Reference* [PDR], 2012). Selective serotonin reuptake inhibitors (SSRIs) will induce "activation adverse events," including increased activity, impulsivity, insomnia, and disinhibition in 45% of children (Reinblatt, dosReis, Walkup, & Riddle, 2009).

Some of the side effects of the antidepressants that are covered in Chapter 4 are likely to be more distressing for young people than for middle-aged persons. SSRIs are associated with suppression of growth hormone and suppression of growth (Weintrob, Cohen, Klipper-Aurbach, Zadik, & Dickerman, 2002) and decreased bone mineral density (Calarge, Zimmerman, Xie, Kuperman, & Schlechte, 2010). At a time when dating is initiated, weight gain and suppression of sexual function may disrupt the capacity for establishing relationships. Moreover, young people will be entering the childbearing years. The risks of antidepressant use in pregnancy are becoming better known. The incidence of an increased risk for autism, pulmonary hypertension, developmental delays, premature birth, and preeclampsia is established (see Chapter 4, Drug Treatment section). Should a young woman opt to discontinue her antidepressant prior to pregnancy, withdrawal may be a problem. There is very little published data on the duration of withdrawal from antidepressants, although it is more protracted (range of 1 to 52 days) than the duration of withdrawal from heroin (2 to 3 days) or alcohol (at most a week; Haddad, 2001). Haddad (1997, 2001) indicates that 20% to 86% of samples of individuals in withdrawal report dizziness, nausea, lethargy, headache, anxiety, tingling and burning sensations, confusion, tremor, sweating insomnia, irritability, sweating, memory problems, and anorexia. Given that young people are also establishing careers, protracted withdrawal may be very damaging. Additionally, for men, antidepressants suppress sperm production (Akasheh, Sirati, Noshad Kamran, & Sepehrmanesh, 2014). Thus, the potential impact on future family formation is considerable.

ATTENTION DEFICIT HYPERACTIVITY DISORDER

ADHD is diagnosed in the United States at far higher rates than elsewhere on the globe (Hinshaw & Scheffler, 2014). According to the CDC, 11% of children in the age group of 4 to 17 years were diagnosed with ADHD in 2011 (www.cdc.gov/ncbddd/adhd/data.html). In the United States, the lifetime risk of diagnosis in boys is 20% (Schwarz, 2014).

Social factors contribute to whether a child will be diagnosed as having ADHD. A study in Canada found that kindergartners whose birthdays were toward the end of the deadline for starting school were much more likely than children who were almost a year older to receive a diagnosis of ADHD (Morrow et al., 2012). In the United States, in those states that strongly observe "no child left behind" requirements, the rates of ADHD diagnoses are higher. The test scores of children with ADHD diagnoses are not included in the calculations of school performance (Hinshaw &

Scheffler, 2014). Thus, the more school administrators experience pressure for high average test scores, the more likely children are to being diagnosed with ADHD. Although technically a physician provides the diagnosis, teachers and school administrators often initiate the process that results in a diagnosis.

Genetics and Neurobiology

The number of neurobiological routes to problems with attention are many. Many studies find that men with a primary diagnosis of alcoholism were hyperactive children. In adoption studies, the male adopted-out children of alcoholics have a higher incidence of ADHD (Littrell, 1991). Some children who have problems attending are dyslexic and their attention problems resolve when they are given remedial reading instructions (Kibby, Pavawalla, Fancher, Naillon, & Hynd, 2009). Maternal smoking during gestation is associated with a higher risk of ADHD in the offspring (Thapar et al., 2003). Volkow et al. (2009) noted lower levels of the dopamine transporter and lower levels of D2 receptors in the nucleus accumbens of children with ADHD.

Despite the heterogeneity of those receiving the diagnosis, some findings relevant to common neurological underpinnings are emerging. Consistent with the prefrontal cortex's (PFC) role in regulating behavior and emotions, Brennan and Arnsten (2008) review the case for deficit connections with the PFC accounting for inattention and hyperactivity. Researchers at the National Institute of Mental Health (NIMH) have data suggesting that ADHD involves a developmental lag in the growth of neuronal connections of the part of the brain connecting the two hemispheres (the corpus callosum), in the development of lateralization of brain function (Gilliam et al., 2011; Shaw et al., 2009), and in the thickening of the frontal lobe (Hinshaw & Scheffler, 2014).

Killeen, Russell, and Sergeant (2013) have posited the idea that hyperactivity is a problem of supplying fuel to neurons. Glial cells store fuel, which, in response to norepinephrine, is released for the uptake of the neurons. In those with ADHD, the release of fuel (lactic acid) is sluggish. As evidence for their theory, Killeen et al. have shown a correspondence between glial cell function and the pattern of performance displayed by those with ADHD. According to their theory, the excessive movement observed in those with ADHD is compensatory. Given movement, more norepinephrine is released in the brain, which goads the glial cells to release fuel needed by the neurons. If the theory is correct, then increases in movement should increase capacity to attend.

Stimulant Treatment Efficacy

Stimulant drugs are the mainstay of treatment for ADHD. Stimulants do increase dopamine release and, as discussed in Chapter 2, dopamine focuses attention, facilitates memory formation, and increases vigilance (Soetens, D'Hooge, & Hueting, 1993). School performance in the short term does improve. Early on, Rapoport et al. placed an entire grade-school class on stimulant medications. Everyone's vigilance and concentration improved (Sostek, Buchsbaum, & Rapoport, 1980).

Despite the performance-enhancing effects of stimulants, their efficacy may not be uniform across all populations. Drury and Gleason (2012) suggest that stimulants are less effective and carry higher risk of side effects in preschoolers. Moreover, even with treatment, considerable deficits remain in 32% to 64% of treated children (Halperin & Healey, 2011).

Stimulants generally do improve short-term performance, but questions can be asked about whether improvement in the short term translates into long-term improvement. The Multisite Multimodal study funded by the NIMH followed children for 8 years. Some of the children had been medicated, with some continuing with medication, whereas others had never been medicated. At 8 years, there was no difference in school performance among the children who had been medicated and those who had not (Molina et al., 2009). Even for those who had continued on medication, there were few differences between the medicated and nonmedicated children, except for better performance in math among the medicated. In examining the data, Volkow and Swanson (2013) concluded that although short-term benefits with stimulants for ADHD are shown, evidence is lacking for long-term benefits. According to Halperin and Healey's (2011) review, "the collective evidence suggests that stimulant medication use has few, if any, long-term benefits for children with ADHD" (p. 625).

Stimulants inhibit the dopamine transporter. (Inhibition of the dopamine transporter implies that dopamine remains in the synaptic cleft for a longer period of time.) Neurons from the ventral tegmental area (VTA) projecting to the nucleus accumbens have dopamine transporters. Thus, amphetamines potentially can increase activity in the nucleus accumbens. In the discussion of the neurology underlying attention deficits, the role of the PFC has been assigned importance. However, the dopamine projections from the VTA to the PFC do not have dopamine transporters (Morón, Brockington, Wise, Rocha, & Hope, 2002). Because amphetamines (used to treat ADHD) operate on the dopamine transporter, their mechanism of action will not be relevant for the PFC. Thus, stimulant drugs may have the wrong target for actually targeting an underlying issue.

Side Effects

Stimulants suppress growth hormone secretion and, with continued use, may limit height (Faraone, Biederman, Morley, & Spencer, 2008; Zhang, Du, & Zhuang, 2010). They suppress appetite and disrupt sleep (*PDR*, 2012). They can induce motor tics, psychosis, and mania (DelBello et al., 2001; *PDR*, 2012). Concerns about cardiovascular damage with amphetamines have been raised (Kaye, McKetin, Duflou, & Darke, 2007; Treweek, Wee, Koob, Dickerson, & Janda, 2007). Stimulants carry FDA warnings for heart attack and priapism (extended-duration erections) and the FDA recommends that patients be monitored (FDA, 2013, 2014).

Across all species of mammals, young animals engage in playful behavior. Stimulants suppress playfulness (Beatty, Dodge, Dodge, White, & Panksepp, 1982; Trezza, Baarendse, & Vanderschuren, 2010). Researchers have investigated the purpose of playful behavior in young animals. Playfulness facilitates social development and the maturation of the orbitofrontal cortex and PFC (Bell, Pellis, & Kolb, 2010). Playfulness and laughter share circuitry in brain (Gervais & Wilson, 2005). According to reports of stimulant abusers, stimulants focus attention intensely, decreasing relaxed positive mood behaviors such as laughter. Laughter has a social function of promoting cooperation and group cohesion (Gervais & Wilson, 2005). Stimulants thus deprive the uses of playfulness and joyful behavior that contribute to social skill development.

There has been research on the effects of dopamine agonist drugs on the risk for Parkinson's disease. Dopamine neurons from the substantia nigra pars compacta (SNpc) in the midbrain deteriorate in Parkinson's disease. Amphetamines can block the operation of the degrading enzymes (called proteasomes) that clean out inappropriately folded proteins in a cell. In those who use stimulants, inclusion bodies containing aggregated proteins, such as those observed in Parkinson patients, have been found in SNpc neurons as well as damage to dopamine neuron terminals (Castino et al., 2008; Fornai et al., 2008; Lazzeri et al., 2007; Moszczynska & Yamamoto, 2011). In rats, chronic methylphenidate (Ritalin) administration results in "reduced expression of neurotrophic factors, increased neuroinflammation, and a small, but significant loss of SNpc dopamine neurons" (Sadasivan et al., 2012). There is an increased risk of Parkinson's disease in those exposed to methamphetamine (Callaghan, Cunningham, Sykes, & Kish, 2012). Thus, long-term use of stimulants may increase the risk of Parkinson's disease.

Dopamine agonists are addicting drugs. Amphetamine use does decrease D2 receptors in the nucleus accumbens (Dalley, Cardinal, & Robbins, 2004). Nora Volkow, the director of National Institute on Drug Abuse, finds that those with fewer D2 receptors do like cocaine better than those who have more receptors (Volkow et al., 2002). Chapter 8 explains the process of sensitization in which continued exposure to stimulant drugs progressively increases the amount of dopamine released in response to the drug over time. The sensitization process is correlated with increased compulsion to use the drug and increased sensitivity to stressors. Perhaps the routine administration of stimulants to children will fail to induce sensitization. Animal work shows that rodents develop compulsive use patterns for stimulants when they self-administer in novel environments but not when the drug is administered in the home cage with meals (Caprioli et al., 2007; Littrell, 2010). Molina et al. (2013) did not find that those adolescents with long-term exposure to stimulants differed from those who were not in their substance abuse status. The routine administration of stimulants may explain the absence of drug sensitization effects.

Atomoxetine/Strattera is listed as a nonstimulant treatment for ADHD. It blocks the reuptake of norepinephrine. It carries an FDA warning for serious liver injury and suicidal ideation (FDA, 2014). As with other stimulants, it carries a warning for stimulating effects on blood pressure and heart rate (FDA, 2014).

Hard Choices

Stimulant drugs are performance enhancing for everyone. This raises questions for the society. Competition in school is fierce. On college campuses, students have been known to sell their "addies" and snort the contents before examinations (Setlik, Bond, & Ho, 2009). As with drug use in professional sports, the pressure to use in order to compete favorably at top-level universities will probably continue (Cakic, 2009). In fact, a neurophilosopher, Nicole A. Vincent (2014), at a lecture to the Neuroscience Institute at Georgia State raised the question of whether persons with demanding jobs (e.g., surgeons) should be required to take stimulants in order to maximize their performance. Given the pressure to excel in the United States, prioritizing winning over long-term risks will always be a temptation.

Alternatives

Many alternatives are available for improving attention. There is a literature evaluating nicotine patches in the treatment of ADHD. In fact, nicotine patches yield effects equivalent to stimulants on improving attention span and cognitive performance (Levin, Conners, Silva, Canu, & March, 2001). The advantage of nicotine is that it is associated with fewer side effects, although nicotine does increase blood pressure. Cigarettes increase cancer risk and cardiovascular risk; however, the negative effects are attributable to the delivery mechanism. Nicotine patches do not result in escalating levels of consumption (Levin, Simon, & Conners, 2000; Zevin & Benowitz, 2000). Unfortunately, limited information on long-term effects of nicotine patches is available.

According to Killeen et al.'s theory of ADHD, described earlier in the chapter, the problem is a sluggish release of fuel by the glial cells. The excessive movement observed in those with ADHD induces the glial cells to release fuel. This suggests that increasing exercise will increase the attention span of children with ADHD. In fact, exercise does increase cognitive control and academic achievement in children and improves the function in those with ADHD (Halperin & Healy, 2011; Hillman et al., 2009; Pontifex, Saliba, Raine, Picchietti, & Hillman, 2013). (In the Pontifex et al. study, duration of exercise was 20 minutes.) Children can learn multiplication tables while doing jumping jacks. At a Summit Conference on Childhood Obesity at Morehouse School of Medicine in 2013, presenters advocated just that. Perhaps altering some classrooms so that children could run as they learn might solve the American child obesity epidemic as well as improve performance for those with ADHD. In fact, my friend Marlene Zyler, when she worked in the Children's Unit at the Georgia State Hospital, taught a hyperactive 4-year-old to read while running. Marlene distributed the alphabet around the perimeter of the room. She told the child to, for example, to go get the "ba" sound to teach phonemes. Then Marlene and the little boy put the sounds together to determine the word. (Jump up and down, yeah, yeah, yeah.) Some children can learn if you combine reading with gym class.

Directed play is also useful for ADHD (Halperin & Healey, 2011). The Vygosky method was developed by a contemporary of Piaget. Activities, including having children practice carrying a bell without letting it ring, and having children practice singing a song before responding, are used as strategies for increasing cognitive control (Bodrova & Leony, 1996). Pretending to be the teacher forces children to stay in role and furthers the development of cognitive control. Interventions based on the Vygosky method were particularly likely to improve the behavior of children with the highest levels of initial inattention (Diamond & Lee, 2011). In line with exercises for increasing cognitive control, mindfulness meditation (discussed in Chapter 4) does increase cognitive control in adults (Larson, Steffen, & Primosch, 2013). Mindfulness meditation has been shown to improve performance in children with ADHD (Searight, Robertson, Smith, Perkins, & Searight, 2012; Zylowska et al., 2008).

Omega-3s are found in lower levels in children with ADHD and dietary interventions may ameliorate symptoms (Freeman et al., 2006; Gow, Vallee-Tourangeau, et al., 2013a; Gow, Sumich, et al., 2013). In a study of pediatric bipolar disorder, Wozniak et al. (2007) did find that, with children who were not on medication, taking omega-3s did decrease manic symptoms. Sleep deprivation increases impulsivity in children (Gruber, Cassoff, Frenette, Wiebe, & Carrier, 2012); so ensuring adequate sleep is important. Pediatrician Bos Ravenel (2013) tests children with symptoms of ADHD for allergies to gluten and for alleles for improper processing of methionine and use of folate (see discussion in Chapter 4, "Depression"). Dietary modifications do improve the behavior of children with enzyme deficiencies. In fact, in the United Kingdom, the guidelines suggest that children be treated first with dietary modifications, and parental instruction on consistency of rules before stimulant medications is employed (Murphy et al., 2014).

The Triple Positive Program of family intervention was designed to assist parents to be more confident and consistent so that annoying behaviors in their children could be ameliorated (Prinz, Sanders, Shapiro, Whitaker, & Lutzker, 2009; Sanders, 2008; Turner & Sanders, 2006). Broadly based on behavioral principles of Albert Bandura and Gerald Patterson, the program also includes elements of public health. Sessions with parents are held to discuss age-appropriate expectations. Although there is respect for cultural variations in desired goals for children, information on what can be expected from children at various age levels is also provided. The aim is to involve as many families in the community as possible so that contagion in emulating good parental practices can develop. Phone support is provided. There are websites for service providers (www.triplep.org; www.triplep.net).

With regard to assisting parents in the Triple Positive Program, parents are coached in being consistent and making requests without shouting or engaging in extended lecturing. They are taught emotional regulation skills so that they maximize their own cognitive capacities when approaching their children. Other strategies include selecting ground rules for specific situations; giving clear, calm, age-appropriate instructions and requests; presenting logical consequences; and using time-out and planned ignoring. Children are taught emotional regulation skills, such as breathing deeply to regain calm, avoiding catastrophizing (e.g., "I will never get to go outside again"), and taking time-outs.

FOSTER CARE

The number of children in foster care receiving antipsychotic drugs is particularly notable. According to the Medicaid Medical Directors Learning Network and Rutgers Center for Education and Research on Mental Health Therapeutics (2010), 12.37% of children in foster care are being treated with antipsychotic drugs. dosReis et al. (2011) examined prescriptions for 16,969 children younger than 20 years in a Mid-Atlantic state Medicaid Program. For foster children not awaiting adoption, 19% were prescribed multiple antipsychotic drugs and 24% of those awaiting adoption were receiving multiple antipsychotics. Although the numbers of those children in foster care receiving antipsychotics are particularly striking, higher percentages of children in foster care are receiving all classes of psychotropics (Breland-Noble et al., 2004; dosReis, Zito, Safer, & Soeken, 2001; Littrell & Lyons, 2010b; Raghavan & McMillen, 2008). With regard to psychiatric drugs, law professor Angela Burton (2010) reviews the medication of children in foster care in an article entitled "They Use It Like Candy." She argues that obstreperous children are being restrained with these drugs in violation of international law.

To receive a prescription for antipsychotic medication, the diagnosis does not seem to matter. Of the children in foster care with prescriptions for an antipsychotic, dosReis et al. (2011) found that 53% had a diagnosis of ADHD, 34% had a diagnosis of depression, 21% had a diagnosis of bipolar disorder, and 5% had a diagnosis of schizophrenia. In terms of demographic predictors of receiving an antipsychotic, being male and African American increased the probability. Many of the children being prescribed antipsychotics also had prescriptions for other classes of drugs as well. Consistent with the dosReis et al. study, another recent study also found that children in foster care with ADHD diagnoses were often medicated with antipsychotics (Burcu, Zito, Ibe, & Safer, 2014). A particular comment by a child psychiatrist suggesting what can underlie antipsychotic prescriptions was illuminating. I was a participant at a conference on the medication of children in Georgia's foster care system at the Barton Law Clinic at Emory University on April 12, 1202. As a member of the conference panel, the child psychiatrist stated, "child psychiatrists medicate symptoms, not diagnoses." Apparently, some psychiatrists feel justified in restraining children so that their caretakers can have an easier time.

The medication of foster children, particularly with antipsychotics, has drawn attention from the U.S. Congress and national television. The Washington state Medicaid Director Jeffrey Thompson organized the Medicaid Medical Directors Learning Network (2010) to examine the practice of prescribing prescriptions of strong medications for children in foster care. Senators Charles Grassley and Mary Landrieu developed the Senate Caucus on Foster Care Youth (Samuels, 2011). On December 1, 2011, Senator Tom Carper of Delaware convened the Senate Sub-Committee on Financial Management, Government Information, Federal Services, and International Security to hear expert testimony and to discuss the findings of the Government Accounting Office on a five-state survey on the extent of medicating children in foster care. The Public Broadcasting

Service program *The Watch List* (2011) aired "The Medication of Foster Children." Diane Sawyer and Sharyn Alfonsi of ABC News, during the first week of December 2011, ran a series on the medication of children in foster care (Sawyer & Alfonsi, 2011).

In September 2011, Congress passed the Child and Family Services Improvement and Innovation Act. States applying for certain child welfare grants are required to establish protocols for appropriate use and monitoring of psychotropic drugs prescribed for children. The American Academy of Child and Adolescent Psychiatry requires obtaining informed consent for medical treatment of children (Kutz, 2011). For children in foster care, ambiguity exists on who might be authorized to provide informed consent. According to Sato's (2011) testimony at Tom Carper's Sub-Committee hearing, states "had to abandon an attempt to strengthen the hand of foster care workers in these situations, when it became clear that BA/BS or MSW educated workers would face significant liability issues when disagreeing with prescribers." The financial pressures on prescribers to continue medicating children with strong medications are great. Many state Medicaid programs allow more psychiatric visits for children with extreme diagnoses. Extreme diagnoses can entitle children to meet criteria for Supplemental Security Income through the Social Security Administration. Given extreme diagnoses, it is harder to argue for restrained prescribing.

Posttraumatic Stress Disorder

For all children in foster care who are exhibiting symptoms, the diagnosis of PTSD cannot be ruled out. All children in foster care have experienced the trauma of being removed from their parents. For many, they will have experienced physical abuse, mental abuse, or witnessed horrifying violence. The symptoms of PTSD not only include dysphoria and heightened response to signals of alarm, but also, as in returning soldiers, irritability and violence have been noted (Tyre, 2004). The American Academy of Child and Adolescent Psychiatry recommends against medicating PTSD in children (Gleason et al., 2007).

Psychiatrists Bruce Perry and Maia Szalavitz (2012), in their book *The Boy Who Was Raised as a Dog*, describe Perry's experience in working with severely traumatized children. Although some children received individual therapy, for the most part, this type of traditional weekly talk therapy (as provided for adults) was not very effective. In fact, Perry reports that discussing past trauma at scheduled times can exacerbate the child's symptomatic behavior. Perry works with the caregivers of traumatized children. Caregivers are taught to comfort small children when they are symptomatic. Experiencing an environment of supportive caregivers can ameliorate distressing experiences as well as increasing expectations of the children to the possibility of establishing supportive relationships.

For older children in foster care, Pace et al. (2012; Reddy et al., 2012) trained children in compassion meditation. (In compassion meditation, people focus on wishing good things to particular individuals and broaden it to include good wishes for the world.) Pace et al. found that training in compassion meditation resulted in improvements in both inflammatory markers and in behavior. Rather than exhibiting acting-out behavior, the children trained in compassion meditation developed skills in conflict resolution.

Sometimes children in foster care and elsewhere may struggle with anxiety disorders. Wilson and Lyon (2013) offer specific techniques for working with anxious children and their caregivers in their book *Anxious Kids, Anxious Parents*. At Wilson's website (anxieties.com), a version of the book written for older children can be downloaded.

GENERAL ALTERNATIVES FOR CHILDREN

In Chapter 4, various interventions for increasing heart rate variability, for decreasing inflammation, and for decreasing symptoms of anxiety and depression were described. Although small children might not be easy converts to yoga and meditation, physical activity in the context of games is particularly suitable for youth of all ages. Group activities that emphasize cooperation can help in teaching social skills. Additionally, attention to diet is important. Not only might omega-3 consumption be increased, but inflammatory foods (high-fat and high-fructose foods) should be avoided.

It should be noted that the guidelines for the treatment of depression and ADHD issued by the UK National Institute for Health and Care Excellence recommend against medications as a first-line alternative. In the United States, the American Academy of Pediatrics and the American College of Child and Adolescent Psychiatry have issued far more permissive guidelines for medications (Murphy et al., 2014). (According to child psychiatrist, Vicki Martin, MD, who blogs for Mad in America, the bulk of the training in child psychiatry is concentrated on medications.) Although the rates of childhood depression and ADHD are roughly equivalent in the United Kingdom and the United States, children in the United States are far more likely to be medicated (Murphy et al., 2014). Murphy et al. (2014) recognize the discrepancy between the U.S. and U.K. recommendations and suggest that time will tell which is the better course of action. As with adults, alternative treatments to medications are emerging for children. Many of these alternatives (diet and exercise) not only improve functioning but also are good for physical health.

REFERENCES

Akasheh, G., Sirati, L., Noshad Kamran, A. R., & Sepehrmanesh, Z. (2014). Comparison of the effect of sertraline with behavioral therapy on semen parameters in men with primary premature ejaculation. *Urology, 83*(4), 800–804.

Akiskal, H. S., Bourgeois, M. L., Angst, J., Post, R., Möller, H., & Hirschfeld, R. (2000). Re-evaluating the prevalence of and diagnostic composition within the broad clinical spectrum of bipolar disorders. *Journal of Affective Disorders, 59*(Suppl. 1), 5–30.

Akiskal, H. S., Downs, J., Jordan, P., Watson, S., Daugherty, D., & Pruitt, D. B. (1985). Affective disorders in referred children and younger siblings of manic-depressives. Mode of onset and prospective course. *Archives of General Psychiatry, 42*(10), 996–1003.

American Psychiatric Association. (1994). *Diagnostic and statistical manual of mental disorders* (4th ed.). Washington, DC: Author.

American Psychiatric Association. (2013). *Diagnostic and statistical manual of mental disorders* (5th ed.). Arlington, VA: American Psychiatric Press.

Anthony, J., & Scott, P. (1960). Manic-depressive psychosis in childhood. *Journal of Child Psychology and Psychiatry, 4*, 53–72.

Banu, S. H., Jahan, M., Koli, U. K., Ferdousi, S., Khan, N. Z., & Neville, B. (2007). Side effects of phenobarbital and carbamazepine in childhood epilepsy: Randomised controlled trial. *British Medical Journal, 334*(7605), 1207.

Beatty, W. W., Dodge, A. M., Dodge, L. J., White, K., & Panksepp, J. (1982). Psychomotor stimulants, social deprivation and play in juvenile rats. *Pharmacology, Biochemistry, and Behavior, 16*(3), 417–422.

Bell, H. C., Pellis, S. M., & Kolb, B. (2010). Juvenile peer play experience and the development of the orbitofrontal and medial prefrontal cortices. *Behavioural Brain Research, 207*(1), 7–13.

Biederman, J., Mick, E., Faraone, S. V., Spencer, T., Wilens, T. E., & Wozniak, J. (2000). Pediatric mania: A developmental subtype of bipolar disorder? *Biological Psychiatry, 48*(6), 458–466.

Biederman, J., Mick, E., Wozniak, J., Monuteaux, M. C., Galdo, M., & Faraone, S. V. (2003). Can a subtype of conduct disorder linked to bipolar disorder be identified? Integration of findings from the Massachusetts General Hospital Pediatric Psychopharmacology Research Program. *Biological Psychiatry, 53*(11), 952–960.

Birmaher, B., Axelson, D., Goldstein, B., Strober, M., Gill, M. K., Hunt, J.,... Keller, M. (2009). Four-year longitudinal course of children and adolescents with bipolar spectrum disorders: The Course and Outcome of Bipolar Youth (COBY) study. *American Journal of Psychiatry, 166*(7), 795–804.

Birmaher, B., Axelson, D., Strober, M., Gill, M. K., Valeri, S., Chiappetta, L.,... Keller, M. (2006). Clinical course of children and adolescents with bipolar spectrum disorders. *Archives of General Psychiatry, 63*(2), 175–183.

Blader, J. C., & Carlson, G. A. (2007). Increased rates of bipolar disorder diagnoses among U.S. child, adolescent, and adult inpatients, 1996–2004. *Biological Psychiatry, 62*(2), 107–114.

Bodrova, E., & Leony, D. J. (1996). *Tools of the mind: The Vygotskian approach to early childhood education.* Columbus, OH: Merrill.

Breland-Noble, A. M., Elbogen, E. B., Farmer, E. M., Dubs, M. S., Wagner, H. R., & Burns, B. J. (2004). Use of psychotropic medications by youths in therapeutic foster care and group homes. *Psychiatric Services, 55*(6), 706–708.

Brennan, A. R., & Arnsten, A. F. (2008). Neuronal mechanisms underlying attention deficit hyperactivity disorder: The influence of arousal on prefrontal cortical function. *Annals of the New York Academy of Sciences, 1129*, 236–245.

Burcu, M., Zito, J. M., Ibe, A., & Safer, D. J. (2014). Atypical antipsychotic use among Medicaid-insured children and adolescents: Duration, safety, and monitoring implications. *Journal of Child and Adolescent Psychopharmacology, 24*(3), 112–119.

Burton, A. O. (2010). "They use it like candy"—How the prescription of psychotropic drugs to state-involved children violates international law. *Brooklyn Journal of International Law, 35*, 454–513.

Cakic, V. (2009). Smart drugs for cognitive enhancement: Ethical and pragmatic considerations in the era of cosmetic neurology. *Journal of Medical Ethics, 35*(10), 611–615.

Calarge, C. A., Zimmerman, B., Xie, D., Kuperman, S., & Schlechte, J. A. (2010). A cross-sectional evaluation of the effect of risperidone and selective serotonin reuptake inhibitors on bone mineral density in boys. *Journal of Clinical Psychiatry, 71*(3), 338–347.

Callaghan, R. C., Cunningham, J. K., Sykes, J., & Kish, S. J. (2012). Increased risk of Parkinson's disease in individuals hospitalized with conditions related to the use of methamphetamine or other amphetamine-type drugs. *Drug and Alcohol Dependence, 120*(1–3), 35–40.

Caprioli, D., Paolone, G., Celentano, M., Testa, A., Nencini, P., & Badiani, A. (2007). Environmental modulation of cocaine self-administration in the rat. *Psychopharmacology, 192*(3), 397–406.

Castino, R., Lazzeri, G., Lenzi, P., Bellio, N., Follo, C., Ferrucci, M.,...Isidoro, C. (2008). Suppression of autophagy precipitates neuronal cell death following low doses of methamphetamine. *Journal of Neurochemistry, 106*(3), 1426–1439.

Chang, K., Howe, M., Gallelli, K., & Miklowitz, D. (2006). Prevention of pediatric bipolar disorder: Integration of neurobiological and psychosocial processes. *Annals of the New York Academy of Sciences, 1094*, 235–247.

Chang, K., & Kowatch, R. A. (2007). Is this child bipolar? What's needed to improve diagnosis? *Current Psychiatry, 6*(10), 23–33.

Chang, K. D. (2010). Course and impact of bipolar disorder in young patients. *Journal of Clinical Psychiatry, 71*(2), e05.

Child and Family Services Improvement and Innovation Act, Pub. L. No. 112–134, H. R. 2883, S. 1013 (2011). Retrieved from http://www.govtrack.us/congress/bills/112/hr2883

Cicero, D. C., Epler, A. J., & Sher, K. J. (2009). Are there developmentally limited forms of bipolar disorder? *Journal of Abnormal Psychology, 118*(3), 431–447.

Consoli, A., Brunelle, J., Bodeau, N., Louët, E., Deniau, E., Perisse, D.,...Cohen, D. (2014). Diagnostic transition towards schizophrenia in adolescents with severe bipolar disorder type I: An 8-year follow-up study. *Schizophrenia Research, 159*(2–3), 284–291.

Correll, C. U., & Carlson, H. E. (2006). Endocrine and metabolic adverse effects of psychotropic medications in children and adolescents. *Journal of the American Academy of Child and Adolescent Psychiatry, 45*(7), 771–791.

Craney, J. L., & Geller, B. (2003). A prepubertal and early adolescent bipolar disorder-I phenotype: Review of phenomenology and longitudinal course. *Bipolar Disorders, 5*(4), 243–256.

Dalley, J. W., Cardinal, R. N., & Robbins, T. W. (2004). Prefrontal executive and cognitive functions in rodents: Neural and neurochemical substrates. *Neuroscience and Biobehavioral Reviews, 28*(7), 771–784.

DelBello, M. P., Soutullo, C. A., Hendricks, W., Niemeier, R. T., McElroy, S. L., & Strakowski, S. M. (2001). Prior stimulant treatment in adolescents with bipolar disorder: Association with age at onset. *Bipolar Disorders, 3*(2), 53–57.

Diamond, A., & Lee, K. (2011). Interventions shown to aid executive function development in children 4 to 12 years old. *Science, 333*(6045), 959–964.

Dickstein, D. P., Towbin, K. E., Van Der Veen, J. W., Rich, B. A., Brotman, M. A., Knopf, L.,…Leibenluft, E. (2009). Randomized double-blind placebo-controlled trial of lithium in youths with severe mood dysregulation. *Journal of Child and Adolescent Psychopharmacology, 19*(1), 61–73.

dosReis, S., Yoon, Y., Rubin, D. M., Riddle, M. A., Noll, E., & Rothbard, A. (2011). Antipsychotic treatment among youth in foster care. *Pediatrics, 128*(6), e1459–e1466.

dosReis, S., Zito, J. M., Safer, D. J., & Soeken, K. L. (2001). Mental health services for youths in foster care and disabled youths. *American Journal of Public Health, 91*(7), 1094–1099.

Drury, S. S., & Gleason, M. M. (2012). A delicate brain: Ethical and practical considerations for the use of medications in very young children. *Psychiatric Times, 29*(3), 1–6.

Duffy, A., Alda, M., Hajek, T., & Grof, P. (2009). Early course of bipolar disorder in high-risk offspring: Prospective study. *British Journal of Psychiatry, 195*(5), 457–458.

Duke, P., & Hochman, G. (1991). *A brilliant madness: Living with manic-depressive illness.* New York, NY: Bantam Books.

Faraone, S. V., Biederman, J., Mennin, D., Wozniak, J., & Spencer, T. (1997). Attention-deficit hyperactivity disorder with bipolar disorder: A familial subtype? *Journal of the American Academy of Child and Adolescent Psychiatry, 36*(10), 1378–1387; discussion 1387.

Faraone, S. V., Biederman, J., Morley, C. P., & Spencer, T. J. (2008). Effect of stimulants on height and weight: A review of the literature. *Journal of the American Academy of Child and Adolescent Psychiatry, 47*(9), 994–1009.

Food and Drug Administration. (2007, May 2). *FDA proposes new warnings about suicidal thinking, behavior in young adults who take antidepressant medications.* News & Events. Retrieved from http://www.fda.gov/NewsEvents/Newsroom/PressAnnouncements/2007/ucm108905.htm

Food and Drug Administration. (2013). *FDA drug safety communication: FDA warns of rare risk of long-lasting erections in males taking methylphenidate ADHD medications and has approved label changes.* Retrieved from http://www.fda.gov/Drugs/DrugSafety/InformationbyDrugClass/ucm283449.htm

Food and Drug Administration. (2014). *Strattera (atomoxetine hydrochloride capsule).* Retrieved from http://www.fda.gov/safety/medwatch/safetyinformaiton/ucm223889.htm

Fornai, F., Lenzi, P., Capobianco, L., Iacovelli, L., Scarselli, P., Lazzeri, G., & De Blasi, A. (2008). Involvement of dopamine receptors and beta-arrestin in metamphetamine-induced inclusions formation in PC12 cells. *Journal of Neurochemistry, 105*(5), 1939–1947.

Freeman, M. P., Hibbeln, J. R., Wisner, K. L., Davis, J. M., Mischoulon, D., Peet, M.,...Stoll, A. L. (2006). Omega-3 fatty acids: Evidence basis for treatment and future research in psychiatry. *Journal of Clinical Psychiatry, 67*(12), 1954–1967.

Geller, B., Bolhofner, K., Craney, J. L., Williams, M., DelBello, M. P., & Gundersen, K. (2000). Psychosocial functioning in a prepubertal and early adolescent bipolar disorder phenotype. *Journal of the American Academy of Child and Adolescent Psychiatry, 39*(12), 1543–1548.

Geller, B., Sun, K., Zimerman, B., Luby, J., Frazier, J., & Williams, M. (1995). Complex and rapid-cycling in bipolar children and adolescents: A preliminary study. *Journal of Affective Disorders, 34*(4), 259–268.

Geller, B., Tillman, R., Bolhofner, K., & Zimerman, B. (2008). Child bipolar I disorder: Prospective continuity with adult bipolar I disorder; characteristics of second and third episodes; predictors of 8-year outcome. *Archives of General Psychiatry, 65*(10), 1125–1133.

Gervais, M., & Wilson, D. S. (2005). The evolution and functions of laughter and humor: A synthetic approach. *Quarterly Review of Biology, 80*(4), 395–430.

Ghaemi, S. N., Hsu, D. J., Soldani, F., & Goodwin, F. K. (2003). Antidepressants in bipolar disorder: The case for caution. *Bipolar Disorders, 5*(6), 421–433.

Ghaemi, S. N., & Martin, A. (2007). Defining the boundaries of childhood bipolar disorder. *American Journal of Psychiatry, 164*(2), 185–188.

Gilliam, M., Stockman, M., Malek, M., Sharp, W., Greenstein, D., Lalonde, F.,...Shaw, P. (2011). Developmental trajectories of the corpus callosum in attention-deficit/hyperactivity disorder. *Biological Psychiatry, 69*(9), 839–846.

Gleason, M. M., Egger, H. L., Emslie, G. J., Greenhill, L. L., Kowatch, R. A., Lieberman, A. F.,...Zeanah, C. H. (2007). Psychopharmacological treatment for very young children: Contexts and guidelines. *Journal of the American Academy of Child and Adolescent Psychiatry, 46*(12), 1532–1572.

Goldstein, T. R., Frye, M. A., Denicoff, K. D., Smith-Jackson, E., Leverich, G. S., Bryan, A. L.,...Post, R. M. (1999). Antidepressant discontinuation-related mania: Critical prospective observation and theoretical implications in bipolar disorder. *Journal of Clinical Psychiatry, 60*(8), 563–567; quiz 568.

Goodwin, F. K., & Jamison, K. R. (2007). *Manic-depressive illness: Bipolar disorders and recurrent depression* (2nd ed.). New York, NY: Oxford Press.

Goodman, W. K., Murphy, T. K., & Storch, E. A. (2007). Risk of adverse behavioral effects with pediatric use of antidepressants. *Psychopharmacology, 191*(1), 87–96.

Gow, R. V., Sumich, A., Vallee-Tourangeau, F., Crawford, M. A., Ghebremeskel, K., Bueno, A. A.,...Rubia, K. (2013). Omega-3 fatty acids are related to abnormal emotion processing in adolescent boys with attention deficit hyperactivity disorder. *Prostaglandins, Leukotrienes and Essential Fatty Acids, 88*(6), 419–429.

Gow, R. V., Vallee-Tourangeau, F., Crawford, M. A., Taylor, E., Ghebremeskel, K., Bueno, A. A.,...Rubia, K. (2013). Omega-3 fatty acids are inversely related to callous and unemotional traits in adolescent boys with attention deficit hyperactivity disorder. *Prostaglandins, Leukotrienes and Essential Fatty Acids, 88*(6), 411–418.

Gruber, R., Cassoff, J., Frenette, S., Wiebe, S., & Carrier, J. (2012). Impact of sleep extension and restriction on children's emotional liability and impulsivity. *Pediatrics, 130*(5), e1155–e1161.

Haddad, P. (1997). Newer antidepressants and the discontinuation syndrome. *Journal of Clinical Psychiatry, 58*(Suppl. 7), 17–21; discussion 22.

Haddad, P. M. (2001). Antidepressant discontinuation syndromes. *Drug Safety, 24*(3), 183–197.

Hagino, O. R., Weller, E. B., Weller, R. A., Washing, D., Fristad, M. A., & Kontras, S. B. (1995). Untoward effects of lithium treatment in children aged four through six years. *Journal of the American Academy of Child and Adolescent Psychiatry, 34*(12), 1584–1590.

Halperin, J. M., & Healey, D. M. (2011). The influences of environmental enrichment, cognitive enhancement, and physical exercise on brain development: Can we alter the developmental trajectory of ADHD? *Neuroscience and Biobehavioral Reviews, 35*(3), 621–634.

Hillman, C. H., Pontifex, M. B., Raine, L. B., Castelli, D. M., Hall, E. E., & Kramer, A. F. (2009). The effect of acute treadmill walking on cognitive control and academic achievement in preadolescent children. *Neuroscience, 159*(3), 1044–1054.

Hinshaw, S. P., & Scheffler, R. M. (2014). *The ADHD explosion: Myths, medication, and money.* New York, NY: Oxford University Press.

Jureidini, J. N., Doecke, C. J., Mansfield, P. R., Haby, M. M., Menkes, D. B., & Tonkin, A. L. (2004). Efficacy and safety of antidepressants for children and adolescents. *British Medical Journal, 328*(7444), 879–883.

Kaye, S., McKetin, R., Duflou, J., & Darke, S. (2007). Methamphetamine and cardiovascular pathology: A review of the evidence. *Addiction, 102*(8), 1204–1211.

Kennard, B. D., Silva, S. G., Tonev, S., Rohde, P., Hughes, J. L., Vitiello, B.,...March, J. (2009). Remission and recovery in the Treatment for Adolescents with Depression Study (TADS): Acute and long-term outcomes. *Journal of the American Academy of Child and Adolescent Psychiatry, 48*(2), 186–195.

Kibby, M. Y., Pavawalla, S. P., Fancher, J. B., Naillon, A. J., & Hynd, G. W. (2009). The relationship between cerebral hemisphere volume and receptive language functioning in dyslexia and attention-deficit hyperactivity disorder (ADHD). *Journal of Child Neurology, 24*(4), 438–448.

Killeen, P. R., Russell, V. A., & Sergeant, J. A. (2013). A behavioral neuroenergetics theory of ADHD. *Neuroscience and Biobehavioral Reviews, 37*(4), 625–657.

Kutz, G. D. (2011, December 1). United States Accountability Office testimony before the Subcommittee on Federal Financial Management, Government Information, Federal Services, and International Security, Committee on Homeland Security and Governmental Affairs, U.S. Senate. *Congressional Record, 157*(183) (Thursday, December 1, 2011) [Daily Digest] [pp. D1299–D1300].

Larson, M. J., Steffen, P. R., & Primosch, M. (2013). The impact of a brief mindfulness meditation intervention on cognitive control and error-related performance monitoring. *Frontiers in Human Neuroscience, 7,* 308.

Lazzeri, G., Lenzi, P., Busceti, C. L., Ferrucci, M., Falleni, A., Bruno, V.,...Fornai, F. (2007). Mechanisms involved in the formation of dopamine-induced intracellular bodies within striatal neurons. *Journal of Neurochemistry, 101*(5), 1414–1427.

Levin, E. D., Conners, C. K., Silva, D., Canu, W., & March, J. (2001). Effects of chronic nicotine and methylphenidate in adults with attention deficit/hyperactivity disorder. *Experimental and Clinical Psychopharmacology, 9*(1), 83–90.

Levin, E. D., Simon, B. B., & Conners, C. K. (2000). Nicotine effects and attention-deficit/hyperactivity disorder. In M. Piasecki & P. A. Newhouse (Eds.), *Nicotine in psychiatry: Psychopathology and emerging therapeutics* (pp. 203–214). New York, NY: American Psychiatric Press.

Lewinsohn, P. M., Klein, D. N., & Seeley, J. R. (2000). Bipolar disorder during adolescence and young adulthood in a community sample. *Bipolar Disorders, 2*(3, Pt. 2), 281–293.

Littrell, J. (1991). *Understanding and treating alcoholism: Biological, psychological, and social aspects of alcohol consumption and abuse.* Hillsdale, NJ: LEA Press.

Littrell, J. (2001). What neurobiology has to say about why people abuse alcohol and other drugs. *Journal of Social Work Practice in the Addictions, 1,* 23–40.

Littrell, J., & Lyons, P. (2010a). Pediatric bipolar disorder: Part I—Is it related to classical bipolar? *Children and Youth Services Review, 32*(7), 945–964.

Littrell, J., & Lyons, P. (2010b). Pediatric bipolar disorder: An issue for child welfare. *Children and Youth Services Review, 32*(7), 965–973.

Loranger, A. W., & Levine, P. M. (1978). Age at onset of bipolar affective illness. *Archives of General Psychiatry, 35*(11), 1345–1348.

March, J. S., Silva, S., Petrycki, S., Curry, J., Wells, K., Fairbank, J.,...Severe, J. (2007). The Treatment for Adolescents With Depression Study (TADS): Long-term effectiveness and safety outcomes. *Archives of General Psychiatry, 64*(10), 1132–1143.

Martin, A., Young, C., Leckman, J. F., Mukonoweshuro, C., Rosenheck, R., & Leslie, D. (2004). Age effects on antidepressant-induced manic conversion. *Archives of Pediatrics & Adolescent Medicine, 158*(8), 773–780.

Medicaid Medical Directors Learning Network and Rutgers Center for Education and Research on Mental Health Therapeutics. (2010). *Antipsychotic medication use in Medicaid children and adolescents: Report and resource guide from a 16-state study.* MMDLN/Rutgers CERTs, Publication 1. Retrieved from http://rci.rutgers.edu/~cseap/MMDLNAPKIDS/Antipsychotic_Use_in_Medicaid_Children_Report_and_Resource_Guide_Final.pdf

Molina, B. S., Hinshaw, S. P., Eugene Arnold, L., Swanson, J. M., Pelham, W. E., Hechtman, L.,... MTA Cooperative Group. (2013). Adolescent substance use in the multimodal treatment study of attention-deficit/hyperactivity disorder (ADHD) (MTA) as a function of childhood ADHD, random assignment to childhood treatments, and subsequent medication. *Journal of the American Academy of Child and Adolescent Psychiatry, 52*(3), 250–263.

Molina, B. S., Hinshaw, S. P., Swanson, J. M., Arnold, L. E., Vitiello, B., Jensen, P. S.,... MTA Cooperative Group. (2009). The MTA at 8 years: Prospective follow-up of children treated for combined-type ADHD in a multisite study. *Journal of the American Academy of Child and Adolescent Psychiatry, 48*(5), 484–500.

Morón, J. A., Brockington, A., Wise, R. A., Rocha, B. A., & Hope, B. T. (2002). Dopamine uptake through the norepinephrine transporter in brain regions with low levels of the dopamine transporter: Evidence from knock-out mouse lines. *Journal of Neuroscience, 22*(2), 389–395.

Morrow, R. L., Garland, E. J., Wright, J. M., Maclure, M., Taylor, S., & Dormuth, C. R. (2012). Influence of relative age on diagnosis and treatment of attention-deficit/hyperactivity disorder in children. *CMAJ: Canadian Medical Association Journal, 184*(7), 755–762.

Moszczynska, A., & Yamamoto, B. K. (2011). Methamphetamine oxidatively damages Parkin and decreases the activity of 26S proteasome in vivo. *Journal of Neurochemistry, 116*(6), 1005–1017.

Murphy, J. M., McCarthy, A. E., Baer, L., Zima, B. T., & Jellinek, M. S. (2014). Alternative national guidelines for treating attention and depression problems in children: Comparison of treatment approaches and prescribing rates in the United Kingdom and United States. *Harvard Review of Psychiatry, 22*(3), 179–192.

Nock, M. K., Green, J. G., Hwang, I., McLaughlin, K. A., Sampson, N. A., Zaslavsky, A. M., & Kessler, R. C. (2013). Prevalence, correlates, and treatment of lifetime suicidal behavior among adolescents: Results from the National Comorbidity Survey Replication Adolescent Supplement. *JAMA Psychiatry, 70*(3), 300–310.

Olfson, M., Blanco, C., Wang, S., Laje, G., & Correll, C. U. (2014). National trends in the mental health care of children, adolescents, and adults by office-based physicians. *JAMA Psychiatry, 71*(1), 81–90.

Olfson, M., He, J. P., & Merikangas, K. R. (2013). Psychotropic medication treatment of adolescents: Results from the National Comorbidity Survey–Adolescent Supplement. *Journal of the American Academy of Child and Adolescent Psychiatry, 52*(4), 378–388.

Pace, T. W., Negi, L. T., Dodson-Lavelle, B., Ozawa-de Silva, B., Reddy, S. D., Cole, S. P.,...Raison, C. L. (2013). Engagement with cognitively-based compassion training is associated with reduced salivary C-reactive protein from before to after training in foster care program adolescents. *Psychoneuroendocrinology, 38*(2), 294–299.

Perry, B., & Szalavitz, M. (2007). *The boy who was raised as a dog.* New York, NY: Basic Books.

PDR Network, LLC. (2012). *Physicians' desk reference.* Montvale, NJ: Author.

Pontifex, M. B., Saliba, B. J., Raine, L. B., Picchietti, D. L., & Hillman, C. H. (2013). Exercise improves behavioral, neurocognitive, and scholastic performance in children with attention-deficit/hyperactivity disorder. *Journal of Pediatrics, 162*(3), 543–551.

Presne, C., Fakhouri, F., Noel, L. H., Stengel, B., Even, C., Kreis, H.,...Grunfeld, J. P. (2003). Lithium-induced nephropathy: Rate of progression and prognostic factors. *Kidney International, 64*(2), 585–592.

Prinz, R. J., Sanders, M. R., Shapiro, C. J., Whitaker, D. J., & Lutzker, J. R. (2009). Population-based prevention of child maltreatment: The U.S. Triple P system population trial. *Prevention Science, 10*(1), 1–12.

Raghavan, R., & McMillen, J. C. (2008). *Patterns of psychotropic medication use among older adolescents in foster care.* Orlando, FL: Academy Health Annual Research Meeting.

Ratzoni, G., Gothelf, D., Brand-Gothelf, A., Reidman, J., Kikinzon, L., Gal, G.,...Weizman, R. (2002). Weight gain associated with olanzapine and risperidone in adolescent patients: A comparative prospective study. *Journal of the American Academy of Child and Adolescent Psychiatry, 41*(3), 337–343.

Ravenel, S. D. (2013). An integrative approach to common behavior and learning problems in children: A role for gluten sensitivity and MTHFR polymorphism. *Ethical Human Psychology and Psychiatry, 15*(2), 100–108.

Reddy, S. D., Negi, L. T., Dodson-Lavelle, B., Ozawa-de Silva, B., Pace, T. W. W., Cole, S. P.,...Craighead, L. W. (2012) Cognitive-based compassion training: A promising prevention strategy for at-risk adolescents. *Journal of Child and Family Studies, 22*(2), 219–230. doi:10.1007/s10826–012-9571-7

Reinblatt, S. P., DosReis, S., Walkup, J. T., & Riddle, M. A. (2009). Activation adverse events induced by the selective serotonin reuptake inhibitor fluvoxamine in children and adolescents. *Journal of Child and Adolescent Psychopharmacology, 19*(2), 119–126.

Rohde, P., Silva, S. G., Tonev, S. T., Kennard, B. D., Vitiello, B., Kratochvil, C. J., . . . March, J. S. (2008). Achievement and maintenance of sustained response during the Treatment for Adolescents With Depression Study continuation and maintenance therapy. *Archives of General Psychiatry, 65*(4), 447–455.

Sadasivan, S., Pond, B. B., Pani, A. K., Qu, C., Jiao, Y., & Smeyne, R. J. (2012). Methylphenidate exposure induces dopamine neuron loss and activation of microglia in the basal ganglia of mice. *PLoS ONE, 7*(3), e33693.

Samuels, B. (2011). *Testimony of the commissioner for Administration of Children, Youth and Families and Administration of Children and Families, U.S. Department of Health and Human Services before the Senate Homeland Security and Government Affairs Committee.* Retrieved from http://hsgac.senate.gov/public/index.cfm? FuseAction=Hearings.Hearing&Hearing_Ib=9fc194de-2a7c-4417–8f2b-6b90cadacede

Sanders, M. R. (2008). Triple P-Positive Parenting Program as a public health approach to strengthening parenting. *Journal of Family Psychology, 22*(4), 506–517.

Sato, M. (2011). *The financial and societal cost of medicating America's foster children.* Testimony of executive director for the National Association of Medicaid Directors before the Senate Homeland Security and Government Affairs Committee. Retrieved from http://hsgac.senate.gov/public/index .cfm?FuseAction=Hearings.Hearing&Hearing_Ib=9fc194de-2a7c-4417–8f2b-6b90cadacede

Sawyer, D., & Alfonsi, S. (2011, December). *Overmedication of children in the U.S. foster care system* [Television broadcasts]. New York, NY: ABC News. Retrieved from http://abcnews.go.com/blogs/headlines/2011/11/abc-news-investigation-diane-sawyer-and-sharyn-alfonsi-to-report-on-the-overmedication-of-children-in-the-u-s-foster-care-system

Schwarz, A. (2014, May 17). Among experts, scrutiny of attention disorder diagnoses in 2- and 3-year olds. *The New York Times,* pp. A11–A14.

Searight, H. R., Robertson, K., Smith, T., Perkins, S., & Searight, B. K. (2012). Complementary and alternative therapies for pediatric attention deficit hyperactivity disorder: A descriptive review. *ISRN Psychiatry, 2012,* 804127.

Setlik, J., Bond, G. R., & Ho, M. (2009). Adolescent prescription ADHD medication abuse is rising along with prescriptions for these medications. *Pediatrics, 124*(3), 875–880.

Shaw, P., Lalonde, F., Lepage, C., Rabin, C., Eckstrand, K., Sharp, W., . . . Rapoport, J. (2009). Development of cortical asymmetry in typically developing children and its disruption in attention-deficit/hyperactivity disorder. *Archives of General Psychiatry, 66*(8), 888–896.

Soetens, E., D'Hooge, R., & Hueting, J. E. (1993). Amphetamine enhances human-memory consolidation. *Neuroscience Letters, 161*(1), 9–12.

Sostek, A. J., Buchsbaum, M. S., & Rapoport, J. L. (1980). Effects of amphetamine on vigilance performance in normal and hyperactive children. *Journal of Abnormal Child Psychology, 8*(4), 491–500.

Spetie, L., & Arnold, L. E. (2007). Ethical issues in child psychopharmacology research and practice: Emphasis on preschoolers. *Psychopharmacology, 191*(1), 15–26.

Thapar, A., Fowler, T., Rice, F., Scourfield, J., van den Bree, M., Thomas, H.,... Hay, D. (2003). Maternal smoking during pregnancy and attention deficit hyperactivity disorder symptoms in offspring. *American Journal of Psychiatry, 160*(11), 1985–1989.

Tillman, R., Geller, B., Nickelsburg, M. J., Bolhofner, K., Craney, J. L., DelBello, M. P., & Wigh, W. (2003). Life events in a prepubertal and early adolescent bipolar disorder phenotype compared to attention-deficit hyperactive and normal controls. *Journal of Child and Adolescent Psychopharmacology, 13*(3), 243–251.

Treweek, J., Wee, S., Koob, G. F., Dickerson, T. J., & Janda, K. D. (2007). Self-vaccination by methamphetamine glycation products chemically links chronic drug abuse and cardiovascular disease. *Proceedings of the National Academy of Sciences of the United States of America, 104*(28), 11580–11584.

Trezza, V., Baarendse, P. J., & Vanderschuren, L. J. (2010). The pleasures of play: Pharmacological insights into social reward mechanisms. *Trends in Pharmacological Sciences, 31*(10), 463–469.

Turner, K. M., & Sanders, M. R. (2006). Help when it's needed first: A controlled evaluation of brief, preventive behavioral family intervention in a primary care setting. *Behavior Therapy, 37*(2), 131–142.

Tyre, P. (2004, December). Battling the effects of war. *Newsweek.* Retrieved September 14, 2008, from http://www.newsweek.com/id/5598

U.S. Food and Drug Administration. (2007). *Antidepressant use in children and adults: Revisions to medication guide.* Retrieved March 1, 2011, from http://www.fda.gov/Drugs/DrugSafety/Informationby DrugClass/ucm096273.htm

Vincent, N. A. (2014, February 4). *Neuroscientific solutions to legal problems and legal problems with neuroscientific solutions.* Georgia State University to the Neuroscience Institute, Atlanta, GA.

Volkow, N. D., & Swanson, J. M. (2013). Clinical practice: Adult attention deficit-hyperactivity disorder. *New England Journal of Medicine, 369*(20), 1935–1944.

Volkow, N. D., Wang, G. J., Fowler, J. S., Thanos, P. P., Logan, J., Gatley, S. J.,... Thanos, P. (2002). Brain DA D2 receptors predict reinforcing effects of stimulants in humans: Replication study. *Synapse, 46*(2), 79–82.

Volkow, N. D., Wang, G. J., Kollins, S. H., Wigal, T. L., Newcorn, J. H., Telang, F.,...Swanson, J. M. (2009). Evaluating dopamine reward pathway in ADHD: Clinical implications. *Journal of the American Medical Association, 302*(10), 1084–1091.

Watch List (Producer) & Shoshana Guy (Producer & Correspondent). (2011, January 7). *The medication of children in foster care* [DVD]. Judith Starr Wolf (Editor); Mar Cabra & Sarah Fitzpatrick (Directors). United States: PBS. Retrieved from www.pbs.org/wnet/need-to-know/health/video-the-watch-list-the-medication-of-foster-children/6232. Also available at video.pbs.org/video/1967228102. "Drugs in the System" original broadcast date: January 7, 2011.

Weintrob, N., Cohen, D., Klipper-Aurbach, Y., Zadik, Z., & Dickerman, Z. (2002). Decreased growth during therapy with selective serotonin reuptake inhibitors. *Archives of Pediatrics & Adolescent Medicine, 156*(7), 696–701.

Wilson, R., & Lyons, L. (2013). *Anxious kids, anxious parents.* Deerfield Beach, FL: Health Communications.

Wozniak, J., Biederman, J., Mick, E., Waxmonsky, J., Hantsoo, L., Best, C.,...Laposata, M. (2007). Omega-3 fatty acid monotherapy for pediatric bipolar disorder: A prospective open-label trial. *European Neuropsychopharmacology, 17*(6–7), 440–447.

Wozniak, J., Biederman, J., Mundy, E., Mennin, D., & Faraone, S. V. (1995). A pilot family study of childhood-onset mania. *Journal of the American Academy of Child and Adolescent Psychiatry, 34*(12), 1577–1583.

Zevin, S., & Benowitz, N. L. (2000). Pharmacokinetics and pharmacodynamics of nicotine. In M. Piasecki & P. A. Newhouse (Eds.), *Nicotine in psychiatry: Psychopathology and emerging therapeutics* (pp. 37–57). New York, NY: American Psychiatric Press.

Zhang, H., Du, M., & Zhuang, S. (2010). Impact of long-term treatment of methylphenidate on height and weight of school age children with ADHD. *Neuropediatrics, 41*(2), 55–59.

Zuvekas, S. H., & Vitiello, B. (2012). Stimulant medication use in children: A 12-year perspective. *American Journal of Psychiatry, 169*(2), 160–166.

Zylowska, L., Ackerman, D. L., Yang, M. H., Futrell, J. L., Horton, N. L., Hale, T. S.,...Smalley, S. L. (2008). Mindfulness meditation training in adults and adolescents with ADHD: A feasibility study. *Journal of Attention Disorders, 11*(6), 737–746.

10

New Opportunities
and How to Proceed

Our current mental health system is focused on what is wrong. The bulk of the prior chapters considered various forms of distress. Facts about the relatively high rates of disorders were covered in previous chapters. The first section of this chapter begins by asking why the rates of mental health diagnoses are so high in the modern Western world. Part of the reason for our high rates of illness may be that we have the wrong focus. This chapter considers whether current diagnostic practices have served us well and looks at an alternative focus for delivering mental health services. In this chapter, a paradigm shift is suggested. This chapter focuses on happiness and optimal functioning. The case is made for focusing on flourishing and increasing the frequency of the positive moods and positive experiences of the population.

The second section of this chapter asks about those behaviors that promote flourishing and well-being. It begins by examining the behavior of the resilient, that is, those who maintain a positive focus during stressful periods. Following this, those activities and behaviors that are correlated with maintenance of positive moods are reviewed. Topics here include cultivating social support, experiencing gratitude, meditating, enjoying music, and laughing. Eating an anti-inflammatory diet and exercising are certainly on this list. These topics were covered in Chapters 4 and 5 and are not reexamined here. Because engaging in some of the useful strategies (exercising, learning to meditate) will require implementation of new habits and lifestyle modifications, a brief overview of the literature on changing behavior and arranging the environment to cue to new habits is provided.

The final section of this chapter considers the new use of behavioral health specialists in primary care. The integration of behavioral health into primary care was written in the Patient Protection and Affordable Care Act. Screening for behavioral health will probably be a component of integrating behavioral health into primary care. Screening tools are discussed. The chapter ends with some suggestions for broad-based social policy that could support the changes needed to enhance people's health.

MENTAL ILLNESS IN THE UNITED STATES IS AN EPIDEMIC

In the Western world, between 50% and 65% of the general population have met criteria for a *Diagnostic and Statistical Manual of Mental Disorders, Fourth Edition* (*DSM IV*; American Psychiatric Association, 1994; Kessler et al., 2005) diagnosis during their lifetimes and 27% currently meet criteria for anxiety or depression (Chapter 1, The *DSM-IV* Continues the Tradition of Medicalizing More of Us section). These rates are higher than they were in previous decades. Each succeeding generation since 1900 has exhibited higher rates of distress than those born in earlier times. Moreover, rates of mental illness are higher in the United States than in Mexico and China (see Chapter 4, Prevalence Over Time and Cultures section). A variety of explanations have been proffered to explain the high rates of mental illness in the Western world. In looking at some possible explanations, the purpose is to identify avenues for decreasing the current trends toward greater numbers of mentally ill persons.

1. Inflammation is associated with many mental disorders and may play a causal role in anxiety and depression. Exercise reduces inflammation, but many Americans have a sedentary lifestyle. Many components of the American diet are high in inflammation-inducing foods, such as high levels of saturated fats and high levels of high-fructose corn syrup. Moreover, the preservatives in packaged food change the microbiota and contribute to leaky gut, which may also explain the exploding rates of inflammatory bowel disease. The hygiene hypothesis suggests that exposure to pathogens early in life can increase regulatory factors in the immune system (T regulatory cells and more interleukin [IL]-10), which will serve to reign in inflammation. With fewer T regulatory cells, levels

of asthma, depression, and diabetes increase, which is consistent with the current status of these conditions in the United States (References section and section on inflammation in Chapter 4). Finally, America is witnessing an obesity epidemic. Weight carried around the middle (a component of the highly prevalent metabolic syndrome) is bad. Fat tissue around one's middle is loaded with activated macrophages spewing inflammatory cytokines into circulation (Shelton & Miller, 2010).

2. Social support can mitigate the impact of stressor exposure and happier people are more likely to make more social contacts (Boscarino, 1995; Krueger et al., 2009). Sociologist Robert Putnam (2001) in *Bowling Alone* suggests a loss of social connection in the United States. Fewer people participate in community activities, including religious events and civic events. More adults are living alone. Many jobs are temporary and job turnover is higher than before, further limiting the opportunity to create enduring social relationships. Fewer families eat dinner together. People do connect on the Internet but these connections are more fragile and less enduing than face-to-face relationships. Although, even according to Putnam's data, people do spend time informally socializing with friends, they do so less than in the past. The absence of social connection may play a role in explaining the higher rates of mental distress in contemporary, Western society.

3. Another major change in the last several decades has been a collective change in attitude. Marty Seligman has discussed his extended years of experience in reading bedtime stories to his children. Although in the 1950s and 1960s, the story of "Puff and Toot" dominated, in recent years, the focus has turned to self-esteem (Seligman, 2002, 2011). People in this society are thus encouraged to reflect on themselves, asking questions about their feelings and their thoughts. Rather than promoting subjective well-being, the learned self-focus may have undermined subjective well-being.

4. Parker, Gladstone, and Chee (2001) examined the rates of major depression in China and reported them to be much lower than those in the United States. Parker believes that the rates of depression in China and the United States may be more equivalent, although the Chinese are more likely to describe physical symptoms (fatigue, lack of energy, etc.) than feelings. In fact, the research described

throughout this book suggests that the same brain phenomena underlie both response to infection and response to social exclusion. Distress in an organ of the body is registered in the same brain area as the pain of loss of a loved one. Psychological distress and physical symptoms share a common brain representation (Lieberman, 2013). Thus, for the Chinese, reporting fatigue is just as valid as reporting sadness. The question should be "which explanation yields the better outcome?" Arguably, believing one is fatigued may be the better explanation. It is less stigmatizing. Alternatively, if persons are diagnosed with major depression, and they do even a cursory review of the outcome studies, they will not be very optimistic about the long-term outcomes. Some have argued (Fava & Offidani, 2011; Whitaker, 2010) that current pharmaceuticals change an acute condition into a chronic one. Regardless of the explanation, reading the outcome research carries the possibility of creating a self-fulfilling prophecy. Explaining one's state as physically ill carries a more benign prognosis than our current practice of labeling ourselves as mentally ill.

Case Against Diagnoses That Create Harm

General population surveys find that many people who are distressed fail to access services (Corrigan, Druss, & Perlick, 2014). When a physician makes a referral to a mental health practitioner, only 50% of the referred follow through with the referral (Adams & Grieder, 2014; Kessler, Stafford, & Messier, 2009). Up to 45% of people meeting the criteria for mental illness do not seek treatment because of low perceived need. Those rating their need as greater may prefer to handle the situation themselves and many drop out of treatment because of this preference or because of perceived improvement. The National Comorbidity Survey–Replication found that the attitude toward mental health treatment was a more likely reason for failure to engage in treatment than was the lack of access (Mojtabai et al., 2011). Being labeled "mentally ill" carries public and self-stigma and may discourage persons from seeking treatment (Held & Owens, 2013). For the person who accepts the label, although it may allow access to services, it comes with a price. Labels serve a self-definitional function. Rating one's distress as low level and preferring to handle the situation alone may reflect an appraisal that one can handle it alone. Such appraisals are components of self-efficacy. Perhaps the failure to engage in treatment is a positive finding.

Empirical findings support the view that self-efficacy regarding one's capacity for maintaining positive mental health is associated with positive outcomes. A person who endorses such statements as "If they want to, people can change the emotions they have," experiences fewer negative emotions and garners more social support from others under challenging conditions (Tamir, John, Srivastava, & Gross, 2007). Tamir, John, Srivastava, and Gross (2007) found that self-efficacy about being able to alter their own negative emotions was the mediator of lower levels of depression in those who believed people can change their emotions. Accepting a mental illness diagnosis can undermine self-efficacy. Persons who present themselves in a self-enhancing manner exhibit higher self-esteem and more productive functioning (Taylor & Brown, 1994).

The literature on bereavement has focused on another group that presents itself in an overly positive manner. Repressors of negative affect have been the focus of bereavement studies. *Repressors* are defined as those reporting low levels of subjective distress while exhibiting high levels of sympathetic nervous system activity, a possible physical measure of distress. Repressors may not be aware of their proclivity to focus on the positive and away from the negative. They may not be denying in the sense that denial is measured on self-report measures on which people endorse items such as "I refuse to believe that this has happened." George Bonanno and his colleagues have followed repressors longitudinally after bereavement. Repressors, that is, those who self-report positive moods failing to reflect their physiological response, have better long-term outcomes (Bonanno, 2005; Bonanno, Keltner, Holen, & Horowitz, 1995; Coifman, Bonanno, Ray, & Gross, 2007). The studies on repressors are consistent with the idea that presenting oneself as "coping well" can be construed as a component of mental health.

A variety of empirical findings support the idea that presenting oneself as "coping well" is a correlate of positive mental health. The current system requires an admission of defeat in order to gain services. Perhaps it is possible to deliver services that promote and emphasize well-being rather than ministering to distress. The reduced stigmatization may yield some benefits.

LESSONS FROM THE RESILIENCE LITERATURE

Throughout this book, the focus has been on disorder. Stressful environments are associated with the emergence of anxiety disorders and mood disorders. There is a literature, however, examining characteristics of those who are able to maintain adaptive function despite having been tested by adversity. Feder, Nestler, and Charney (2009) label these individuals as "resilient." Feder et al. suggest that in the resilient, some of the processes that are induced by stress not only fail to occur, but other processes that enhance stability of the system do occur. For example, under stress, many animals will exhibit an increase in brain-derived neurotrophic factor (BDNF) in the ventral tegmental area (which is a correlate of distress). This does not occur in resilient animals. As explained in Chapter 4, (Brain-Derived Neurotrophic Factor section) BDNF in the VTA is a marker of distress.

A large literature exists that measures the coping styles of those experiencing stressors such as bereavement, caring for incapacitated significant others, or experiencing trauma. Coping styles are measured with instruments, such as coping inventories, that ask whether a person has used various coping strategies. Then outcomes (depression, anxiety, and moods) are correlated with various coping mechanisms. Active coping and problem solving are associated with positive outcome, whereas denial, avoidant coping, behavioral disengagement, and venting are associated with negative outcome. In terms of personality style, those who score high on measures of optimism display better outcomes. Those with purpose in life and those who find meaning in adversity also achieve better outcomes (Feder, Nestler, & Charney, 2009).

Folkman and Moskowitz (2000) alert us to additional beneficial coping mechanisms. Folkman and Moskowitz (2000), reviewing their own studies as well as those of others, find that in coping with stressful events, such as caretaking of a loved one dying from HIV or life-threatening illness, many people experience both positive and negative emotions. Folkman and Moskowitz identify the following strategies as instrumental in experiencing positive emotions under stress of caring for a dying loved one: finding meaning or benefit, such as developing a skill or a strength as a consequence of the adversity; noticing small pleasant blessings; pursuing of realistic, attainable goals; and focusing on proximal tasks even when the loved one's death cannot be prevented. Even with situational constraints, making plans and setting goals are possible, and are associated with greater positive affect in those who have experienced the loss of a loved one (Robinson & Tamir, 2011; Stein, Folkman, Trabasso, & Richards, 1997).

Other researchers have identified other facets of resilience. Kent and Davis (2014) define *resilience* as the capacity to maintain a sense of agency, that is, maintaining the sense of being an actor rather than an object that is acted on. Persons under adverse circumstances (such as being confined in a prison camp) who engage in goal-directed imagery (planning for constructing a house or imagining playing an instrument) as a coping strategy are able to escape symptoms of posttraumatic stress disorder (PTSD). In fact, Kent and Davis view PTSD as a disorder characterized by the loss of a subjective sense of agency. For treating PTSD, Kent and Davis use exercises in setting goals and encourage active working toward these goals as an antithesis to an absence of agency. Active coping focuses attention and maintains a sense of mastery (Folkman & Moskowitz, 2000).

The emphasis on active coping fits well with the model of learned helplessness discussed in Chapter 2. Exposure to uncontrollable shock will activate the lateral habenula that leads to activation of the amygdala (increased anxiety) and downregulation of the nucleus accumbens (less goal-directed activity). With downregulation of the nucleus accumbens, there is less movement and less exploration. In contrast to uncontrollable stress, animals that have had the controllable shock experience become resistant to later exposure to lack of control. The animals exposed to prior solvable problems continue to be active when facing unsolvable problems later.

To summarize, many avenues of research in animals and people converge on active coping. The key seems to be to engage in active behavior, to set goals, and moving toward a goal. Although the larger issue may be uncontrollable, other benefits can be derived by continuing to strive.

THE GOAL OF FLOURISHING

Keyes (2007) distinguishes languishing from flourishing. Those who languish are not depressed in the sense of experiencing distress. Rather, they describe their lives as hollow and empty. Fredickson and Losada (2005) suggest that the ratio of positive to negative affect is low in those who languish. The ratio of positive to negative emotion experienced during a day should be greater than 2.9 for flourishing to occur, that is, there should be about three times as many positive moods as negative. In large general-population surveys in Western cultures, the ratio of positive to negative affect relates to a subjective sense of well-being (Diener, 2000; Fredrickson & Losada, 2005).

In order to increase the ratio of positive to negative emotions experienced during a day, we can ask about those activities and events that increase the probability of positive emotions. There are some surprises here. Those events or conditions that create distress are distinct from events or conditions that create satisfaction and happiness. Duckworth, Steen, and Seligman (2005) reviewed early work establishing this point. In a work environment, Herzberg, Mausner, and Snyderman (1959) showed that lack of appreciation and low pay create aggravation. However, satisfaction derives from meaningful and engaging work, not just the absence of aggravation. As discussed by Duckworth et al., early on Norman Bradburn established that both positive and negative moods can co-occur. Many people experience both positive and negative emotions within the same time period. Because good and bad can occur within the same time frame, each individual can choose where to focus. Duckworth et al. (2005) suggest that giving more attention to the positive emotions offers a way to optimize overall function.

The experience of positive emotions can offset the experience of stress. Workers who report positive emotions during their day exhibit lower levels of cortisol and reduced inflammatory markers in response to stress (Steptoe, Wardle, & Marmot, 2005). Good moods are associated with increased heart rate variability, stronger response to vaccination, and better sleep architecture (Dockray & Steptoe, 2010; Steptoe, Dockray, & Wardle, 2009). In studies wherein a cold virus is sprayed into the nasal cavity, those who experience more daily pleasant events display fewer symptoms (Cohen, Doyle, Turner, Alper, & Skoner, 2003b). People who rate higher on experiencing positive mood and those who view their lives as meaningful are lower on the expression of inflammatory factors, but higher on the expression of immune system responses for fighting viruses (Fredrickson et al., 2013). Positive emotions impact health not only in the short term but also in the long term. Those who experience high levels of positive mood enjoy greater longevity (Fredrickson & Losada, 2005; Krueger, Kahneman, Schkade, Schwarz, & Stone, 2009).

Positive mood also facilitates adaptation to new situations. Relative to neutral mood, being in a positive mood state will induce a broad versus small-detail focus, an increased desire to be active, and increase consideration of a broader range of coping responses (Fredrickson, 2004; Fredrickson & Branigan, 2005; Fredrickson & Joiner, 2002). In fact, positive mood at time 1 predicts more active coping at a future time (Fredrickson & Losada, 2005).

Marty Seligman, the former president of the American Psychological Association, spent most of his early career studying major depression. (He was an originator in developing the learned-helplessness paradigm.) After spending a considerable degree of his life focusing on deficit functioning, Seligman, along with Mihaly Csikszentmihalyi (Csikszentmihalyi & Nakamura, 2011), decided to switch focus to study positive psychology. In the process of defining the good life, Seligman (Duckworth, Steen, & Seligman, 2005) distinguished three kinds of positive moods: momentary enjoyment, flow, and transcendence. The momentary experience of enjoyment is strongly associated with having an extroverted personality. The other forms of positive mood are less associated with personality factors. Engagement or absorption in a task (called flow) is not associated with a particular personality type. "Flow is the experience associated with engaging one's highest strengths and talents to meet just-doable challenges" (Duckworth et al., 2005, p. 838). Transcendence derives from engagement in activities and tasks that the individual considers meaningful. Both flow and transcendence correlate with life satisfaction, whereas momentary enjoyment is independent (Duckworth et al., 2005). Seligman's differentiation of forms of positive mood offers an heuristic for arranging activities to ensure that all the various forms of positive mood are included.

WHAT TO DO TO INCREASE POSITIVE MOOD

Seligman et al. (Duckworth et al., 2005) have identified activities for increasing the experience of satisfaction and positive mood. They recommend helping people identify core character strengths (wisdom and knowledge, courage, love, justice, temperance, transcendence) and then arranging situations in which these core strengths can be manifested. Performing acts of kindness is also associated with positive mood

(Lyubomirsky, Sheldon, & Schkade, 2005). Furthermore, religious activities are associated with positive mood (Catalino & Fredrickson, 2011).

It is also worth reiterating Tracey Shors findings, discussed in Chapter 4 in section on exercise, that both exercise and learning new things increase new neurons being integrated into circuits, a sign of brain health. New neurons in the hippocampus help to distinguish new situations from old memories of similar situations. Being able to distinguish the present from the past may be particularly important for overcoming traumatic experiences (Kheirbek & Hen, 2014). Other ways to ensure the experience of positive emotions follow.

Primacy of Social Support

The importance of social support has been demonstrated in many types of investigation. Social interactions with others are associated with positive mood during the day (Krueger et al., 2009). All of the very happy people identified by Diener and Seligman (2002), in their investigation of daily mood, had good social relationships and they spent less of their time alone. The Alameda County studies found that persons with more social contacts were two to three times less likely to die of cardiovascular disease, cancer, and all-cause mortality during a 9-year period (Berkman, 1995). Those individuals who are high in sociability are less likely to develop cold symptoms after their nasal passages are sprayed with a virus (Cohen, Doyle, Turner, Alper, & Skoner, 2003a).

In Chapter 5, the buffering effect of social support of those enduring trauma was covered. Brief mention is reiterated here. Those who have social support are less likely to develop PTSD after controlling for trauma exposure (Boscarino, 1995; Charuvastra & Cloitre, 2008). Abused children carrying the short form of the serotonin transporter (a risk factor for depression) are less likely to become depressed adults if they have had high levels of social support (Kaufman et al., 2004). When people are subjected to laboratory stressors, their anticipated rises in blood pressure and heart rate are attenuated when they are with someone (Kamark, Annunziato, & Amateau, 1995; Lepore, Allen, & Evans, 1993). Holding one's spouse's hand when anticipating a shock is associated with lower levels of anxiety and lower activation in brain alarm areas (Coan, Schaefer, & Davidson, 2006).

Zautra (2014) reviewed the studies on the ameliorative effect of social support on those who experience natural disasters. Particular types of engagement with people are better than others. Listening and giving advice are less important than engaging in joint activities. The hurt individual needs to receive tangible support and feel connected.

Other studies have drilled down to examine the mediators of the effect of social support. Eisenberger, Taylor, Gable, Hilmert, and Lieberman (2007) had research participants talk about their most embarrassing moment to an audience of scowling people. Those who reported more social support during the week exhibited less activation in the dorsal anterior cingulate cortex and lower levels of cortisol during the talk. In a similar experiment, Heinrichs, Baumgartner, Kirschbaum, and Ehlert (2003) also found that under stress, those with social support exhibit an attenuated rise in cortisol, and this attenuation was further enhanced by exogenous oxytocin, the hormone of social connection.

The converse of social support is loneliness. Because people vary in their need for frequency of close social relationships, loneliness is best assessed by instruments, such as the UCLA Loneliness Scale, which assesses subjective craving and distress regarding the absence of contact. Besides the distress, loneliness exacts additional tolls. Lonely people process information less effectively. Although they may be more attentive to social cues, they interpret information about others in a style that alienates people, causing a negative response from others. Thus, their behavior toward others may push people away rather than inviting desired contact (Cacioppo & Patrick, 2008). In terms of physiology, lonely people pay a price. Lonely people exhibit a larger increase in cortisol in the morning and experience sleep problems (Steptoe, Owen, Kunz-Ebecht, & Brydon, 2004). They are higher on inflammatory factors (Cacioppo & Patrick, 2008).

In summary, many areas of study attest to the importance of engaging with others. The list of findings attesting to the importance of human interaction for both happiness and health is very long. Planning for how to access connection with others may be a way of increasing positive affect. Many forms of psychotherapy involve only the therapist and the client; however, engaging with a group may offer a more tangible and more sustainable form of social support. Thus, arranging for group activities of those who have been through similar experiences or those who wish to achieve the same behavioral goal (changing diet, exercising, yoga, meditation, quitting smoking, learning to cook healthy foods) may often be the best way to achieve productive results.

Humor

Weems (2014) characterizes humor as both a coping mechanism for alleviating stress and a mechanism for building connection to others. Weems has analyzed the process of humor. According to Weems, who is a neuroscientist, the brain is a series of independently functioning modules. Sometimes conflicting perceptions/cognitions can occur simultaneously. Just as a computer needs to reboot when confronted with contradictions, the human brain's response is sometimes laughter. Indeed, laughter can be elicited by a sudden change in perspective, similar to what occurs when given a flash of insight. This is illustrated in the old Henny Youngman one liner referring to his spouse, "Take my wife...please!"

Humor and tickling activate some of the same brain structures (Gervais & Wilson, 2005). JaakPanksepp and his laboratory colleagues have been tickling rats for several years now. When they are tickled, the rats produce 50-kHz ultrasonic vocalizations just as they do during rough-and-tumble play. Rats that have been the recipients of tickling approach the laboratory members in order to be tickled. The tickling has very salubrious effects on the rats. Tickled rats exhibit less fear in response to humans and they exhibit enhanced neurogenesis in the hippocampus. Higher levels of insulin-like growth factor (IGF) are implicated in enhanced neurogenesis in the hippocampus. Consistent with enhanced neurogenesis, rough-and-tumble play increases higher levels of IGF-1 in the parietal and frontal cortex in rodents (Burgdorf, Kroes, Beinfeld, Panksepp, & Moskal, 2010).

In addition to being a substance for maintaining brain health, IGF-1 may be the chemical mediator of this particular type of pleasure. Burgdorf et al. also showed that direct application of IGF-1 into the brain will increase pleasure vocalization and removing IGF-1 with an antagonist will block pleasure vocalization.

It behooves us to find ways to take more seriously the truism that there is much to be said for both laughter and play. When experienced in the company of others, laughter is contagious (Gervais & Wilson, 2005).

Music

Music does arouse emotions and can be a source of joy. Music can activate the nucleus accumbens and increase dopamine release in this area (Salimpoor, Benovoy, Larcher, Dagher, & Zatorre, 2011). Fancourt, Ockelord, and Belai (2014) reviewed studies assessing the impact of exposure to music on measures of mood and physiology. In a variety of studies, listening to relaxing music was associated with a decrease in anxiety, an increase in oxytocin, and lower levels of cortisol.

In his exposition of the polyvagal theory, Porges (2011) discusses the fact that the myelinated vagus nerve also controls facial muscles and the tuning of the ear to particular frequencies. He speculates that "since melodic music contains acoustic properties similar to vocal prosody, music may be used to recruit the social engagement system by challenging and modulating the neural regulation of the middle ear muscles. If the social engagement system is effectively recruited, positive facial expressions will emerge, . . . and the traumatized individual will shift to a more calm and positive physiological state" (p. 253). For Porges, then, there is reason to believe that music can be exploited for beneficial effects. In fact, a recent study finds that toddlers who are rhythmically bounced are more likely to hand a dropped object back to an adult. Synchronized walking, singing, and finger tapping have also been shown to increase cooperative behavior and liking (Cirelli, Einarson, & Trainor, 2014).

The type of sounds that people listen to may be important in determining the effect produced. Thoma et al. (2013) found that listening to rippling water in contrast to listening to music produced a greater degree of relaxation. The impact of different sounds on stress reduction was evaluated. Just prior to engaging in the Trier Social Stress Test in which speech and arithmetic calculations were performed in front of an audience, subjects listened to relaxing music, the sound of rippling water, or were in a "just-resting" control condition. Thoma et al. found higher cortisol levels in those who had not listened to the music, whereas cortisol levels were lowest in the group listening to rippling water. Listening to rippling water also facilitated faster recovery of heart rate variability (Kirschbaum, Pirke, & Hellhammer, 1993; Thoma et al., 2013). In a similar study, Radstaak, Geurts, Brosschot, and Kompier (2014) found that both happy and relaxing music hastened the return of blood pressure to baseline levels following a laboratory stressor.

Even when the music experience is jarring, the effect produced may be similar to the effects of controllable shock. As discussed in Chapter 2, section on creating learned helplessness, creating a resilient animal, exposure to controllable shock "immunizes" against the deleterious effects of later exposure to uncontrollable shock. In a study examining the later effects of music on stress, Toyoshima, Fukui, and Kuda (2011) assigned college students to play piano, mold clay, practice calligraphy, or be in a no-intervention control condition. Those in the music condition exhibited decreased cortisol and lower levels of anxiety scores later in the week. Music may also distract from stressors. Studies of exposure to music in patients undergoing surgical procedures have noted lower levels of cortisol in those who listened to music (Leardi et al., 2007).

There are many unanswered questions regarding the types of music that can yield a salubrious effect. Some music can induce unpleasant emotions, whereas other melodies are soothing or pleasantly arousing. Music can be listened to passively or can be generated actively. Finally, making music or listening to music can be done communally. The data are inconsistent as to whether music has an effect on immune system parameters (Fancourt, Ockelord, & Belai, 2014). Perhaps more consistent findings will emerge when questions are asked more systematically.

In terms of harnessing music for beneficial effects, client preferences should be relied on. For those who are deficient in positive emotions, music may offer another source for eliciting positive mood.

Making Blessings Salient

There is a strong correlation between an attitude of gratitude and reported well-being (Emmons & Mishra, 2011). After 9/11, the self-report of gratitude was associated with better postcrisis coping and resilience (Fredrickson, Tugade, Waugh, & Larkin, 2003). High levels of gratitude distinguished between veterans with and without PTSD after controlling for the same level of trauma exposure (Kashdan, Uswatte, & Julian, 2006). Those with higher levels of gratitude are more successful in recasting unpleasant memories (Watkins, Cruz, Holben, & Kolts, 2008). Gratitude is positively correlated with self-esteem and self-satisfaction (Emmons & Mishra, 2011). Gratitude is also correlated with kindness, extroversion, emotional stability, generosity, and trust (Emmons & Mishra, 2011).

Momentary gratitude correlates with increased heart rate variability (McCarty & Childre, 2004).

The previously cited research is correlational. Manipulated-variable research has been conducted. Emmons and McCullough (2003) randomly assigned people to write either about five things for which they were grateful or about daily events. Research participants wrote for 10 weeks. At the end of the time, those writing about gratitude scored higher on measures of how they felt about life in general, displayed greater optimism about the coming week, reported better sleep, were more likely to have helped others, and were more likely to feel connected to others.

Meditation and Yoga

In mindfulness meditation, people attempt to concentrate on a mantra. They notice when their minds wander. They maintain a nonjudgmental stance and refocus their attention on their mantra. They pay attention to the sensory aspects of an emotion, but do not make judgments about the significance of the emotion. According to Farb et al. (2010, p. 26), "mindfulness training may reduce chronic reactivity by shifting attention away from subjective appraisals of affect, toward the incorporation of more sensory-based representations of emotions." The idea is to focus on immediate sensory experiences rather than engaging in speculation about those experiences, making judgments, or linking to prior memories (Farb et al., 2007).

Manipulated-variable studies of mindfulness and compassionate meditation have demonstrated that meditation has a wide range of positive benefits on mood and health. (Compassionate meditation adds to mindfulness meditation a specific focus on wishing good things for others.) Time spent in compassionate meditation predicts a daily increase in positive mood which is associated with lower levels of physical symptoms (headache, chest pain, etc; Fredrickson, Cohn, Coffey, Pek, & Finkel, 2008). After meditating for 8 weeks, people exhibit more left-brain activation and less anxiety. (See Chapter 2, Putting It All Together: BAS and BIS section.) Strong immune system function as a result of meditation has been demonstrated. Those who have undergone 8 weeks of mindfulness meditation have higher antibody levels following vaccination, which is correlated with their increase in left-brain activation (Davidson et al., 2003). As mentioned in Chapter 2,

Telomeres section, meditation also increases telomerase activity, a measure of less stress on the body. Pace et al. (2009) found that those research participants who engaged in more practice of mindfulness exhibited lower levels of inflammation and subjective distress when subjected to the Trier Social Stress Test (Kirschbaum, Pirke, & Hellhammer, 1993). Mindfulness training (which includes aspects of meditation and yoga) will also increase activation in brain areas that exercise inhibitory control (the lateral prefrontal cortex [PFC]; Farb et al., 2007). A meta-analysis of mindfulness meditation concluded that meditation yields positive effects on mood, sensory pain, and quality of life in both clinical and nonclinical populations (Grossman, Niemann, Schmidt, & Walach, 2004).

In contrast to meditation, yoga involves mindfulness and focus on bodily sensation as an individual moves. Hatha yoga involves stretching of all muscle groups for strength, flexibility, and balance. In a review of the literature on yoga, Ross and Thomas (2010) found that yoga decreases levels of negative mood and subjective stress, decreases sleep disturbance, increases parasympathetic tone (heart rate variability), and decreases inflammatory markers. Balasubramaniam, Telles, and Doraiswamy (2013) drew similar conclusions.

Envisioning Positive Future Selves

In this chapter, the importance of staying active and moving toward goals has been emphasized. Lyubomirsky (2007; Layous, Nelson, & Lyubomirsky, 2012) had people write logs envisioning their positive future selves and moving toward desired goals. She found that this strategy did improve daily moods and was useful in helping people to develop realistic strategies for actually achieving their goals.

Being Able to Forgive

Although forgiveness is a way of coping with adversity, it may also contribute to happiness. Forgiveness has been identified as a type of active coping mechanism. An inverse relationship between rumination over negative events and forgiveness has been found in various studies. Those who are able to forgive experience lower blood pressure, better sleeping patterns, high self-acceptance, and lower levels of depression (Stoia-Caraballo et al., 2008; Worthington, Witvliet, Pietrini, & Miller, 2007).

INCREASING THE PROBABILITY OF TAKING ACTION

Throughout this book alternatives for enhancing well-being and relieving distress have been proffered. In Chapters 4 and 5, the beneficial effects of a noninflammatory diet (omega-3s, curcumin or turmeric, and the Mediterranean diet) and exercise were highlighted. In this chapter, we provided more information on ways to increase flourishing. The list of ways to increase positive mood and to decrease distress include meditation, exercise, increasing exposure to humor, spending time with friends, taking stock of what one is grateful for, and learning new physical and mental things. Because implementing these changes requires follow-through, this section highlights the bottom lines from the literature on maximizing the implementation of goals.

Peter Gollwitzer's research has focused on identifying strategies for maximizing the implementation of goals. Gollwitzer and Sheeran (2006) have conducted a meta-analysis of a large number of studies. Their analysis suggests that the more specific the intention to do something (exercise, see friends), the more likely the intention will be realized. It is important to identify the "when," "where," and "how" of implementation. It is important to consider how a behavioral intention might be thwarted and to make contingency plans. Contingency plans should also specify the "when," "where," and "how."

Making a commitment to even small changes in routine can be helpful. The latest research on exercise suggests that even small amounts of exercise, such as daily walking and taking the stairs, can yield big payoffs. Indeed, an active lifestyle was associated with lower inflammation, decreased insulin resistance, and smaller waist circumference (Loprinzi, Lee, & Cardinal, 2014). Similar results were obtained by Church, Earnest, Skinner, and Blair (2007). People may be more willing to commit to small changes than big changes. Moreover, because modest goals often take less time to be reached, their success can be celebrated more often and more quickly, making it easier to more readily sustain these commitments.

Bargh, Lee-Chai, Barndollar, Gollwitzer, and Trotschel (2001) have considered the automaticity of behaviors. Environmental cues—stimuli in the environment—even when not consciously processed, can alter behavior. In order to maximize the probability of realizing a behavioral change, the environment needs to be organized to cue the desired behavior. This could mean setting out exercise clothing the night before in order to cue exercise in the morning. This could mean having nutritious foods in the refrigerator.

A big "automatic" cue for either desired or undesired behavior is what others are doing. Obesity is contagious (Christaski & Fowler, 2007). Both smoking and quitting smoking are contagious (Christakis & Fowler, 2008). Much of human behavior is contagious. Laughter is contagious. Yawning is contagious (Weems, 2014). Support groups for making changes and enlisting the support of persons with whom one is in daily contact can increase goal attainment.

In studying the impact of time perspective, Carstensen (2006, 2011; Lang & Carstensen, 2002) found that older people tend to experience more happiness and positive moods than younger persons. In investigating the reasons for the positive mood, they found that the shortened sense of the future prioritizes opportunities for good mood. Elderly people just do not have time for activities that lead to distress. With the awareness that the time for positive moments is running out, the focus on positives more readily becomes a priority. Older people have a preference for positive information and stimuli. Positive memories come to mind more readily than do the negative. There is a lesson to be learned from the elderly. We have examined many activities for increasing the daily ratio of positive mood (time with friends, exercise, yoga, meditation, humor, etc.). Making the experience of these activities a priority and building pleasant activities into each day can yield big payoffs.

INTEGRATING BEHAVIORAL HEALTH INTO PRIMARY CARE

With the passage of the Patient Protection and Affordable Health Care Act in 2010 and the Mental Health Parity and Addiction Equity Act of 2008, new models of health care delivery may be upon us. Although the specifics of these laws are not yet clear, much has been written about the goals (Beronio, Po, Skopec, & Glied, 2013; U. S. Department of Health and Human Services, 2013). A goal of health care reform is to support "proven interventions to address behavioral, social, and environmental determinants of positive behavioral health" (Adams & Grieder, 2014, p. 17). The goal for the patients is to receive both physical and behavioral health care in one setting, the "medical home." The emphasis is on what Berkwick (2009), the former administrator for the Center for Medicare and Medicaid Services, calls "person-centered care." There are several components to person-centered care: (a) the needs of the patient come first, (b) the motto is "nothing about me done without me," and (c) every patient is the only patient such that general rules regarding care are avoided. According to the person-centered care philosophy, treatment plans should be developed with the patient rather than given to the patient. Care is to be integrated across domains of physical and mental health with one treatment plan integrating both areas. Rather than treating disease, the emphasis is on supporting health and treating the person. All this is reminiscent of Hippocrates' maxim, "it's more important to know what sort of person has the disease than to know what sort of disease a person has."

As discussed in a document prepared for the Agency for Healthcare Research and Quality (Peek & The National Integration Academy Council, 2013, p. 2), the target for the integration of behavioral health and primary care is "mental health and substance abuse conditions, health behaviors (including their contribution to chronic medical illness), life stressors and crises, stress-related physical symptoms, and ineffective patterns of health care utilization." The targets for intervention may also include maintenance of wellness and involving the patient in his or her health maintenance. The case has been made that inflammation is a factor in negative mood as well as diagnosable depression, anxiety, and psychosis. Many chronic medical conditions (cancer, type 2 diabetes, heart disease) are also inflammatory conditions (Aggarwal & Harikumar, 2009; Kumar, Takada, Boriek, & Aggarwal, 2004). Exercise, yoga, meditation, nonsaturated fat diets, omega-3s, and social support reduce inflammation. Thus, what is good for mental health is also very good for physical health.

The advantages of integrating behavioral health into primary care are many. For example, after feedback regarding liver enzyme scores in those who are heavy drinkers, clients may be more likely to follow-through if someone can talk to them immediately. Sometimes patients seek assistance from physicians for problems that are better served with behavioral interventions. In fact, 70% of primary care visits are for behavioral health needs (Hunter, Goodie, Oordt, & Dobmeyer, 2009). Many patients with chronic conditions, such as rheumatoid arthritis, diabetes, cancer, chronic obstructive pulmonary disease (COPD), have behavioral components that complicate their treatment. Again, offering help "on the spot" may be advantageous.

Specifics about what to do to integrate care are not heavily articulated in the Patient Protection and Affordable Care Act or in the *Federal Register*. (The *Federal Register* is the executive branch's interpretation of the law.) Much of the language in the law, and the language used by those writing about integration of behavioral health into primary care, allows for broad interpretations supportive of the practice of proactive, preventive medicine. For those employed as behavioral health clinicians in primary care, there are ways to proceed. Introductory education on the importance of keeping the ratio of positive to negative moods can alert people to the importance of attending to their daily mental health. In terms of the range of behavioral interventions that might be offered, support groups, dietary interventions along with guidance on how to implement suggestions, yoga, and exercise classes are possibilities. Traditional psychotherapy is also a possibility. Whether these services are offered in the same building or "referred out" remains to be seen. There is an advantage to the "medical home" concept, because, with patient permission, information can more readily be shared between the behavioral health clinician and the physician. However, for information to be shared, in a health maintenance organization (HMO) setting, there should be some assurance that information communicated in confidence by the client to a behavioral health clinician will not be used to "disenroll" the client.

Screening

The Medicare and Medicaid billing system does allow for screening and prevention interventions in primary care. There are screening instruments for major depression that are in the public domain, such as the Center for Epidemiologic Studies Depression Scale (CES-D; Radloff, 1977) and the Hamilton Depression Rating Scale (1960). The Beck Depression Inventory (1984) is frequently used for screening but is costly. Pollard, Margolis, Niemiec, Salas, and Aatre (2013) also developed an instrument to screen for distress in primary health settings. The problem with these instruments as well as interviewing for depression is that they do screen for deficits. When a person is focused on conveying his or her current level of distress, the individual may neglect to convey strengths. The individual may therefore provide a distorted image even to himself or herself. Without assessing for strengths or observing an individual when discussing the more positive aspects of his or her life, the opportunities for identifying resources for promoting change are missed. A recent study by researchers at the University of California at Davis did find that brief screening for depression does result in more people being diagnosed, who probably represented false positives (Jerant et al., 2014). In fact, because of the problem of "too many false positives" when screening for depression, the Canadian guidelines are to no longer recommend screening for depression (Canadian Task Force on Preventive Health Care, 2013).

In line with concerns about the danger of too many false positives, Frances (2013) in the *Essentials of Psychiatric Diagnoses: Responding to the Challenge of the DSM-5* recommends stepped diagnosis. Because people often come in for treatment during their most difficult periods, Frances recommends reserving a diagnosis until the client is seen on multiple occasions. Because the rates of spontaneous remissions are high, allowing time for the crisis to subside may provide a more accurate view of the client's capacity for resilience.

An alternative to screening for distress would be to screen for strengths and daily activities that will prevent the emergence of severe *DSM* disorders. From the research on positive emotions, we have learned that the ratio of positive to negative emotions is predictive of resilience. Screening for the frequency of positive and negative emotional experiences during the course of a day can be done. In the research literature, meaningful divisions between those who flourish, those who languish, or those who function in the distressed range have been made on the basis of the frequency of positive and negative emotions. For screening in primary care, clients might be asked to complete daily tallies of positive emotions and negative emotions, and then the ratio of positive to negative mood can be calculated. The adjectives used by Fredrickson and Losada (2005) were "amusement," "awe," "compassion," "contentment," "gratitude," "hope," "interest," "love," "pride," "sexual desire," "anger," "contempt," "disgust," "embarrassment," "fear," "guilt," "sadness," and "shame," each assessed on a 4-point scale from "not at all" to "extremely." Ed Diener is known for his research examining happiness and life satisfaction. His assessments did relate to outcomes in meaningful ways. Diener's five-question measure might be used as a screen. Diener, Emmons, Larsen, and Griffin's (1985) open-access measure of life satisfaction includes five questions. These five questions along with the CES-D scale are provided in the Appendix of this book.

It should be noted that happiness, like self-esteem, is a by-product of how one spends his or her time (Lyubomirsky et al., 2005; Lyubomirsky & Layous, 2013). Judging oneself unfavorably for not being sufficiently happy is self-defeating. If one is experiencing few positive emotions, then routines need to be changed. Screening for the frequency of activities correlated with an increase in positive moods is a strategy to use to increase positivity. The combined administration of the UCLA Loneliness Scale (Russell, 1996) and screening for frequency of enjoyable activities and physical exercise offer a way to proceed. Screening in this fashion will identify those activities that need to be added to one's daily routine. The focus should be on engaging in activities that promote well-being.

LARGER SOCIAL CHANGE

Many of the interventions discussed in this book involve diet and exercise. Our current society is organized around fast foods and a sedentary lifestyle. The modern family, with two employed parents, does not have time to cook. If cooking does occur, families reach for packaged foods or processed foods containing preservatives and stabilizers. Lecturing people with limited monetary and time resources on developing healthy lifestyles would not work. A realistic plan is required that acknowledges the exigencies operating in people's lives. Given where the society is, and where it needs to be in this regard, suggests that big changes are required. One possibility in less affluent neighborhoods would be the establishment of neighborhood kitchens staffed by unemployed individuals or those with prison records (who have trouble finding employment) trained in the preparation of low-fat, high-fiber meals. These neighborhood centers could also offer sports activities, meditation, and yoga for both adults and children. Although such an investment would be costly initially, the savings in treatment for obesity-associated conditions (depression, diabetes, heart disease, and cancer) will, over the long run, cover the cost of creating these centers. Health is not an individual responsibility. Good health requires healthy communities.

REFERENCES

Adams, N., & Grieder, D. M. (2014). *Treatment planning for person-centered care: Shared decision making for whole health* (2nd ed.). New York, NY: Academic Press.

Aggarwal, B. B., & Harikumar, K. B. (2009). Potential therapeutic effects of curcumin, the anti-inflammatory agent, against neurodegenerative, cardiovascular, pulmonary, metabolic, autoimmune and neoplastic diseases. *International Journal of Biochemistry and Cell Biology, 41*(1), 40–59.

Balasubramaniam, M., Telles, S., & Doraswamy, P. M. (2013). Yoga on our minds: A systematic review of yoga for neuropsychiatric disorders. *Frontiers in Psychiatry, 3,* Article 117. doi:10.3389/fpsyl.2012.00117

Bargh, J. A., Lee-Chai, A., Barndollar, K., Gollwitzer, P. M., & Trotschel, R. (2001). The automated will: Nonconscious activation and pursuit of behavioral goals. *Journal of Personality and Social Psychology, 81*(6), 1014–1027.

Beck, A. T., & Steer, R. A. (1984). Internal consistencies of the original and revised Beck Depression Inventory. *Journal of Clinical Psychology, 40*(6), 1365–1387.

Berkman, L. F. (1995). The role of social relations in health promotion. *Psychosomatic Medicine, 57*(3), 245–254.

Berkwick, D. (2009). What "patient-centered" should mean: Confessions of an extremist. *Health Affairs, 28,* 560–562.

Beronio, K., Po, R., Skopec, L., & Glied, S. (2013). *Assistant Secretary for Planning and Evaluation research brief: Affordable Care Act will expand mental health and substance use disorder benefits and parity protection for 62 million Americans.* Washington, DC: U.S. Department of Health and Human Services: Office of the Assistant Secretary for Planning and Evaluation. Retrieved from http://aspe.hhs.gov

Bonanno, G. A. (2005). Resilience in the face of potential trauma. *Current Directions in Psychological Science, 14*(3), 135–138.

Bonanno, G. A., Keltner, D., Holen, A., & Horowitz, M. J. (1995). When avoiding unpleasant emotions might not be such a bad thing: Verbal-autonomic response dissociation and midlife conjugal bereavement. *Journal of Personality and Social Psychology, 69*(5), 975–989.

Boscarino, J. A. (1995). Post-traumatic stress and associated disorders among Vietnam veterans: The significance of combat exposure and social support. *Journal of Trauma and Stress, 8*(2), 317–336.

Burgdorf, J., Kroes, R. A., Beinfeld, M. C., Panksepp, J., & Moskal, J. R. (2010). Uncovering the molecular basis of positive affect using rough-and-tumble play in rats: A role for insulin-like growth factor 1. *Neuroscience, 168,* 789–777.

Cacioppo, J. T., & Patrick, W. (2008). *Loneliness: Human nature and the need for social connection.* New York, NY: W. W. Norton.

Canadian Task Force on Preventive Health Care. (2013). Guidelines: Recommendations on screening for depression in adults. *Canadian Medical Association Journal, 185*(9), 775–782.

Carstensen, L. (2011). *Older people are happier.* Retrieved from www.ted.com/talks/laura_carstensen_older_people_are_happier

Carstensen, L. L. (2006). The influence of a sense of time on human development. *Science, 321*(5782), 1913–1915.

Catalino, L. I., & Frederickson, B. L. (2011). A Tuesday in the life of a flourisher: The role of positive emotional reactivity in optimal mental health. *Emotion, 11*(4), 938–950.

Charuvastra, A., & Cloitre, M. (2008). Social bonds and posttraumatic stress disorder. *Annual Review of Psychology, 59*, 301–328.

Christakis, N. A., & Fowler, J. H. (2007). The spread of obesity in a large social network, over 32 years. *New England Journal of Medicine, 357*(4), 370–379.

Christakis, N. A., & Fowler, J. H. (2008). The collective dynamics of smoking in a large social network. *New England Journal of Medicine, 358*(21), 2249–2258.

Church, T. A., Earnest, C. P., Skinner, J. S., & Blair, S. N. (2007). Effect of different doses of physical activity on cardiorespiratory fitness among sedentary, overweight or obese postmenopausal women with elevated blood pressure: A randomized controlled trial. *Journal of the American Medical Association, 297*(19), 2081–2091.

Cirelli, L. K., Einarson, K. M., & Trainor, L. J. (2014). Interpersonal synchrony increases prosocial behavior in infants. *Developmental Science,* 1–9. doi:10.1111/desc.12193

Coan, J. A., Schaefer, H. S., & Davidson, R. J. (2006). Lending a hand: Social regulation of the neural response to threat. *Psychological Science, 17*(12), 1032–1039.

Cohen, S., Doyle, W. J., Turner, R., Alper, C. M., & Skoner, D. P. (2003a). Sociability and susceptibility to the common cold. *Psychological Science, 14*(5), 389–395.

Cohen, S., Doyle, W. J., Turner, R. B., Alper, C. M., & Skoner, D. P. (2003b). Emotional style and susceptibility to the common cold. *Psychosomatic Medicine, 65*, 652–657.

Coifman, K. G., Bonanno, G. A., Ray, R. D., & Gross, J. J. (2007). Does repressive coping promote resilience? Affective-autonomic response discrepancy during bereavement. *Journal of Personality and Social Psychology, 92*(4), 745–758.

Corrigan, P. W., Druss, B. G., & Perlick, D. A. (2014). The impact of mental illness stigma on seeking and participating in mental health care. *Psychological Science in the Public Interest, 15*(2), 37–70.

Csikszentmihalyi, M., & Nakamura, J. (2011). Positive psychology: Where did it come from, where is it going? In K. M. Sheldon, T. B. Kashdan, & M. F. Steger

(Eds.), *Designing positive psychology: Taking stock and moving forward* (pp. 3–8). New York, NY: Oxford University Press.

Davidson, R. J., Kabat-Zinn, J., Schumacher, J., Rosenkranz, M., Muller, D., Santorelli, S. F.,…Sheridan, J. F. (2003). Alterations in brain and immune function produced by mindfulness meditation. *Psychosomatic Medicine, 65,* 564–570.

Diener, E. (2000). Subjective well-being: The science of happiness and a proposal for a national index. *American Psychologist, 55,* 34–43.

Diener, E., Emmons, R. W., Larsen, R. J., & Griffin, S. (1985). The Satisfaction with Life Scale. *Journal of Personality Assessment, 49*(1), 71–75.

Diener, E., & Seligman, M. E. P. (2002). Very happy people. *Psychological Science, 13*(1), 81–84.

Dockray, S., & Steptoe, A. (2010). Positive affect and psychobiological processes. *Neuroscience and Biobehavioral Reviews, 35*(1), 69–75.

Duckworth, A. L., Steen, T. A., & Seligman, M. E. P. (2005). Positive psychology in clinical practice. *Annual Review of Clinical Psychology, 1,* 629–651.

Eisenberger, N. I., Taylor, S. E., Gable, S. L., Hilmert, C. J., & Lieberman, M. D. (2007). Neural pathways like social support to attenuated neuroendocrine stress responses. *NeuroImage, 35*(4), 1601–1612.

Emmons, R. A., & McCullough, M. E. (2003). Counting blessings versus burdens: An experimental investigation of gratitude and subjective well-being in daily life. *Journal of Personality and Social Psychology, 84*(2), 377–389.

Emmons, R. A., & Mishra, A. (2011). Why gratitude enhances well-being: What we know, what we need to know. In K. M. Sheldon, T. B. Tashdan, & M. F. Steger (Eds.), *Designing positive psychology: Taking stock and moving forward* (pp. 248–264). New York, NY: Oxford University Press.

Fancourt, D., Ockelford, A., & Belai, A. (2014). The psychoneuroimmunological effects of music: A systematic review and a new model. *Brain, Behavior, and Immunity, 36,* 15–26.

Farb, N. A. S., Anderson, A. K., Mayberg, H., Bean, J., McKeon, D., & Segal, Z. V. (2010). Minding one's emotions: Mindfulness training alters the neural expression of sadness. *Emotion, 10*(1), 25–33.

Farb, N. A. S., Segal, Z. V., Mayberg, H., Bean, J., McKeon, D., Fatima, Z., & Anderson, A. K. (2007). Attending to the present: Mindfulness meditation reveals distinct neural modes of self-reference. *Scan, 2,* 313–322.

Fava, G. A., & Offidani, E. (2011). The mechanisms of tolerance in antidepressant action. *Progress in Neuropsychopharmacology and Biological Psychiatry, 35*(7), 1593–1602.

Feder, A., Nestler, E. J., & Charney, D. S. (2009). Psychobiology and molecular genetics of resilience. *Nature Reviews Neuroscience, 19*(6), 446–457.

Folkman, S., & Moskowitz, J. T. (2000). Positive affect and the other side of coping. *American Psychologist, 55*(6), 647–654.

Frances, A. (2013). *Essentials of psychiatric diagnosis: Responding to the challenge of the DSM-5, revised edition.* New York, NY: Guilford Press.

Fredrickson, B., Tugade, M. M., Waugh, C. E., & Larkin, G. R. (2003). What good are positive emotions in crises? A prospective study of resilience and emotions following the terrorist attacks on the United States on September 11th, 2001. *Journal of Personality and Social Psychology, 84*(2), 365–376.

Fredrickson, B. L. (2004). The broaden-and-build theory of positive emotions. *Philosophical Transactions of the Royal Society of London. Series B: Biological Sciences, 359,* 1367–1377.

Fredrickson, B. L., & Branigan, C. A. (2005). Positive emotions broaden the scope of attention and thought-action repertoires. *Cognition and Emotion, 19,* 313–332.

Fredrickson, B. L., Cohn, M. A., Coffey, K. A., Pek, J., & Finkel, S. M. (2008). Open hearts build lives: Positive emotions, induced through loving-kindness meditation, build consequential personal resources. *Journal of Personality and Social Psychology, 5,* 1045–1062.

Fredrickson, B. L., Grewen, K. M., Coffey, K. A., Algoe, S. B., Firestine, A. M., Arevalo, J. M. G.,...Cole, S. W. (2013). A functional genomic perspective on human well-being. *Proceedings of the National Academy of Sciences of the United States of America, 110*(33), 13684–13689.

Fredrickson, B. L., & Joiner, T. (2002). Positive emotions trigger upward spirals toward emotional well-being. *Psychological Science, 13,* 172–175.

Fredrickson, B. L., & Losada, M. F. (2005). Positive affect and the complex dynamics of human flourishing. *American Psychologist, 60*(7), 678–686.

Gervais, M., & Wilson, D. S. (2005). The evolution and functions of laughter and humor: A synthetic approach. *Quarterly Review of Biology, 80*(4), 395–430.

Gollwitzer, P. M., & Sheeran, P. (2006). Implementation intentions and goal achievement: A meta-analysis of effects and processes. *Advances in Experimental Social Psychology, 38,* 69–119.

Grossman, P., Niemann, L., Schmidt, S., & Walach, H. (2004). Mindfulness-based stress reduction and health benefits: A meta-analysis. *Journal of Psychosomatic Research, 57,* 35–43.

Hamilton, M. (1960). A rating scale for depression. *Journal of Neurology, Neurosurgery, and Psychiatry, 23,* 56–62.

Heinrichs, M., Baumgartner, T., Kirschbaum, C., & Ehlert, U. (2003). Social support and oxytocin interact to suppress cortisol and subjective responses to psychosocial stress. *Biological Psychiatry, 54*(12), 1389–1398.

Held, P., & Owen, G. P. (2013). Stigmas and attitudes toward seeking mental health treatment in a sample of veterans and active duty service members. *Traumatology, 19*(2), 136–142.

Herzberg, F., Mausner, B., & Snyderman, B. B. (1959). *The motivation to work* (2nd ed.). New York, NY: John Wiley.

Hunter, C. L., Goodie, J. L., Oordt, M. S., & Dobmeyer, A. C. (2009). *Integrated behavioral health in primary care: Step-by-step guidance for assessment and intervention.* Washington, DC: American Psychological Association.

Jerant, A., Kravitz, R. L., Fernandez y Garcia, E., Feldman, M. D., Cipri, C., Nishio, D.,...Franks, P. (2014). Potential antidepressant overtreatment associated with office use of Brief Depression Symptom measures. *Journal of the American Board of Family Medicine, 27*(5), 611–620.

Kamark, T. W., Annunziato, B., & Amateau, L. M. (1995). Affiliation moderates the effects of social threat on stress-related cardiovascular responses: Boundary conditions for a laboratory model of social support. *Psychosomatic Medicine, 57*(2), 183–194.

Kashdan, T. B., Uswatte, G., & Julian, T. (2006). Gratitude and hedonic and eudaimonic well-being in Vietnam War veterans. *Behavior Research and Therapy, 44*, 177–199.

Kaufman, J., Yang, B. Z., Douglas-Palumberi, H., Houshyar, S., Lipschitz, D., Krystal, J. H., & Gelernter, J. (2004). Social support and serotonin transporter gene moderate depression in maltreated children. *Proceedings of the National Academy of Sciences of the United States of America, 101*(49), 17316–17321.

Kent, M., & Davis, M. C. (2014). Resilience training for action and agency to stress and trauma: Becoming the hero in your life. In M. Kent, M. C. Davis, & J. W. Reich (Eds.), *The resilience handbook: Approaches to stress and trauma* (pp. 227–255). New York, NY: Routledge.

Kessler, R. C., Berglund, P., Demler, O., Jin, R., Merikangas, K. R., & Walters, E. E. (2005). Lifetime prevalence and age-of-onset distributions of DSM-IV disorders in the National Comorbidity Survey Replication. *Archives of General Psychiatry, 62*(6), 593–602.

Kessler, R., Stafford, D., & Messier, R. (2009). The problem of integrating behavioral health in the medical home and the questions it leads to. *Journal of Clinical Psychology in Medical Settings, 16*, 4–12.

Keyes, C. L. M. (2007). Promoting and protecting mental health as flourishing. *American Psychologist, 62*(2), 95–108.

Kheirbek, M. A., & Hen, R. (2014, July). Add neurons; subtract anxiety. *Scientific American*, pp. 62–67.

Kirschbaum, C., Pirke, K. M., & Hellhammer, D. H. (1993). The 'Trier Social Stress Test'—a tool for investigating psychobiological stress responses in a laboratory setting. *Neuropsychobiology, 28*(1–2), 76–81.

Krueger, A. B., Kahneman, D., Schkade, D., Schwarz, N., & Stone, A. A. (2009). National time accounting: The currency of life. In A. B. Krueger (Ed.), *Measuring the subjective well-being of nations: National accounts of time use and well-being* (pp. 9–86). Chicago, IL: University of Chicago Press.

Kumar, A., Takada, Y., Boriek, A. M., & Aggarwal, B. B. (2004). Nuclear factor-KB: Its role in health and disease. *Journal of Molecular Medicine, 82*(7), 434–448.

Lang, F. R., & Carstensen, L. L. (2002). Time counts: Future time perspective, goals, and social relationships. *Psychology and Aging, 17*(1), 125–129.

Layous, K., Nelson, S. K., & Lyubomirsky, S. (2012). What is the optimal way to deliver a positive activity intervention? The case for writing about one's best possible selves. *Journal of Happiness Studies, 14*(2), 635–654.

Leardi, S., Pietroletti, R., Angeloni, G., Necozione, S., Ranalletta, G., & Del Gusto, B. (2007). Randomized clinical trial examining the effect of music therapy in stress response to day of surgery. *British Journal of Surgery, 94*, 943–947.

Lepore, S. J., Allen, K. S., & Evans, G. W. (1993). Social support lowers cardiovascular reactivity to an acute stressor. *Psychosomatic Medicine, 55*(6), 518–524.

Lieberman, M. D. (2013). *Social: Why our brains are wired to connect.* New York, NY: Crown.

Loprinzi, P. D., Lee, H., & Cardinal, B. J. (2014). Evidence to support including lifestyle light-intensity recommendations in physical activity guidelines for older adults. *American Journal of Health Promotion.* Retrieved from http://dx.doi.org/10.4278/ajhp.130709-QUAN-354

Lyubomirsky, S. (2007). *The how of happiness: A new approach to getting the life you want.* New York, NY: Penguin Books.

Lyubomirsky, S., & Layous, K. (2013). How do simple positive activities increase well-being? *Current Directions in Psychological Science, 22*(1), 57–62.

Lyubomirsky, S., Sheldon, K. M., & Schkade, D. (2005). Pursuing happiness: The architecture of sustainable change. *Review of General Psychology, 9*, 111–131.

McCarty, R., & Childre, D. (2004). The grateful heart: The psychophysiology of appreciation. In R. A. Emmons & M. E. McCullough (Eds.), *The psychology of gratitude* (pp. 230–255). New York, NY: Oxford University Press.

Mental Health Parity and Addiction Equity Act of 2008, Pub. L. No. 110–343. § 511, 110th Congress. (2013). Rules and regulations. *Federal Register, 78*(219). Retrieved from http://www.gpo.gov/fdys/pkg/FR-2013-27086.pdf

Mojtabai, R., Olfson, M., Sampson, N. A., Jin, R., Druss, B., Wang, P. S.,...Kessler, R. C. (2011). Barriers to mental health treatment: Results of the National Comorbidity Survey Replication (NCS-R). *Psychological Medicine, 41*(8), 1751–1761.

Pace, T. W. W., Negi, L. T., Adame, D. D., Cole, S. P., Sivilli, T. I., Brown, T.,...Raison, C. L. (2009). Effect of compassion meditation on neuroendocrine, innate immune and behavioral response to psychosocial stress. *Psychoneuroendocrinology, 34*(1), 87–98.

Parker, G., Gladstone, G., & Chee, K. T. (2001). Depression in the planet's largest ethnic group: The Chinese. *American Journal of Psychiatry, 158*, 857–864.

Patient Protection and Affordable Care Act of 2010, Pub. L. No. 111–148, 124, Stat. 119 (2010).

Peek, C. J., and the National Integration Academy Council. (2013). *Lexicon for behavioral health and primary care integration: Concepts and definitions developed by expert consensus (AHRQ Publication No. 13-IP011EF)*. Rockville, MD: Agency for Healthcare Research and Quality.

Pollard, C. A., Margolis, R. B., Niemiec, R., Salas, J., & Aatre, G. (2013). Psychometric properties of the primary care behavioral health screen. *Journal of Clinical Psychology in Medical Settings, 20,* 302–310.

Porges, S. W. (2011). *The polyvagal theory: Neurophysiological foundations of emotions, attachment, communication, and self-regulation*. New York, NY: Norton.

Putnam, R. (2001). *Bowling alone: The collapse and revival of American community*. New York, NY: Simon & Shuster.

Radloff, L. S. (1977). The CES-D scale: A self-report depression scale for research in the general population. *Applied Psychological Measures, 1*(3), 385–401.

Radstaak, M., Geurts, S. A. E., Brosschot, J. F., & Kompier, M. A. J. (2014). Music and psychophysiological recovery from stress. *Psychosomatic Medicine, 76,* 529–537.

Robinson, M. D., & Tamir, M. (2011). A task-focused mind is a happy and productive mind: A processing perspective. In K. M. Sheldon, T. B. Kashdan, & M. F. Steger (Eds.), *Designing positive psychology: Taking stock and moving forward* (pp. 160–174). New York, NY: Oxford University Press.

Ross, A., & Thomas, S. (2010). The health benefits of yoga and exercise: A review of comparison studies. *Journal of Alternative and Complementary Medicine, 16*(1), 3–12.

Russell, D. W. (1996). UCLA loneliness scale (version 3): Reliability, validity, and factor structure. *Journal of Personality Assessment, 66*(1), 20–40.

Salimpoor, V. N., Benovoy, M., Larcher, K., Dagher, A., & Zatorre, R. J. (2011). Anatomically distinct dopamine release during anticipation and experience of peak emotion to music. *Nature Neuroscience, 14*(2), 257–262.

Seligman, M. E. P. (2002). *Authentic happiness*. New York, NY: Free Press.

Seligman, M. E. P. (2011). *Flourish: A visionary new understanding of happiness and well-being*. New York, NY: Free Press.

Shelton, R. C., & Miller, A. H. (2010). Eating ourselves to death (and despair): The contribution of adiposity and inflammation to depression. *Progress in Neurobiology, 91,* 275–299.

Stein, N. L., Folkman, S., Trabasso, T., & Richards, T. A. (1997). Appraisal and goal processes as predictors of psychological well-being in bereaved caregivers. *Journal of Personality and Social Psychology, 72,* 872–884.

Steptoe, A., Dockray, S., & Wardle, J. (2009). Positive affect and psychobiological processes relevant to health. *Journal of Personality, 77*(6), 1747–1776.

Steptoe, A., Owen, N., Kunz-Ebecht, S. R., & Brydon, L. (2004). Loneliness and neuroendocrine, cardiovascular, and inflammatory stress responses in middle-aged men and women. *Psychoneuroendocrinology, 29,* 593–611.

Steptoe, A., Wardle, J., & Marmot, M. (2005). Positive affect and health-related neuroendocrine, cardiovascular, and inflammatory processes. *Proceedings of the National Academy of Sciences of the United States of America, 102,* 6508–6512.

Stoia-Caraballo, R., Rye, M. S., Pan, W., Kirschman, K. J. B., Lutz-Zois, C., & Lyons, A. M. (2008). Negative affect and anger rumination as mediators between forgiveness and sleep quality. *Journal of Behavioral Medicine, 31,* 478–488.

Tamir, M., John, O. P., Srivastava, S., & Gross, J. J. (2007). Implicit theories of emotion: Affective and social outcomes across a major life transition. *Journal of Personality and Social Psychology, 92*(4), 731–744.

Taylor, S. E., & Brown, J. D. (1994). Positive illusions and well-being revisited; separating fact from fiction. *Psychological Bulletin, 24,* 399–406.

Thoma, M. V., La Marcha, R., Brönnimann, R., Finkel, L., Ehlert, U., & Nater, U. M. (2013). The effect of music on the human stress response. *PLoS ONE, 8*(8), e70156.

Toyoshima, K., Fukui, H., & Kuda, K. (2011). Piano playing reduces stress more than other creative art activities. *International Journal of Music Education, 29,* 257–264.

U.S. Department of Health and Human Services. (2013). 45 CRF Parts 147, 155, 156, Patient Protection and Affordable Care Act; Standards related to essential health benefits, actuarial value, and accreditation, final rule. *Federal Register, 78*(37), 12834–12872.

Watkins, P. C., Cruz, L., Holben, H., & Kolts, R. L. (2008). Taking care of business? Grateful processing of unpleasant memories. *Journal of Positive Psychology, 3,* 87–99.

Weems, S. (2014). *Ha!: The science of when we laugh and why.* New York, NY: Basic Books.

Whitaker, R. (2010). *Anatomy of an epidemic.* New York, NY: Crown.

Worthington, E. L., Witvliet, C. V. O., Pietrini, P., & Miller, A. J. (2007). Forgiveness, health, and well-being: A review of evidence for emotional versus decisional forgiveness, dispositional forgivingness, and reduced unforgiveness. *Journal of Behavioral Medicine, 30,* 291–302.

Zautra, A. J. (2014). Resilience is social, after all. In M. Kent, M. C. Davis, & J. W. Reich (Eds.), *The resilience handbook: Approaches to stress and trauma* (pp. 185–196). New York, NY: Routledge.

Appendix: Screening Instruments

ALCOHOL USE DISORDERS IDENTIFICATION TEST

How often do you have a drink containing alcohol?

(0) Never
(1) Monthly or less
(2) 2 to 4 times a month
(3) 2 to 3 times a week
(4) 4 or more times a week

How many drinks containing alcohol do you have on a typical day when you are drinking?

(0) 1 or 2
(1) 3 or 4
(2) 5 or 6
(3) 7, 8, or 9
(4) 10 or more

How often do you have 6 or more drinks on one occasion?

(0) Never
(1) Less than monthly
(2) Monthly
(3) Weekly
(4) Daily or almost daily

How often during the last year have you found that you were not able to stop drinking once you had started?

(0) Never
(1) Less than monthly
(2) Monthly
(3) Weekly
(4) Daily or almost daily

How often during the last year have you failed to do what was normally expected from you because of drinking?

(0) Never
(1) Less than monthly
(2) Monthly
(3) Weekly
(4) Daily or almost daily

How often during the last year have you been unable to remember what happened the night before because you had been drinking?

(0) Never
(1) Less than monthly
(2) Monthly
(3) Weekly
(4) Daily or almost daily

How often during the last year have you needed an alcoholic drink first thing in the morning to get yourself going after a night of heavy drinking?

(0) Never
(1) Less than monthly
(2) Monthly
(3) Weekly
(4) Daily or almost daily

How often during the last year have you had a feeling of guilt or remorse after drinking?

(0) Never
(1) Less than monthly
(2) Monthly
(3) Weekly
(4) Daily or almost daily

Have you or someone else been injured as a result of your drinking?

(0) No
(2) Yes, but not in the last year
(4) Yes, during the last year

Has a relative, friend, doctor, or another health professional expressed concern about your drinking or suggested you cut down?

(0) No
(2) Yes, but not in the last year
(4) Yes, during the last year

A score of 8 or greater is suggestive of a problem.

Source: http://pubs.niaaa.nih.gov/publications/aa65/AA65.html

CAGE QUESTIONNAIRE

Have you ever felt you should **c**ut down on your drinking?

Have people **a**nnoyed you by criticizing your drinking?

Have you ever felt bad or **g**uilty about your drinking?

Have you ever had a drink first thing in the morning to steady your nerves or to get rid of a hangover (**e**ye opener)?

A positive response to two or more items suggests a problem.

Source: http://niaaa.nih.gov/publications/AssessingAlcohol/InstrumentPDFs/16_CAGE.pdf

THE SATISFACTION WITH LIFE SCALE

In most ways my life is close to my ideal.

The conditions of my life are excellent.

I am satisfied with my life.

So far I have gotten the important things I want in life.

If I could live my life over, I would change almost nothing.

Source: http://internal.psychology.illinoisedu/_ediener/scales.html

THE CENTER FOR EPIDEMIOLOGIC STUDIES DEPRESSION SCALE

The following is a list of the ways you might have felt or behaved. Please tell me how often you have felt this way during the past week.

0 Rarely or none of the time (less than 1 day)

1 Some or a little of the time (1–2 days)

2 Occasionally or a moderate amount of the time (3–4 days)

3 Most or all of the time (5–7 days)

   1. __ I was bothered by things that usually do not bother me.
   2. __I did not feel like eating; my appetite was poor.
   3. __I felt that I could not shake off the blues even with help from my family or friends.
  *4. __I felt that I was just as good as other people.
   5. __I had trouble keeping my mind on what I was doing.
   6. __I felt depressed.
   7. __I felt that everything I did was an effort.
  *8. __I felt hopeful about the future.
   9. __I thought my life had been a failure.
  10. __I felt fearful.
  11. __My sleep was restless.
 *12. __I was happy.
  13. __I talked less than usual.

14. __I felt lonely.
15. __People were unfriendly.
*16. __I enjoyed life.
17. __I had crying spells.
18. __I felt sad.
19. __I felt that people disliked me.
20. __I could not get "going."

*Items 4, 8, 12, and 16 are reverse scored. Scores can range from 0 to 60. Cutoff score for depression is 16. A score of 15 to 21 is in the mild to moderate depression range.

Source: http://cesd-r.com/about-cesdr

Index

changing recommendations, 160
dosage of, 157
efficacy, 154–156
  in children with major depression,
    336–337
ketamine, 160
for neurotransmitter deficiency, 10
novel drugs, 160–161
for obsessive-compulsive disorders, 10
and pharmaceutical industry, 125, 126
and pregnancy, 159
and serotonin, 43
side effects of, 128, 132, 158–159
  in children with major depression,
    337–339
for smoking cessation, 317
withdrawal, 155–158
antidopaminergic drugs, for psychosis,
    239, 243, 248
anti-inflammation factors, and
    depression, 152
anti-inflammatory drugs, for
    schizophrenia, 246
antipanic neurons, 43–44
antipsychotics, 103–104
  atypicals. *See* atypical antipsychotics
  for children in foster care, 346–348
  and dopamine, 40, 41
  dosage of, 237
  extrapyramidal effects of, 104
  neuroleptics, 104
  for obsessive-compulsive disorders, 10–11
  for pediatric bipolar disorders, 8
  and pharmaceutical industry, 125
  for psychosis, 238–240, 250
  for refractory depression, 10
  side effects of, 239–240
  withdrawal from, 131–132
antisocial behavior, societal sanctions
    against, 3
anxiety, 74–75, 195–230. *See also*
    depression; fear
  and cannabinoids, 47
  and inflammation, 151
  and learned helplessness, 56
  as neurosis, 6

and oxytocin, 73
physiology of, 195–201
  differentiating anxiety from fear,
    197–198
  extinction, 199
  fear, 195–197
  fear memories, 198
  reconsolidation, 199–201
  teaching active coping, 201
  role of prefrontal cortex in suppressing, 60
  and serotonin circuits, 43
anxiety disorders, 202–212
  generalized anxiety disorder, 202–205
  obsessive-compulsive disorder, 205–208
    super recollectors, 206–207
    targeted treatment, 207–208
  posttraumatic stress disorder, 208–212
    factors associated with enhanced risk
      for, 208–210
    recovery, 211–212
  treatments, 212–220
    medications, 213–214
    nondrug treatments, 214–215
    reestablishing connections to others,
      217–218
    selection of, 220
    self-concept, 218–220
    talking about and dealing with past
      traumatic events, 215–220
    talk therapies, 212–213
appetitive signaling, 52–54
  turning off activity in nucleus
    accumbens, 53–54
area of executive control, 58
aripiprazole (Abilify, Abilify Maintena),
    104, 105, 112, 250
  for refractory depression, 10
Asch paradigm, 79
Asian Americans, capacity for
    metabolizing antipsychotics, 104
aspirin
  for depression, 165
  for schizophrenia, 246
Association of Medical Superintendents
    of American Institutions for the
    Insane, 3

panic disorder, 202
  and stigma, 16
  treatment of, 214
paper and pencil measures, for behavioral
    inhibition system, 62
parabrachial nucleus, and pleasure, 75
parasympathetic nervous system (PNS),
    68–70
  polyvagal theory, 68–69
  role in anxiety, 203
  and self-regulation, 69–70, 315
parietal cortex, and pleasure, 76
Parkinson's disease, 99
  and dopamine agonists, 40–41, 342–343
  treatment, and addiction, 297
paroxetine (Paxil, Pexeva), 113, 124
  for generalized anxiety disorder, 214
parvalbumin-positive (PV+), and
    schizophrenia, 232, 233, 235
past traumatic events, talking about and
    dealing with, 215–220
  reestablishing connections to others,
    217–218
patent rights, for drugs, 116–117
  extensions, 119
pathogen-related inflammation, and
    depression, 150
pathophysiology of mental disorders, 10
Patient Protection and Affordable Care
    Act, 11, 18, 119, 123, 380, 382
pay for delay, 119
pediatric bipolar disorders, 8, 332–336
  diagnosis of, 336
  medication, 334–335
  drug side effects, 335–336
peptide, 28
periaqueductal gray (PAG), 37, 43, 74–75
peripheral inflammation, and depression,
    150
peripheral nervous system, and
    acetylcholine, 45
persistence, and ventromedial prefrontal
    cortex, 61
personal characteristics, influence on
    posttraumatic stress disorder, 209
personality traits

and addiction, 302
  and behavioral activation system, 63
  and heart rate variability, 69
person-centered care, 381
pharmaceutical industry
  and behavioral health clinicians
      regarding, 127–132
  health threats regarding, 117–118
  mechanisms controlling medical
      practice, 122–125
  off-label protection, 123–125
  money spending by, 121
pharmaceutical treatments. See drugs
pharmacodynamics, 98–102
pharmacokinetics, 98–102
Pharmed Out, 118
phenelzine (Nardil), 113
phenobarbital (Luminal sodium), 114
phenothiazine, 104
phobias
  and genetics, 203
  talk therapies for, 212
physical pain, associated with social
    rejection, 60–61
physical stress, role of cortisol in, 71–72
Physician Payment Sunshine Act, 123
physicians
  influence of pharmaceutical industry
      on, 123
  prescribing off-label drugs, 124
physiology, 25–96
  of anxiety, 195–201
    differentiating anxiety from fear,
        197–198
    extinction, 199
    fear, 195–197
    fear memories, 198
    reconsolidation, 199–201
    teaching active coping, 201
  circuits, 52–64
    appetitive signaling, 52–54
    behavioral activation system, 62–64
    behavioral inhibition system, 62–63
    creating anxiety/fear, 56
    creating learned helplessness, 54–58
    creating resilient animals, 57–58

emotional inhibition/regulation in
  BAS high scorers, 63–64
habenula to caudal dorsal raphe, 56
motor behavior changes, 56–57
regulation of impulses, motor activity,
  and emotions, 58–62
turning off activity in nucleus
  accumbens, 53–54
emotions, 64–77
  autonomic nervous system, 66–70
  cooperative social communication, 70
  cortisol, 71–72
  disgust, 75
  distress/anxiety, 74–75
  hormonal activity, 70–73
  oxytocin, 73
  parasympathetic nervous system, 68–70
  pleasure, 75–76
  polyvagal theory, 68–69
  preparing for a burst of energy, 70
  rage/anger, 76–77
  self-regulation, 69–70
  sympathetic nervous system, 67–68
genes, 26–31
  epigenetics, 29–31
  making of protein, 26–29
  telomeres, 31
human brain as social, 77–79
immune system, 48–52
  adaptive, 50–51
  glial cells, 51–52
  innate, 49–50
neurons, 32–48
neurotransmitters, 32–48
  acetylcholine, 45
  cannabinoids, 47
  dopamine, 40–43
  GABA, 46–47
  glutamate, 45–46
  investigation of functions of, 34–40
  life cycle of, 34
  norepinephrine/noradrenaline, 44–45
  opioids, 47–48
  serotonin, 43–44
regulation of impulses, motor activity,
  and emotions, 58–62

pineal gland, 37
pituitary–adenylate cyclase-activating
  polypeptide (PACAPR), 210
pituitary gland, 37, 40
pKa of drugs, 98
placebo, 13, 116, 121
  for depression, 155, 166, 167
  for generalized anxiety disorder, 214
plans, for sobriety, 313
playfulness, effect of stimulants on, 342
pleasure, 75–76
  and addiction, 293–294
  and opioids, 48
polyvagal theory, 68–69, 375
pons, 36
Porges, Stephen, 68, 69
positive drug trials, 122
positive emotions, 370–371
  and depression, 147
  strategies under stress of caring,
    368–369
positive moods, 371
  activities to increase, 371–379
positive signs of schizophrenia, 231
positive stimulus, of anxiety, 197–198
postganglionic neuron, 67
posttraumatic stress disorder (PTSD),
  208–212
  in foster children, 348–349
  recovery, 211–212
  risk factors for, 208–210
  treatment, fear reconsolidation in, 200
prefrontal cortex (PFC), 42, 43, 58
  and behavioral activation system, 63
  and depression, 145
  dorsolateral. See dorsolateral prefrontal
    cortex (DLPFC)
  left, 63
    and behavioral inhibition system, 62
    and depression, 145
    and negative affect, 64
  medial, 69
    and pleasure, 76
  right
    and behavioral inhibition system, 62
    and depression, 145